With
Gun, Rifle and Bow

With
Gun, Rifle and Bow
Stories for the Field Sportsman

James Douglas

BLANDFORD

A BLANDFORD BOOK

First published 1994
by Cassell
Villiers House
41/47 Strand
London
WC2N 5JE

Distributed in the United States
by Sterling Publishing Co., Inc.
387 Park Avenue South, New York, New York 10016-8810

Distributed in Australia
by Capricorn Link (Australia) Pty Ltd
2/13 Carrington Road, Castle Hill, NSW 2154

British Library Cataloguing-in-Publication Data
A catalogue record for this book is available from
the British Library

ISBN 0-7137-2343-2

Typeset by Method Limited, Epping, Essex
Printed and bound in Great Britain by
Mackays of Chatham plc, Chatham, Kent

Contents

*This book is dedicated to all those who enjoy the outdoors
and field sports and have a spirit of adventure and, of course,
Doran and Lyle, so that they may know a little of
my earlier years.*

Introduction

THERE ARE FEW CITIES in Britain or Europe that have quite the wonderful outdoor facilities enjoyed by the city of Glasgow. You can, within a short journey, enjoy wonderful hill-walking, sailing, fishing (both sea and freshwater) and shooting, whilst a little extra journey brings you to the ski resorts. Anyone living in Glasgow therefore does not have to travel far to leave the city behind; if they care to look for it, there is an abundance of country sports.

Over a period of years, starting in the early 1960s, I discovered the joys of field sports. To get rough shooting, one only had to ask the farmers; then, as I became more ambitious, particularly in the pursuit of deer, it was necessary to become a poacher. It would have been impossible for me, a working-class lad from Lambhill in the north of Glasgow, to have had anything like the experiences that I enjoyed if I had not been prepared to go shooting wherever I thought it safe; indeed, I regarded this as the right of all Scotsmen. I couldn't understand how an accident of birth allowed some individuals to enjoy such privilege whilst others were expected to look but not touch. How else was a city boy, born with no silver spoon in his mouth and with no influence, to enjoy country pursuits? So I did — in the company of one or two like-minded lads. Poaching of course, was not regarded in those days as particularly serious. Shotgun ownership was simply a case of buying the gun; the licence you obtained from the Post Office. You were, if you were cautious, relatively free to enjoy your shooting — and poaching was regarded as slightly romantic. You just had to be careful not to get caught.

Whilst the facilities are still there, the freedom enjoyed by my generation has largely gone. It has all changed with a tightening of the laws, an increase in the penalties and a more vigorous enforcement attitude from the police and gamekeepers.

But the land is still held by the privileged and fortunate few, so whilst sport is now more readily available to all, it is largely dependent on the individual's ability to pay for it. The situation still exists of young men, without privilege or resources, who are drawn to enjoy our wonderful field sports, being denied access.

Myself, Cunning John and a few others grandly declared that we were resurrecting the ancient society of 'Free Foresters and Gentlemen Adventurers'. I had my arguments rehearsed for the day we might face capture, though fortunately I never had to use them. I visualised myself standing in some court declaring that, since it said in the Bible that Man would rule over the fowl of the air, the fish of the streams and the beasts of the field, I was only doing exactly that and nowhere in the Bible does it mention that this should apply only to the chosen few. Part of our collective naiveté was that not only were we anti-Establishment but, since we associated the land-owning community generally with the English (when indeed they were purely that peculiar form of Scot that affects an English accent), we were all fervently anti-English. Serious young men, we steeped ourselves in what we thought was 'Scottishness', grew beards and enjoyed wearing the kilt and nurturing our anti-Englishness, romancing with the idea of an independent Scotland.

I make no apology, therefore, for any of the exploits described in this book. It is only increased responsibilities, social awareness, opportunity and the fear of being caught that I believe prevents me from doing similar now.

Whilst many of the stories take place around the time that I lived in Scotland, others are located in England. Even after I had moved south and was working in the film industry in London, I retained my love of the outdoors, taking every opportunity to enjoy shooting and stalking.

As my career has developed I have found myself in the fortunate position of being able to travel abroad and enjoy more ambitious and exotic sporting experiences in the USA, Canada, Europe and Africa. Some of these adventures I have related here, all with the common theme of shooting and stalking. Whilst I have been fortunate to have enjoyed these foreign parts, I believe that the foundation of the knowledge and sporting attitudes that I have today was established during those early years when I had, by necessity, to learn how to move through the countryside with caution and silence, keeping my senses alert, not only for the quarry I was pursuing but for those who might be pursuing me.

A little windfall

AS A SCHOOLBOY I had a weekend job, first as a kitchenhand and then as a waiter, in a hotel in Aberfoyle. This was a tasteless, large, modern establishment that specialised in bus parties, mainly from Glasgow. The hotel did a big trade in dinner-dances for factory and shop workers. The emphasis was on cheap prices and getting the customers through the door; no consideration was given to quality or cuisine. Indeed, the motto could have been 'greasy chips with everything'.

There was at the back of the establishment a small bar, frequented by the locals, mainly agricultural workers. It was there I first saw Willie, a tiny, little man who would sit in the corner smoking a disgusting old pipe, packed with 'Thick Black' which he carried in his waistcoat pocket in a little tin. The whole business of getting his pipe going took some time. I would watch him paring the greasy black bar of tobacco with a small knife, then rolling it between his palms to loosen the strands. He would pack it with expert fingers into the bowl, light it with a match and, after much puffing and when satisfied the ignition was complete, would proceed to fill the room with heavy, blue smoke.

Willie kept himself to himself. He had a quiet dignity and seemed to discourage conversation from other than one or two friends. He was long past retirement age, though still fit. I was told he lived in a little cottage two or three miles up a track from the village and travelled down by bike to the pub, pedalling home after two or three pints of Guinness and half a dozen nips of whisky.

After I left school and started work in Glasgow Museum I continued to spend many of my weekends in the Aberfoyle area, often camping in a little glen, where I enjoyed wonderful times stalking roe deer. I had, of course, no permission to be there but had found this little haven of forestry land where the bucks were plentiful. The forestry trapper did occasionally visit the area but I never had the misfortune of meeting him.

My method was to stalk at first light, long before sensible keepers and trappers had got out of bed, and be finished before they had started their day. Stalking in the evening was, of course, more risky but, on the occasions when I fired a shot, I knew that, unless the keeper was close at hand, if he heard it at all it would be extremely difficult to pinpoint.

During one of my early visits to that particular area I had called at

Willie's cottage. I was made very welcome; he lived alone and obviously had few visitors. We would sit by the fireside, drink black tea and slowly, over the months, he opened up to me, telling me of his life, his experiences of the First World War, how he had come to work on the estate as a gardener and his long, happy marriage (his wife had been dead many years). He was obviously very poor, living on a tiny pension. His cottage belonged to the estate and was untouched by the twentieth century: no electricity and a dry toilet in a shed outside. Willie knew what I was doing in the area. I didn't have to tell him. He just mentioned to me one day in a matter of fact sort of way that I would have to watch the keeper, who was 'a right bastard'. After that I would drop in some venison to Willie. He never said much. I would put it down in the kitchen and he would give a nod and put the kettle on.

The estate was owned by a county lady who lived in a smart house and had previously lived in a castle on the estate which had burnt down. One evening I was visiting my old friend. As we sat drinking tea, he seemed a bit pensive. Then, turning to me, Willie asked me if I could keep a secret.

Wasn't it the case that I knew a bit about guns and would I like to see something special, he enquired of me. He got up from his chair and went into his bedroom. Reaching far under the bed, he dragged out a long, metal box. From this he lifted a long, brass-mounted, wooden gun case. He laid it on the kitchen table and opened it. Inside was a magnificent double-barrelled rifle, complete with all accoutrements: bullet moulds, powder measures, little, silver oil bottles, silver-mounted screwdrivers. The whole case was quite beautiful and worth a considerable sum of money. I lifted the rifle stock of finest walnut. The action was beautifully engraved. The gold escutcheon laid into the stock had an elaborately carved crest. Where had he come by such a piece, I enquired.

'Och,' he said. 'After the big house burnt down, her Ladyship asked me to have a look in the ruins in one of the small rooms off the gun room. She told me that the Laird's rifle had been kept there since he died some years since. She wanted to know if it had been destroyed in the fire and, if not, she wanted it found and handed in to the polis. I found it, undamaged, and shoved it under my bed. It was too nice to give to the polis. I told her Ladyship I couldn't find it and it must have been destroyed.'

I asked what he intended to do with it.

'Och, I don't know. You can have it, If you want.'

I said that, much as I would like it, I could not pay him its worth and couldn't imagine how I could register it in my name. I thought it would be better if I could try to find someone who might buy it.

The following Monday, when I arrived at the Museum, I told Jake Taylor all about the wonderful rifle but I was careful not to tell him where it was. He suggested that a friend of his, a well-heeled individual who owned a clothing factory and whom I had met, might buy it. But first, he would have to discuss it with the manager of a large gun shop in central Glasgow.

Some days later Jake suggested I bring the rifle in its case into the Museum. The following weekend when I visited my old friend I took the rifle case and all its contents with me when I left. On the Monday morning I took it to work with me and, at lunchtime, Jake and I hurried by bus into the city centre to see Harry, the shop-manager. Harry examined the rifle, making appreciative noises, and gave Jake an estimated value. Then, with my permission, Harry kept the rifle at the shop.

This was the principal gun shop for that part of Scotland and its base-ment store-room was an Aladdin's cave of wonderful shotguns and rifles. Many of them had been deposited at the shop many years previously for servicing and storage but never collected. There were guns there that had been stored for over 30 years, forgotten and, in many cases, their owners long dead. It was a simple matter for Harry to backdate the entry of the gun into the shop ledger as having been bought by the shop years ago.

This done, it was easy for Jake's well-heeled chum to apply for a firearms certificate of the appropriate calibre, then go into the shop and, on payment of a suitable sum of money to the manager, leave with his perfectly legal, new rifle.

I don't know what the arrangements were between Jake, his friend and Harry. I do know his friend paid me £150, a very considerable sum in those days. The following weekend, when I visited Willie, I gave him the money. He was shocked. It was obviously more money than he had ever seen in his life and would certainly keep him in the few luxuries he required for a long time. He tried to split it with me, then, on my refusal tried to get me to take £50. I eventually accepted £10. Willie lived for several years more, though I saw him less frequently. It was obvious that he was enjoying having money, affording himself a few luxuries. When he died, an old dried-milk tin was found under the bed. In it there was still £30.

An inglorious end

DURING THE WINTER OF 1963 C. E. Palmer, Curator of Natural History in the Kelvingrove Museum and Art Galleries, Glasgow, announced to the museum's taxidermists — myself, John Brackenridge, Jimmy Fraser and Jake Taylor, the head of the department — that, if one of us could procure a quality, Scottish wild goat, the princely sum of £25 would be paid by the Museum. C. E. wanted a billy to complement the two nannies already on display. Such a sum was considerable and I wondered for several days how I might lay my hands upon it.

It was while I was at the University animal laboratory and speaking to Pat O'Brien, one of the animal-house technicians, that I mentioned I was looking for a source of wild goats. Pat told me he was a member of the Scottish Outdoor Club, an amalgam of people who had interests in the outdoors — principally skiing and climbing — and he suggested that, since a trip was planned to the Glen Nevis area that weekend, if I wanted a cheap ride up north I should present myself at Lansdowne Crescent at 6.30 on the Friday evening. He went on to tell me that he had seen wild goats in the area. This was a part of the country that was fairly inaccessible, with few keepers. Pat also emphasised that, if I intended to bring a gun, I should be discreet and not wave it around. I would also meet a fellow, John Andrews, who he told me was an enthusiastic shot who normally took advantage of the communal transport to get to the wild places where he could pursue the red deer.

Over the next few days I looked forward with great anticipation to the coming adventure, packing and repacking my camping equipment and checking my cartridges. I intended to use AAAs with my single-barrelled Bernardelli. I dismantled it and rolled it inside my sleeping-bag. On the Friday morning I went to work at the Museum, dressed in my anorak, breeches and hill-boots with my rucksack on my back.

That night after work, since I had time to kill, I walked up Kelvin Way and had a meal at the Green Gate Indian restaurant, then made my way to Lansdowne Crescent and hung about outside the rooms that Pat and the others rented as a clubhouse. Around 6 o'clock a Volkswagen Dormobile appeared and shortly afterwards various outdoor types started arriving and putting their rucksacks on the roof of the vehicle. It really was an excellent system; each of us paid just a few pounds for our return journey.

Pat arrived and introduced me. There were nine of us altogether. Our gear loaded, we climbed into the back of the vehicle and sat on wooden benches along each side, facing inwards. The man I had hoped to meet was late — a trait which I was to discover over the coming years was the norm. Then, as we were moving off, somebody shouted from the front that John had arrived. The back door opened and a rucksack was thrust in, followed by a broad-shouldered, fit figure who squeezed on to the bench beside me. Pat made the introductions and I turned to meet my new friend. I had a vague impression in the dim interior light of a man with cold, piercing eyes and a 'Weetabix' hairstyle, the long hair on the side of his head care-fully positioned to hide obvious premature baldness. The face was domi-nated by a huge axe-blade of a nose, a large, hooked proboscis, a veritable eagle's beak sticking out of his face, the sides of which were clean-shaven; adorning the end of his chin was a luxurious reddy-fair pointed beard. His whole expression was one of a rather shifty-looking Punch.

I was introduced to him, though I was shortly to christen him with the nickname by which he is still widely known, 'Cunning John'. He had no sooner secured his rucksack on the roof than we were off.

We stopped in Alexandria for fish and chips prior to setting off up Loch Lomond side and across the Rannoch Moor. My fellow passengers sang endless rebel songs — some Irish some Scottish — all with the common theme of being both anti-English and anti-Establishment. To me it was a most magical experience, for here I was in the company of individuals who were exciting and who all shared a common interest in the outdoors. I must confess the significance of some of the songs was lost on me. If I had understood them fully I may not have joined in quite so enthusiastically! My only regret during the journey was the Vindaloo which I had eaten earlier, now in conflict with the greasy fish and chips. The result, trapped inside the back of the vehicle, soon had my new chums gasping.

During the journey I confided in Cunning John my desire to shoot a wild goat for the Museum, though I was careful not to mention the subject of money as I felt it better to keep this information to myself. We had struck up an immediate rapport and were soon exchanging notes on guns and cartridges. John had with him, inside his sleeping-bag, a dismantled, Webley & Scott 700 double-barrelled shotgun.

We arranged with Pat, who was in charge of the vehicle, that John and I would be dropped off to do our own thing, whilst the others went further on for a weekend's climbing, collecting us on their way back. Eventually we arrived at the drop-off point. John and I dismounted. The night was crystal-clear and very cold. After collecting our rucksacks, we set off in the darkness up a small estate road for a couple of miles until John, who was leading, descended to the river where we made our precarious way across to the opposite bank. We pitched our tents on a little, grassy lawn, screened by trees and, after a quick brew, climbed into our sleeping-bags. As I fell asleep I was dreaming of the coming goat hunt and, of course, the £25.

Next morning I awakened early. Pulling on my boots and dressed only in my underpants, I crawled out of the tent. It was a typical, crisp, clear, mountain morning. The air felt very cold on my skin as I looked around the glen. From the river the mountains rose steeply on either side, covered with rocks and heather. They were brooding and barren.

After a breakfast of tea, tinned corned beef, cheese and oatcakes, we set off up the hill in search of goats. We had not gone far before both of us got wind of a strong, pungent odour drifting on the breeze. Although neither of us had shot goats before, I recognised the smell because of the two wild nannies which we had already mounted at the Museum.

We spied a few and started making our way towards them for a better look. Eventually we positioned ourselves slightly above them and lay down in the cover of some rocks to study the beasts. There were nannies and a few young billies but nothing spectacular. Then, as I lay there, an enormous great billy suddenly appeared from behind some rocks. His horns were wide and curved, but most impressive was his silvery white colour.

I planned the stalk, taking wind into account, and set off. It was comparatively easy and I soon found myself in the cover of some rocks 30 yards downwind of the billy. The smell was so strong you could almost taste it! I had my trusty Bernardelli loaded with Alphamax AAAs. As I stood up from my hiding-place the goats started to move. I swung onto the big billy, aiming at his shoulder and fired. The billy fell dead instantly. I rushed towards him full of excitement. He was enormous with great, curving horns and an obvious beard and the whole animal from nose to tail seemed silver. I knew immediately that C. E. would be very happy when he saw this superb specimen.

Carefully I measured the girth of the animal around its belly; this was necessary for its eventual mounting. I rolled the animal on to its back and started parting the hair on its belly to make a careful incision. I had never seen an animal so dirty. Not only was it heavily infested with both ticks and keds, but the lice eggs were so thickly scattered through its underfur that it looked as though someone had sprinkled sugar over it. As quickly as possible I gralloched the beast and the two of us dragged him downhill, stashing him in some bracken near our tent.

We spent the rest of the day stalking red-deer hinds. Since we were using shotguns and were stalking on the open hill, extreme care had to be taken in the stalk; the effective range of the shotgun was only 30 yards. John took a good-sized beast whilst I shot a smaller hind. We gralloched and butchered the beasts, stashing one near the goat, then returned up the hill to collect the other.

I felt no guilt whatsoever in taking either the goat or the hind. We had no permission to shoot but that didn't unduly bother me. I justified my actions by the fact that the goat was to be used as a scientific specimen and the hind, like all game that I shot, was for the pot. We were not greedy and only took what we could use — and carry.

On Sunday late afternoon, in the darkness, we met the vehicle with the others as arranged and, on the promise of some venison, the group set off up the track with us to retrieve the carcasses. We loaded the goat onto the roofrack amongst the rucksacks. With the load tied down and covered with a groundsheet to prevent anyone seeing the goat, we set off back to Glasgow, each of us enthusiastically recounting the tales of our adventures.

We didn't seem to have travelled any distance before we were all aware of the smell of the goat. It seemed that it was being funnelled into the back of the vehicle. I realised that we must have unwittingly put it directly over the roof vent of the Dormobile. By this time it was raining heavily and everyone was anxious to get home so, rather than stop to unload everything from the roof to reposition the goat, we reckoned we would soon get used to the smell and elected to keep going.

It didn't happen. Just as we thought the smell was dissipating, the Dormobile would go over a bump in the road and another blast of the noxious odour would permeate the inside of the vehicle. Various comments were made about the smell being comparable to the smell everyone had endured on the Friday night. I was obviously not greatly appreciated. The queasiness it brought on quickly brought us all to silence. Eventually, after a hellishly smelly journey, I was unceremoniously deposited with the beast at the back door of the Museum and Art Galleries. The relief on the faces as the goat was dropped to the pavement was obvious! The night attendant at the Museum allowed me to dump the goat in one of the corridors and I hurried off to walk the several miles home.

Next morning I arrived at work bright and early, retrieved the goat from the corridor, put it on a trolley and wheeled it along to the taxidermy studio. Old Jimmy Fraser was mildly interested and complimented me on the size of the beast, but when Jake arrived he didn't seem at all pleased. He obviously had the intention of winning the £25 for himself and, as the senior taxidermist, not only regarded me as the apprentice but thought that I had no right to meddle in 'his patch'.

C. E. Palmer arrived at 9 o'clock and I knocked on his door and invited him down to our studio to see the new goat for his collection. As he walked along the corridor with me, C. E. asked me where I had obtained the goat. At my hesitancy in answering, he said with a smile that maybe it would be better for him not to know. He was delighted, exclaiming that he had never seen a better specimen and that he would indent for £25 to be paid to me by the Clerk of Works.

After C. E. had gone back to his office I tried to engage Jake in conversation. He was, after all, one of my heroes and I desperately wanted to impress him with the tale of how I had acquired the goat. Foolishly, I did. He listened with rapt attention, then on the conclusion of my story walked out of the studio. Ten minutes later the studio door opened and Jake, accompanied by C. E. Palmer, walked in. From their expressions, I knew I was in trouble. C. E. ranted at me about poaching, theft and his responsibility. In no way could he consider accepting the beast and I should remove it immediately from the museum. Jake of course stood beside C. E. like a nodding-head dog, agreeing with every point the Curator made. Never had I been so quickly transferred from glory to disgrace.

Since it was too heavy for one man to move, I was allowed the assistance of John Brackenridge and together we wheeled the beast on a trolley out

of the Museum. We decided the only place to dump it was in the River Kelvin, which flows within 300 yards of the Museum, so we pushed the trolley around the outside of the building into Sauchiehall Street. No one questioned the two, official-looking young men with a large, dead goat pushing a trolley down a city street.

We reached the river and dragged the beast between us down the bank. I wanted to keep the horns, so with a few deft strokes of my skinning-knife I quickly removed the billy's head. Then we pushed the body into the river.

I often wonder where it went and what questions must have been asked: why this great, silver, headless beast was floating down a river that flows right through the centre of Glasgow — or perhaps it was never found.

Harry the hedgehog

ONE DAY, when I was working as a trainee taxidermist in the Kelvingrove Museum, I was sent on some errand to Parliamentary Road and was walking along the pavement when I came across some kids playing with a little hedgehog. I took it from them, shoved it into my duffle bag and took it with me back to the Museum.

The hedgehog, naturally, was covered with fleas so I gave it a vigorous spraying with fly spray. At that time there was an ingredient used in such sprays — a rather potent chemical — which caused nerve paralysis. I innocently sprayed it all over the little hedgehog, though taking care not to spray his head for fear of getting it into his eyes. My colleagues and I put him in a small hutch that we kept in the studio and left him. Imagine our surprise the next day when we discovered that the hedgehog was paralysed from the shoulders back. All he was able to do was drag himself around by his front legs, his hindquarters having no apparent movement or feeling. Of course, this meant that he could no longer close or curl into a ball. Over the course of the next few weeks the three of us in the Museum, Jake Taylor, Old Jimmy Frazer and I, took great pleasure in looking after this little chap, whom we had named 'Harry'.

Two or three weeks after I had sprayed him, the paralysis started gradually to wear off and, within a month, Harry showed no signs of it. However, as a result of our handling, he had lost his fear of people in general, and the three of us in particular. If he was curled in a ball sleeping and you poked him with your finger, he would pick up your scent and uncurl, looking for some titbit. Harry lived in the studio, was given free run of the floor and became just another one of our bizarre range of pets. When we were working with chemicals that might harm him, we put him into a little run that we had created from a large, empty aquarium tank. He grew at an alarming speed. He lived on the choicest morsels, particularly enjoying the live white mice which we would put into his run for him to chase. We were fascinated by his highly developed sense of scent. No matter where a mouse might hide, Harry could find it and eat it.

After we had kept him for about a year, Jake and I were asked to give a presentation during one of those occasional 'Open Evenings'. Displays were mounted on the public floors of the museum by various individuals and organisations. One woman, a notable biologist, had as her main display

18

a quite beautiful, large glass tank, inside which she had created a woodland in miniature, with tiny plants and tree seedlings. To gaze into the tank was to look down into some Lilliputian woodland. The lady biologist however had an additional surprise up her sleeve. She would hand you a long set of forceps and invite you to select a mealworm or maggot from a little jar and to hold it quietly above the ground in her miniature woodland. After a few moments the most delightful little pigmy shrew would appear, delicately take the offered morsel and whizz off down a series of paths to his den. If you lifted what seemed to be a tiny fallen log, you revealed the little shrew, Maurice by name, delicately removing the tip of each end of the meal-worm and poking it into his writhing, wriggling larder. This was a tremendous attraction and very popular with the visitors.

Jake and I had been well warned there was to be no repeat disaster like that which had occurred during a previous Open Evening, when my hawk, which I was proudly showing to the Lord Provost, Lady Jean Roberts, suddenly sliced, sending a great stream of white bird shit down the leg of the charcoal-suited Deputy Provost and splashing Lady Jean's feet.

During our tea-break that particular evening, Jake introduced me to his latest interest. He was making home-brewed beer, a ferocious mix which was sufficiently lethal to fell Genghis Khan and certainly stronger than the lager-and-limes which I daringly sipped on rare occasions. We sat down-stairs in the studio and had several bottles of the brown, oily liquid. When it was time to go back on duty Jake thought it would be a marvellous wheeze if I took Harry with me.

We approached the long table where the lady biologist had her woodland set up and Jake suggested to her that the visitors might enjoy seeing Harry. She agreed that this was a wonderful idea and I was told to deposit him on the table. I put Harry down and he sat for a moment, motionless. Then his long nose started to twitch. Oh, what a culinary temptation he must have experienced: wafting toward him was the joyful, mixed scent of choice maggot, delicious mealworm and, of course, succulent mouse. Then he was off; shuffling down the table, he came to the glass tank, stood up on his hind legs and pulled himself over the top, falling into the miniature woodland. Before anyone could intervene he started ripping the woodland apart. Following his accurate nose, he found the mealworms and maggots but, not stopping to eat them, he darted his head to one side and grabbed Maurice.

Crunch, crunch, he bit down on the little mouse. With a shriek the lady biologist grabbed Maurice's tail. Someone should have told her that hedgehogs don't eat the tail. Harry had already neatly snipped it off and she was left holding it while Harry enjoyed his meal of pigmy shrew.

A Highland party

MARR LODGE is a splendid hunting lodge situated on flat ground surrounded by its 60,000-acre mountainous estate, just outside Braemar — a magnificent pink-tinged granite monument to past wealth and grandeur.

I used to stalk there as the guest of the owner and enjoyed many wonderful experiences. The late Bob Scott, the legendary stalker, was retired and still living in the Derry Glen. Dougie and Ackie, two brothers, were stalker and head stalker and, in their company, I had many memorable times.

I was invited to the engagement party of one of the stalker's daughters. They referred to me, tongue in cheek, as their 'token toff' — a term attributed to anyone who was a stalking guest. This invitation was quite an honour. I was being invited into the closed world of stalkers and shepherds — the hill men and their families. There was a great air of excitement and anticipation as the day of the party grew near. Indeed, I was never off the hill so early before, so keen were the boys to get ready for the 'do'.

I was staying in the Lodge in a palatial suite, filled with much of the furniture from one of the bedrooms of the Victorian Royal Family. After a hot bath I dressed for the party. Not quite knowing what to expect, I went downstairs and walked through the falling snow to the ball-room — a separate, timber building which, from the outside, gave the impression of being little more than a very large, wooden hut. Inside, however, it was entirely different. Wood-lined, the great, curved ceiling was adorned with over 3,000 stags' heads, skulls and antlers, whilst lower down the walls were lined with both antlers and full head-mounts of some really spectacular stags. Each mount was accompanied by a small plaque announcing which nobleman or member of the Royal Family had shot the beast. The whole interior of the building was both visually stunning and steeped in stalking history.

Small, wooden dining-tables had been set out by the wives around the central dance floor. They were bare except for an ashtray and paper serviettes. When I arrived there were quite a number of people already there and dancing was in progress to a local Scottish country band. Drink was flowing freely; indeed, many guests were already three sheets to the wind. You could have anything you wanted to drink, as long as it was whisky! Not only had the host families supplied a prodigious amount, but the Laird, who was not in attendance, had donated a generous number of cases and most of the men had brought a bottle with them.

I was handed a very large glass of whisky and, as I made my way to a table, one of the women set down a great plateful of stovies — a mix of mince and mashed potatoes which tasted quite delicious. I was hungry and speedily emptied the plate, washing down the food with the whisky. Another plate of stovies was pressed upon me which, out of good manners, I ate, to the accompaniment of more whisky.

I was only too happy to join in the dancing and general merriment. I was among people whom I both admired and respected. They lived, in the main, fairly isolated lives and were badly paid, poorly housed and not fully appreciated by their employers or guests. These were hard men, fit and tough. These were the men whose ancestors had struck terror into the Romans and the English and, more recently, the Germans. People of simple tastes and pleasures, the downfall of several of them was that same affliction of so many of the small Highland communities: too great an appetite for drink.

The hall filled up as the evening wore on, in a swirl of drink, more

21

stovies, dancing and laughter. Everyone was suffering varying degrees of drunkenness. I cannot quite recall whether we had reached a low point, or what triggered the idea, but I was aware of tables being cleared and positioned around the hall against the walls. Then a party of men started picking up the drunkest individuals, who were slumped in chairs, and placing them, still in their chairs, on top of the tables. Eventually, there was a drunk perched insensible on each table right round the room. I had no idea what was coming but, from the air of expectation, realised everyone thought it to be fun.

The group made their way to the first table. Sitting on the top, a drunk lolled. Someone shook him and said, 'Quick, quick, Willie, there's the polis!'

Willie, of course, staggered to his feet and blearily tried to walk. One pace and he crashed down to the floor. A great roar of delight went up as everyone made their way to the next table.

'Hamish, your wife's kicking up hell, hurry up!' and, of course, Hamish would struggle to his feet, take a step — crunch! — and hit the floor!

We, the slightly less drunk, staggered on from table to table. It seemed the greater the splat as the unfortunate's face hit the floor the greater the cheer it raised!

Eventually, the hall started to clear. Drunks were staggering in all directions, loading themselves into Land Rovers and weaving their way off through the snow, which was still falling in huge, thick, white flakes. Being slightly less drunk than most of the others and having only to walk across to the Lodge to reach my bed, I hung back, feeling responsible for the building. I made sure all the electric fires were off and that all smouldering cigarettes were put out. Then, satisfied that the building was safe, I switched out the lights and staggered out into the snow. No one was about.

I walked round the back of the Lodge to let myself in by the back door. There were still one or two Land Rovers parked and I assumed they belonged to those too drunk to drive. I walked across the broad courtyard and noticed a hump in the snow. Then another. Something made me kick one of the humps with my toe. It grunted! Then I realised it was a drunk. I looked around the courtyard and saw there were several more snowy humps. I knew I couldn't possibly leave them outside. They would never have survived the night in the snow, but what to do? I could not lift them all into the back of a Land Rover and, besides, some of them had wet themselves, whilst others had been sick.

Then I had an idea. I got into one of the Land Rovers — the keys are always in them — and drove down to the game larder and hooked up a large flat-bed trailer. I rolled the drunks one by one onto the trailer and drove back to the ball-room. Systematically I dragged each unconscious body into the room and left them in a pile — a great, stinking heap of urine- and vomit-soaked clothing.

I never heard any adverse comments from any of the partygoers about any aspect of the evening. The whole community had had a wonderful time and even those with obviously bruised faces had one universal comment: 'Aye, a grand night, just grand.'

The carnivorous bed

OVER SEVERAL YEARS Cunning John and I enjoyed many exciting shooting and stalking expeditions to a particular area where there was an abundance of capercaillie, grouse, pheasant, red, roe and fallow deer. It was paradise — too large and geographically difficult to be effectively keepered by the one man that the estate employed. Indeed, in all the time we were there, we never even saw him. However, that may also have been due to the care we took in planning our expeditions.

One Friday night, after travelling from Glasgow, we got off the bus in a blizzard and set off to walk the seven or eight miles to the lochside, where we kept our kayaks in a friend's boat-house. The snow was falling in enormous flakes as we set off to paddle down the long loch, to an island which was dense with game. The island, some three miles long, by about three-quarters of a mile wide, is beautiful, made up of light, birch woodland and Scots pine scattered over its undulating grass and bracken terrain. The island was uninhabited but did have a small cottage, comfortably appointed, used as a holiday home by some far-off city-dweller.

Normally we camped whenever we went to the island, but we had on occasion, if the weather was too atrocious for sleeping under canvas, gained access to the cottage. At no time did we feel we were doing anything wrong; we did no damage, stole nothing, simply used the accommodation. We had several times left a few tins of food, surplus to our needs, with cheeky little notes thanking the owner for his hospitality. One must assume that the owner was getting fed-up sharing his holiday home with his unseen visitors and had decided to take steps to discourage us.

We arrived at the island and, having hidden our kayaks in the bracken to avoid discovery by a passing boat, walked with our sleeping-bags and food through the deep snow up the slope to the cottage. We didn't even consider pitching the tent on such a night, particularly with such facilities available. We gained access through a back door and, shortly afterwards, had a fire blazing in the grate and a meal simmering on the stove.

Tired from our long walk and kayak trip, and since the cold in the unheated rooms was intense, we decided to sleep in the living-room/kitchen. There was an old-fashioned couch which opened out into a comfortable double bed in the kitchen. There we could take advantage of the

24

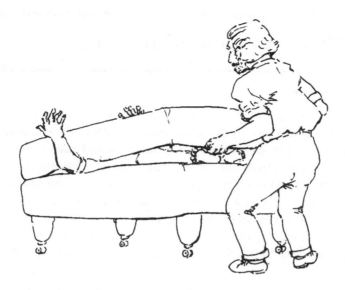

heat from the fire. We opened the bed out, remarking to each other as we opened it how very stiff it seemed.

The technique of getting into a sleeping-bag, if you are going to lie on a bed, is to lay it on the floor, step in and pull it up around your chest, then sit on the edge of the bed and swing your legs up. In this way you don't have to wriggle about trying to get into it.

I was drinking tea as Cunning John stood, pulling his sleeping-bag up around his chest, sat on the bed, swung his legs up and lay flat. Suddenly, to my astonishment, the whole bed snapped shut, like an enormous gin trap, whilst from within I could hear the smothered shrieks of Cunning John. He was bent completely double, his head between his knees, whilst his feet, inside the sleeping-bag, protruded from the top of the jaws of the bed. I struggled and heaved, trying to open the bed as John's cries became more frantic. Slowly I prised it open and there was John, as white as a sheet, looking decidedly shocked.

On examination it was obvious that someone had added some closing springs. Needless to say, we got the message and on our subsequent visits were a great deal more careful. God knows what would have happened if we had both been on the bed. I am sure that the springs were sufficiently hard to have made it virtually impossible for one or two individuals folded flat in the position Cunning John had found himself to have struggled free. We eventually stopped going to the area; probably the owner thought his little ploy had discouraged us. It certainly had.

Weekends in the Trossachs

FOR A LONG PERIOD of time Cunning John and I would leave Glasgow on a Friday night after work, travelling by bus to Aberfoyle, where we would collect our rucksacks from the luggage stowage and set off walking up the Duke's Pass on the road over to Loch Katrine. We had neatly dismantled and rolled our guns inside our sleeping-bags. John had a Webley & Scott 700 double-barrelled shotgun; I had a single-barrelled Bernardelli 12-bore. We carried with us an adequate supply of AAAs plus our entire camping requirements and looked, we hoped, like any other hiking weekenders. Our disguise must have been good: cars would occasionally pull in, offering us a lift. Once during the summer, whilst setting out for roebucks, we were walking up the hill when a tour bus full of middle-aged English women pulled in offering us a lift. We happily accepted and were shown to seats at the back. We soon arrived at our destination and started to walk towards the front. Numerous hands shot out under our kilts and the gangway between the seats became a gauntlet of cackling women, each one determined to outdo the other by having a quick 'feel'. Finally, once we were safely off the bus, it started to pull away. The considerable noise of shrieks and giggles coming from the bus reached a crescendo when John and I lifted our kilts as we waved them goodbye.

At the top of the Duke's Pass we would cut right, down through the heather, over the deer fence and into the forest which led down to Loch Drunkie. There we would pitch our tent in a tiny glade where, unless someone walked within a few yards of us, we would remain unseen. By restricting ourselves to firing very few shots we were difficult for anyone to pinpoint and we could relax and enjoy some delightful woodland stalking for red and roe deer.

One particularly memorable occasion — it was the end of the second week in October and the rut was in full swing — John and I were lying in our sleeping-bags in the early morning; we could hear stags roaring some distance away. John cupped his hands to his mouth and roared back; the call appeared to be answered almost immediately. For the next few minutes John and the stag called to each other. Then there was silence and, though John called occasionally, he had no reply. Suddenly, there was a thunder of hooves and something 'pinged' outside. Poking my head out of our small, mountain tent I was shocked to discover a large stag standing a few yards

away. As my head appeared he gave a grunt and raced off into the trees. The 'pinging' sound had been him snapping one of our guy ropes with his hooves as he passed.

We quickly dressed and set off up the side of the slope, coming out above the tree-line where we sat glassing the opposite side of the narrow, tree-filled valley. There, in a clearing on the other side of the valley, we could see one or two stags. Working out our best line of approach to stalk them we set off into the trees to work our way in a large, circular stalk to come in on them downwind. If our plan was correct and nothing happened to alert the deer, we expected to come to the edge of the clearing within a short distance of the nearest beasts.

We stalked with great care and eventually found ourselves on the edge of the clearing. We could see one large stag some 60 to 70 yards uphill from us. Using hand signals and the almost telepathic sense developed between two regular companions, we separated and slipped back into the trees, coming through on the same level as the beast, 50 yards apart in a pincer movement. There he was, not more than 30 yards from John, who crept forward a few more yards and then, in one fluid motion, as the beast began to move, lifted his gun, swung through and fired. The stag collapsed and let out a great bellow. John put down his shotgun and bounded forward, drawing his dirk as he ran. He straddled the stag and, holding its left antler in his left hand, he reached down to cut its throat. The stag gave a mighty shake of his head and John dropped the dirk as the beast tried to stand up. Putting my gun down I rushed forward to help but could do nothing as the stag was by now thrashing about like some bucking bronco. John was holding its antlers in both hands, lying along its back, with his kilt up around his waist and his great, bare bum stuck up in the air! The possible seriousness of the situation hardly entered my head as I fell about howling with laughter at the ridiculous sight, which was made even funnier by John's shrieks for help.

Eventually I drew my dirk, went forward and cut the by-now failing stag's throat. We gralloched the beast then, after stashing him, set off looking for another.

When we first started stalking this area we would normally restrict ourselves to shooting one beast, which we would then gralloch and skin, removing the haunches, forelegs and saddle. We buried the skin and gralloch, packed the meat in our bags and carried it out of the forest, over the Duke's Pass and back to Aberfoyle, where we caught the bus to Glasgow on the Sunday night. However, we eventually became more sophisticated and allowed ourselves occasionally to shoot two beasts. These we would carefully hide deep in the forest before returning to the city, our rucksacks empty. The only incriminating items we carried were our guns. We would then return a couple of nights later, being driven out by a friend who had a car. He would drop us off without stopping and continue down to the Loch Achray Hotel for a drink before coming back up the road at a pre-arranged time. We would have the meat bagged and stashed by the roadside. In a matter of moments we had it in the car and were on our way back to the city.

We also enjoyed roe stalking in the same area during the spring and summer months. We would again take the bus to Aberfoyle, walking over the Duke's Pass, and would sleep under the stars with only light sleeping-bags. If there was any danger of rain we would erect a small, two-man tent. We had to be particularly careful in this area since we were camping quite close to the forestry-trapper's cottage, but thought it unlikely he would be about between 4 and 6 o'clock in the morning when we preferred to stalk. We would then spend the day swimming, walking and amusing ourselves.

One weekend, having had a particularly early rise on the Saturday morning and a full day of activities, followed by an early Sunday-morning

rise when we had both been successful in shooting a roebuck each, we
were so tired that, around midday, we lay down in the heather a few yards
apart on a little rise in the ground, beside the river which is, though very
narrow, deep and fast-flowing. We were, we thought, hidden in the trees.
We had never been on the other side of the river and didn't realise that the
public road up to Loch Katrine ran close to it at this point. We were both
lying, sound asleep, our guns and equipment in the heather by our sides,
when we became aware of voices. Peering cautiously through the heather,
we discovered that two young couples had appeared on the opposite bank
of the river close to and just below us. Not wishing to announce our presence we lay where we were, expecting them to go away. But no. They
produced a picnic basket and a couple of bottles of wine, which they put
in the river to cool as they chatted. Then, completely unaware of us, the
four of them enjoyed an alfresco lunch.

John's and my whispered conversation could not, of course, be heard
above the rushing water and we decided to sit it out since it would not
have been possible to creep away with our bulky bags and equipment.

Lunch over, the two young couples separated on either side of a heathery bank so that they were out of sight of each other, but clearly in sight of us and only a few yards away. Then, to our embarrassed amusement, the two fellows successfully managed to remove most of the girls' clothing and all of their own and proceeded to writhe gymnastically in the sunshine.

John and I lay back wishing they would just go away when suddenly a bottle came sailing through the air and landed close to John's legs. He peered through the heather. One of the fellows had obviously chucked his empty away. John picked up the bottle and, waiting till they were engrossed in other things, carefully threw it back to land near them. It was surely one of the funniest things I had ever seen. The four, scantily-clad individuals, thinking themselves completely secluded, could not explain the sudden return of the bottle and quickly jumped to their feet, gathered their belongings and disappeared at a run.

The Loch Lomond monster!

ONE FRIDAY NIGHT, Cunning John and I caught the bus from central Glasgow and travelled out of the city to the small village of Balmaha by the side of Loch Lomond. Retrieving our backpacks from the luggage hold we set off to walk along the narrow road that ran along the lochside to Rowardennan. Our destination that first night was the boat-house where we were allowed to store our kayaks. The weather was very cold. By the time we reached the boat-house it was pretty late so we decided not to pitch our tent but to sleep in the boat-house. We had a quick meal, cooked on our stoves and garnished with a bottle of tomato sauce which Cunning John produced from his bag; then we rolled into our sleeping-bags. Next morning I noticed we had left the top off the sauce bottle and was astonished to discover that not one but two little mice had drowned in the tomato sauce. I still marvel at their ability to climb the sides of the sheer glass bottle.

As we launched our kayaks, the morning was misty and raining that fine, all-penetrating, typical Scottish rain. Cunning John and I intended to paddle down the loch, planning to land on one of the islands where we could enjoy some uninterrupted stalking for fallow deer. We set off out from the shore, turning left down the loch; the water was quite choppy with a reasonable wave running. We had been paddling along for some time and, as is common when travelling by kayak, had become separated by some 50 yards due to our different paddling strengths and the wave action. I, who was leading, suddenly spotted a peculiar sight about a quarter of a mile ahead of us. On the fringes of visibility a series of undulating humps appeared to be travelling from right to left in front of us. I pointed it out to John and we both sat watching. With the combination of poor visibility and our low position sitting in the water, it was difficult to see detail, yet we were sure of what we could see. Then a curtain of rain swept across, obscuring the view. Frantically we started to paddle after the creature. Then, after some 200 yards, we caught sight of it again.

There was no doubt, whatever; it definitely had a long neck and head, with what could be antennae, and between six and eight humps of undulating body. We could not see the creature clearly and, as it was on the fringes of the mist, we decided to continue our pursuit.

We paddled as fast as we could, but the creature seemed to be travelling quickly; then we realised we were gaining on it, just as the mist and rain thickened. Still we could not get a clear view. We paddled on. Then as we drew closer I realised what we were seeing. A stag was swimming across

the loch, followed by several hinds in line astern. We closed right up behind them, as close as we dared without panicking the beasts, and watched them swim into the shore. When they came out of the water, they shook the water from their coats and disappeared into the trees. Cunning John and I continued our journey down the loch toward the islands.

Whilst I believe in the possibility of the existence of a creature in both Loch Ness and Loch Morar, probably a form of plesiosaur — indeed the example of the coelacanth, long-thought extinct yet now caught fairly often, proves that such things can exist — there is no doubt that many of the reported sightings are attributable to other objects, such as otters, logs, and deer swimming.

Ghost story

ONE SEPTEMBER WEEKEND during 1963, Beadie Dougie, Big Ian, Cunning John and I packed our kayaks on to a van, which Big Ian had borrowed — two singles on the roof and an inflatable double inside — and set off for Loch Morar. As we neared our destination we stopped the van and caught and killed a sheep at the side of the road. It was quickly cleaned and skinned, the skin and guts being pushed down a hole out of sight.

We journeyed on to the lochside where we launched our boats, leaving the van in the shed of a local worthy, with whom we had become friendly, by the name of Foxy McLeod. In the gathering darkness we set off down the loch, the deepest freshwater loch in Europe. Loch Morar, like Loch Ness, has long been reputed to hold a beast, similar in appearance to the one in Loch Ness and referred to as 'Morag'.

We had planned to camp on one of the islands for the first night of our journey down the loch and soon arrived at an island we thought looked suitable. Densely forested, the island rises straight out of the water with no incline except for one, tiny, sandy beach not more than four yards wide.

In the moonlight we beached our kayaks, pulled them up on to the sand and made camp. As Dougie, John and I were erecting the two small

bivouacs, Ian started to prepare our evening meal, cutting up lumps of the sheep we had killed a few hours earlier; it simmered away on our little stove as we sat around. Then, as the night wore on, we tasted our stew; it was edible, though no gourmet's delight.

After we had eaten our meal we sat enjoying the bright, moonlit, clear evening, drinking tea and swapping stories. I don't know which one of us first became aware of the figures, but we all saw the same thing: the figures of men standing in the trees. They appeared to be wearing long coats. Speaking for myself I am convinced I saw these figures — six or eight of them.

Our first thought was that they were keepers but, when we called to them, they didn't respond and when Ian, the bravest and oldest of us, went to investigate there was nothing there. I climbed into my kayak and quickly went round the small island. In the moonlight I had clear visibility across the loch. There was no boat anywhere, neither tied up at the island nor on the water. Returning to the boys I reported this. They had satisfied themselves by now that there was no one there; yet we all felt sure of what we had seen.

After a not very relaxed night's sleep, the four of us packed our kit into our kayaks and set off down the loch. It was normal practice for each of us to pay out a length of fishing line, each one with a small spinning lure behind our kayaks as we travelled. In this way we caught occasional sea trout, pulling them in and placing them in a plastic bag, which we stowed between our legs. On previous trips, we had discovered a house at the far end of the loch, used annually during the sheep-gathering. Sacks of potatoes and oatmeal were hung from the rafters to prevent vermin getting to them and these, of course, provided us with additional supplies. In this wilderness area we enjoyed wonderful fishing, stalking and hill-walking; it was so remote we were never bothered. We would return each night to the house, eating venison and trout, augmented with the potatoes and oatmeal, living like kings.

At the end of our two weeks in the area we returned to the other end of the loch and I went with Ian to Foxy McLeod's house to collect the van. Over a cup of tea Foxy enquired where we had been and what we had done. I mentioned we had camped the first night on the island. Foxy looked at us for a moment and then asked, 'Did you see anything unusual when you were on the island?'

Always suspicious, Ian replied, 'Why do you ask?'

'Well,' said Foxy. 'This house [referring to his home] was a seminary. During the '45 rebellion it is said the English troops took the priests from here on to that island and hung them from butcher's hooks. Some people say that if you stay on that island at night you are likely to see the priests.'

'How many?' said Ian.

'I think there were eight,' said Foxy.

We were, to say the least, taken aback and confirmed to him that, indeed, all four of us had seen what could have been figures. They could, however, have been shadows. I have no answer other than to say that we had no prior knowledge of the story to inspire our imaginations and that all of us felt convinced we had seen something.

Big Ian's big bang

BIG IAN was much older than myself and most of my friends. An ex-Special Forces soldier, he had had adventures in Korea and Africa. He had difficulty settling back into civilian life and lived for his trips to the hills. During 1964 three of us had planned a canoe trip around the west coast.

We arranged transport for ourselves and our kayaks, with a friend who had a large Ford van, to a convenient launch site on one of the sea lochs in the northwest. Having made arrangements to meet the vehicle much further north in three weeks' time, we set off on our adventure.

Our kayaks, which we had made ourselves, were light, built of canvas and stretched over wooden frames, to a design based on the Eskimo kayaks of the Arctic. Although they were difficult to handle at first, once you had achieved proficiency, you could confidently handle seas which much larger boats would have found difficult.

We set off northwards in our three, small, canvas boats — Ian, David and I — hoping that the weather would remain calm. The forecast was not good, but we had all experienced bad weather before and, as long as it remained fairly stable, were confident in ourselves and our equipment. Having travelled for several days, with the weather deteriorating daily, we eventually found ourselves held by severe gales near a small village clinging to the land at the edge of the Atlantic Ocean. We erected our small tents in a tiny, sheltered bay at the end of a long promontory, which ran like a crooked finger out into the ocean.

During the time we were there we would, in the evenings, walk along the narrow sheep-track to the 'pub', the front room of one of the handful of houses in the village. The locals were naturally curious about the three, serious, hard young men who had appeared from the ocean in such tiny boats, but they asked few questions and seemed to accept us.

They told us the story of the new landowner, a foreigner who had bought up the surrounding estate, then proceeded to impose his own ideas of privacy and access, all of which were grudgingly accepted by the locals. Things, however, had become rather nasty when the incomer built a concrete dam across the river which flowed through his land, for the purposes of generating his own electricity. The stretch of river from its source in the loch to where it entered the sea in a small sandy bay was short and full of salmon and sea trout below the dam, all vainly trying to run up the river to the loch on their annual journey to spawn in the mountain streams.

The dam was about 30 feet across and well constructed, but the man had neglected to install a fish ladder, preventing the fish from getting into the loch. This was damaging to the ecology of the area and made fishing the loch unproductive. Representations had been made to the authorities but, as the bureaucracy dragged on, nothing was being done. I suppose we were quite a curiosity to the locals; modern tourism had yet to come and these communities were largely isolated. Over the next few days we became friendly with some of the men who gave us lots of lobsters and fish.

Ian had established a relationship with several men with whom he would sit drinking long after David and I had returned to our tents. When we were in the bar together we were gently but firmly excluded from their huddled conversations. One night, saying he would be back shortly, he and two villagers left. They appeared again about an hour later, saying nothing, and I assumed that Ian was setting up some deal or other and was aware that we were not involved in whatever was being discussed.

Next day we were held yet again by severe weather but, by late afternoon, it had improved dramatically and we decided to set off for the Western Isles. Whilst David and I packed the gear, Ian insisted on going to say goodbye to his friends in the village. Eventually he returned and we started away from the shore in the early evening but, instead of turning out to sea, Ian turned towards the river, saying he would catch up with us. Not wishing to be separated on the sea-crossing we said we would go with him and paddled along. All he would say was that he 'had a bit of business to attend to'.

When we came to the foot of the rapids, about 300 yards down-river from the dam, Ian beached his kayak, telling us to wait where we were and disappeared up the side of the river into the undergrowth. David and I sat in our kayaks, keeping our bows into the current, when our attention was drawn to a gentle splashing on the other side of the river. Quietly we paddled over and there, to our delight, was a family of otters playing on a slide, skidding down the bank on their bellies and dropping like brown arrows into the water. We sat watching the animals for some time, when suddenly Ian came down the other bank, pushed his kayak out from the shore and started paddling furiously.

'Go like f--- boys!' he shouted, heading out towards the sea, with David and I in hot pursuit. We were just reaching the point where the bay opened out to meet the incoming rollers when behind us we heard a soft 'crumph'. Ian let out a yell of delight and paddled faster. When we were about a mile out to sea we hove to, positioning our kayaks side by side like a raft. Ian told us he had blown the dam. I found this both exhilarating and frightening, convincing myself as we paddled on that it was nothing to do with me. By the determined way in which we paddled it was obvious we were all anxious to put as much distance as possible between ourselves and whatever had happened. The theory was, I suppose, that the further away from it we could get the further away the consequences were.

Over the next few miles, in what was a 16-mile sea-crossing, the wind started up, the waves got progressively bigger and we realised that it was too dangerous to go on. So reluctantly and with some trepidation, wondering what we would find when we returned, we turned back towards the mainland. The wind rose so quickly that we were soon surfing in our kayaks on top of enormous waves. This was both exciting and terrifying and it was quite impossible to stay together. However, we all made it safely back to the shore we had left a few hours previously.

The following morning, whilst we were preparing breakfast, a police sergeant arrived, having walked out from the village. It appeared he was investigating a spate of vandalism. The previous day a person or persons unknown had broken into a shed at roadworkings some miles away, removing a quantity of explosives and detonators, probably the same that had been used to blow a hole in the new dam, built on the neighbouring estate. Did we know anything about it? Where had we been last night?

We told him the truth. Ian had been in the village, we had packed and we had all gone to sea. After taking our names and details he went off back to the village, telling us not to leave until he returned. The three of us sat around, brewing tea and wondering what would happen. Several hours later the sergeant returned along the track to our tents. He was obviously in his cups, walking in the upright fashion of the determinedly sober and smelling of whisky.

'Well boys, your story seems to be true,' he said solemnly. 'One thing I don't understand though,' he said looking at Ian, 'is the number of people who insist they were with you. I don't understand how you could be in so many places at once.' We sat in silence, then after a few moments the sergeant took the offered cup of tea, sat down, lit a cigarette and with a typical Highland smirk said, 'I think you boys would be better to bugger off out of here and not come back.' With that he drank his tea, got up and walked away. We didn't need any further telling. We hurriedly packed and left. It would have taken a hurricane to have kept us from going to sea. We never heard any more of the incident.

I gave the area a wide berth for several years before risking a return. Things had changed: the pub had disappeared, a new hotel had been built which I booked into with my family. Next day I walked down to the river with my children. We stood and watched the fish in the fish ladder built in the little dam. That night in the hotel bar I chatted to the barman who told me an amazing story. Apparently some years previously the estate had built a dam without a salmon ladder and some of the locals had blown it up. 'Oh,' I enquired. 'What happened?'

'Och,' he replied. 'It all blew over. No one was ever caught.'

Eventually the landowner had rebuilt the dam and this time, being more sensible, he incorporated a fish ladder. I asked the barman again, 'Did you never find out who had done it?'

He looked at me, feigning some secret knowledge. 'Well, we have our ideas, but we never found out. There's many around here would give the man a medal.'

A case of 'help yourself'

A CHUM OF MINE, with whom I shared a flat, applied for and succeeded in getting a job in the principal gunshop in Glasgow, serving behind the counter. He was paid poor wages and, like myself, was a keen shooter. One of the obvious benefits of his new job, which he was quick to identify, was that he could provide himself with free cartridges to augment his low wage. To facilitate the removal of the cartridges from the shop, he bought himself a large anorak and showed me how he achieved this. Prior to going

for lunch he would go downstairs to the basement to collect his anorak and visit the toilet, picking up a box of 25 cartridges from the storage rack in the corridor leading to the loo. Once inside, and with the door firmly locked, he would open the box and distribute the cartridges amongst the anorak's voluminous pockets. Folding the box flat he would push it down the front of his trousers and walk out of the shop under the manager's nose. He found it so easy that he was soon arranging to meet me at lunchtime in a local coffee shop where, in the toilet, he would put the cartridges back in the box and give it to me. Then, later, when he was leaving work at 5 p.m., he would bring a second box out. Over the months, the cupboard in the hallway of our flat filled up with boxes of cartridges until we had many hundreds.

By this time my friend was getting more ambitious and had supplied us with other goodies from the shop, including quality skinning-knives. Then he had what he thought was a flash of inspiration. He developed a bad leg, the result of a supposed fall and began to walk with a pronounced limp. This, of course, gave him the perfect cover for stealing shotguns from the basement store-room, where he had discovered many guns which had been left for servicing years previously and never been collected. It was a simple matter for him to check the name under which the gun had been booked in, then look up the telephone directory and make enquiries of the owner; often he discovered they had been long dead or moved away. Taking the gun, he would go into the loo prior to leaving in the evening. He would place the barrel down his leg, inside his trousers and under his belt, then limp out of the door, unsuspected. Next day he would bring out the stock. In this manner those of his friends who were prepared to grease his palm came by nice, new guns which they could otherwise not have afforded. And, of course, in those days you could have as many shotguns as you wanted since the only legal requirement was to buy a shotgun licence at the Post Office.

I don't know how long he would have got away with it. The discrepancy in the stock would eventually have come to light. It was just as well that the college entry he had applied for came through and he left his employment. After we had used up the substantial stocks of cartridges he had stockpiled over the months, sadly, we once again had to start buying our own! When I think back to that time it wasn't such a big deal — simply theft. Were the same crimes to be committed today it would, of course, be an entirely different kettle of fish. Anyone perpetrating the sort of gun theft I have described would be unlikely to get away with it for long and, with the different attitudes to guns now, would be unlikely to have the stupidity to do it in the first place, knowing that if he were caught it would certainly mean a lengthy period behind bars.

Neil

IN MY LATE TEENS I discovered The Papingo, a little coffee bar in University Avenue in Glasgow, not 200 yards from my flat. It was frequented by lots of students from the nearby university and nurses from the nurses' home of the Western Infirmary. Situated on the ground floor and basement, the dark interior had the perfect mix of mood and music and I quickly realised it was the ideal place to meet girls. I would go there on a regular basis, normally with my little terrier, Ghillie, at heel, and meet up with friends. We would drink coffee and chat, whilst Ghillie would sit under the table at my feet, unnoticed.

It was at The Papingo that I first met Neil, a tall, thin fellow with fair hair and a narrow chest which seemed almost concave with his habit of stooping. He was two or three years older than myself. We were part of the same crowd but, apart from a few occasional chats, hardly knew each other. One night I was sitting in the corner with some friends. No one was paying attention to the two, rough-looking fellows that were sitting at another table trying to chat up the girls. I don't know what started the fight, the two men probably just picked the softest-looking fellow, but suddenly we were all aware of these two slapping Neil about. As I and one or two others started to intervene, Ghillie grabbed the trouser leg of one of the yobs, who turned and kicked him. This I took exception to and, in the ensuing fight between myself and the two, they came off worst and were chucked out the door.

Neil, holding a hanky to his badly bleeding nose, thanked me for intervening and bought me a coffee. Over the next few weeks we became friends. We shared several interests, particularly girls, and as I grew to know him better, I discovered he was keen on shooting. We visited each other's flats — mine fairly squalid, his a little better, furnished with lots of matching wood furniture, all with the feature of a little carved mouse hidden somewhere on it. Neil introduced me to the smart bars in the centre of the city, The Rogano and next door The Gay Gordon, a name that today would carry a quite different inference. He was popular with many of the patrons, mainly young professionals a few years older than me. He was obviously lonely, enjoyed the company of others and constantly threw large parties at his flat, where he was a most generous host. He liked people and, he would admit, didn't like to be alone. As Neil's friend I quickly gained an entrée into this circle which enjoyed smart cars, boats and girls. Neil obviously had more money than I did; all I knew of his work was that he was employed in a large city office. We became firm friends and I invited him to join me on several poaching expeditions. He always brought with him a beautiful Dixon Round Action which he said had belonged to an uncle. He was a very good shot and obviously enjoyed the excitement of poaching. He suffered from ill-health and took drugs to control a blood disorder which he didn't talk about. One of the results of his ailment was that he got boils.

One day, after I had known Neil for about two years, I called at his flat. There were several people there I had never met before. All, from their accents, were obviously upper crust, including his sister, a typical 'horsey type', whom I discovered was married to a Scottish aristocrat. Neil took me aside and told me his father had died. I left and returned to my flat. A few days later he called round, inviting me to go with him for a meal. We walked over to University Avenue to the Indian restaurant where, over our curry, he told me the result of his father's death. The office he worked in was the headquarters of an enormous engineering company that belonged to his family. Their business empire was considerable and, as the only son and principal heir, Neil had found himself suddenly in the enviable position of having inherited a large fortune.

The directors of the company made an agreement with Neil that they would pay him a large annual sum, on condition that he didn't interfere with the running of the company. So it was that Neil found himself with lots of money and nothing to do. I was acutely aware of the enormous difference in our finances and, had it not been for the fact that we had become friends before his inheritance, we may never have had the opportunity of getting to know each other. I was to discover that, though he had had an expensive education and his future had been planned out for him, Neil had rebelled, preferring to choose his own friends and do his own thing. He had long been regarded as a bit of a failure and the black sheep of the family.

Neil decided to buy a boat and asked me if I would like to accompany him round a few boatyards. Eventually he got his eye on a wonderful motor yacht, weighing some 27 tons, by the name of *Northern Lion*. We moved the *Lion* to Dumbarton Yacht Moorings and there, over the coming months, practised sailing her in the Clyde. We had planned a long sailing trip up the west coast of Scotland and, eventually, the day came for us to set off. It was the second week in August and the weather was splendid. Two friends were to accompany us, Peter and Adrian, both experienced sailors. We sailed down the Clyde, up into Loch Fyne and through the Crinnan Canal, passing close to Corryvreckan, the infamous area of water with whirlpools and ferocious tide race, and continued north. We would put in occasionally to the harbour of Tobermory where we would refill our water and fuel tanks, then journey on.

Over the next three weeks we enjoyed the most wonderful sailing, dropping anchor in hidden little bays on the west coast. Our two friends were horrified when we first announced to them our intention of going ashore to shoot, insisting they would have no part of it. On several occasions Neil and I would take the tender and row ashore, climb the hills and enjoy many hours looking for a few grouse. At night I would often see Neil heating a can of kaolin in the galley, making poultices which he would apply to the large boils which appeared on his bum, all something to do with his blood disorder.

One morning when we had anchored in a little bay, Neil appeared on deck with a rifle. I had no idea he had it with him. He was eager for us to row ashore and try to shoot a stag. I readily agreed and, leaving our two chums to enjoy the day fishing and sunbathing, we set off for the shore. Dragging the boat above high-water mark, we set off up the hill to look for stags. We walked for some time, eventually finding ourselves high up the mountain. As we walked over a series of sharp ridges enjoying the hot summer sun, we came on a high plateau.

We took cover by some rocks and cautiously glassed ahead. A party of four stags was lying about half a mile away. Even at that distance we could both see that one of them was enormous, with heavy antlers and deep neck. We checked the ground and wind direction, then started to move closer, keeping to the folds in the grounds. We soon moved ourselves to within about 200 yards and lay down to glass the four deer more accurately. Two of them were small beasts, one a good eight-pointer, and the fourth a quite spectacular royal. I suggested we take the nearest and smallest of the stags as, in the heat, the meat wouldn't keep well and the fridge aboard the boat was tiny. Besides we had to drag the beast back!

We tossed a coin to see who should have first shot. I lost and we set off on the final part of the stalk, crawling in until we were comfortably within 100 yards. We lay in the heather, the unsuspecting stags lying out in front. Neil slid the rifle forward, took careful aim and pulled the trigger. I was watching the nearest beast; instead of its head flopping forward, it sprang to its feet and started to run, as did two others. Momentarily I thought Neil had missed, then realised he had shot the royal. As we walked toward the stag, I asked him why he hadn't shot the smaller beast. He turned to me and stated simply, 'I changed my mind!'

After we had done the gralloch, we started the hard work of dragging the stag, which seemed to be anchored to the ground. Neil, with his thin, weak body, was of little help and it wasn't long before both of us were dripping with sweat. We did, however, eventually manage to get the stag up the long slope to the ridge, then started downhill where the task became easier. Eventually, exhausted, we reached the boat. I still wonder at our ability to load the huge beast into the little wooden tender, though once loaded it was easy to row out to the *Lion*, where, with the aid of a block-and-tackle we soon had the stag on the deck.

Adrian and Peter were aghast at what we had done, but we soon calmed them down. When we had finally stored the venison and were sitting in the small saloon, Neil poured himself a large whisky then, with a twinkle in his eye, stated, 'Next time I'll shoot the little one.'

A few months after our sailing expedition, Neil announced that he had bought an estate in the Borders and jokingly referred to himself as an 'instant laird'. He put a tremendous amount of effort into improving the shooting, planting game crop, establishing plantations and putting down large numbers of pheasants. He quickly became a member of the local Establishment and I found it quite gratifying that he never forgot to invite me for the pheasants. I was obviously not one of the social set, yet I was given the dates of all the shoots in advance since Neil expected me to enjoy his hospitality. I would drive down to the estate the night before the shoot, staying in a guest-room which he had designated as mine. I found it slightly odd that Neil, who so enjoyed the company of others, lived alone. He had never married though he did enjoy the company of a succession of young ladies whom he would invite to stay a few days.

The presentation of the pheasants was paramount — high, curling birds that were challenging to say the least. He insisted that everyone taking part had to adhere to his sporting ideals — no low birds or easy shots. After the shoot he would throw a lavish dinner-party, bringing in a caterer to supply the food and wash up.

The following year I visited Neil a few times over the summer and stalked roebuck on his ground. I was invited to shoot pheasants at the beginning of the season. Unable to journey down the evening before the shoot, I arrived in the morning. The other guns were assembling, cars arriving, but no Neil. Eventually, having knocked on the door loudly, I went round the house looking in the windows. I walked up to the french doors of his large sitting-room and, shielding my eyes from the sun, pressed my nose against the glass. I could see the back of a large, wing, leather chair by the fireside and beside it a small occasional table with a glass of whisky. I could see a pair of slippered feet protruding from the chair. Knocking on the glass and getting no reply, I made the decision to kick in the door. Neil was slumped in the chair, the book he had been reading had slid to the floor, his eyes were closed and he was obviously dead.

It turned out that Neil, knowing I wasn't coming the evening before the shoot, had agreed to visit friends locally that evening, but had telephoned them, cancelling the visit, declaring that, since he was hosting a big day's shooting, he intended to have a few drinks and an early night. Though it was never publicised, the apparent cause of his death was some new drugs that he had been prescribed for his blood disorder. He had taken them and settled down by the fireside with a whisky. The mix was lethal. The drugs should never have been taken with alcohol and Neil, who so much enjoyed the company of others, had died alone. I got the impression that there was so much money involved, and so many prominent people who didn't want publicity, that the matter was kept quiet. Perhaps if I had visited him as I normally did things may have been different. I will never know.

Nerves of steel

DURING THE AUTUMN OF 1962 I met and became friendly with a fellow who used to come into the Museum donating various specimens that he had shot. Roddy was a keen, all-round field sportsman, flying a goshawk and shooting, and as we became friendly I discovered he shared my enthusiasm for the bow and arrows. The son of wealthy parents, Roddy had a car, a rarity amongst my friends. The car made it possible for us to travel distances in our search for shooting and over the months we visited areas up to 150 miles from the city.

Roddy was always searching for excitement. Whilst he had access legally to perfectly good shooting, it didn't have that extra attraction that poaching held for him. He enjoyed the thrill of taking a beast or a few pheasants out from under the nose of gamekeepers. Whilst the rest of us curtailed our poaching exploits to areas that we knew were either free of keepers or so large that the keeper was over-stretched, Roddy would actively seek out the better policed, because richer, game areas. On one occasion he stalked and shot a roebuck, then spent the day sleeping on top of the stacked bales of hay in the hayshed close to the keeper's house, only coming out when darkness fell to collect his roe and slip away.

One July, Roddy invited me to join him poaching roe on an area near Aviemore which had recently been developed as a ski resort. We drove up on the Friday night, leaving the car at a car park, and headed off into the estate. Being the middle of summer, with long, light evenings, we soon found a delightful spot to pitch our small tent and snatch a few hours' sleep before waking at 4 a.m. and setting off to enjoy some excellent roe stalking. We were stalking together. I didn't own a rifle so intended to use

Roddy's. After about half an hour Roddy spotted a good buck. I squatted in the heather as he set off to stalk the beast. After some 20 minutes I heard the shot of his rifle and, making my way towards him, found him gralloching the buck. By the time we had the buck cleaned and carefully hidden for later collection it was getting late, the time when keepers would be up and about, so we returned to our tent, Roddy taking with him the liver and kidneys for our breakfast. Back at the tent Roddy stashed the rifle under his sleeping-bag and I got our small stove going to cook breakfast. We were sitting on the grass in the early morning sun, enjoying our breakfast of bacon, eggs, liver and kidneys, when a springer spaniel suddenly appeared, followed a few minutes later by a gamekeeper accompanied by a police officer.

The police officer asked us what we were doing and we both declared that we were hill-walkers. The keeper and policeman were standing over us when I noticed the spaniel sniffing the plate where the liver was. We had put a plastic bag over it to keep the flies away. Cool as a cucumber Roddy pushed the dog out of the way as he quietly lifted the plate and put it inside one of our knapsacks. The two men were highly suspicious and, announcing that he wished to look around, the police officer crawled into our tent, putting his hand straight upon the rifle. He came out of the tent with a grave look, holding the rifle, and asked us what we were intending to do with it. With a look of complete innocence, Roddy explained that we were heading further north to stalk with a friend of his. The two men looked around but, apart from the rifle and a box of bullets, there was no evidence. I fully expected that the two of us would be arrested but, after checking our names and addresses, the policeman handed Roddy a receipt for the rifle and bullets and, telling us to pack and leave and that we would be hearing more, they left us alone.

After they had gone we packed everything in our bags, returned to Roddy's car and drove to a nearby hotel where we ordered coffee and sat thinking what we might do. Our greatest concern was that the roebuck, hidden no more than 200 yards from our tent, would be found. Roddy hatched a plan. He knew what had to be done. Paying for our coffee we left the hotel and drove back to Glasgow. I offered to go with him but Roddy was insistent that it was something he must do alone. First he went to the nearest car-hire company and hired a car. Then, dressed as he described it 'in his smartest county threads' — brogues, cavalry twills, a white polo neck and houndstooth jacket — he headed back to Aviemore. Arriving in the early evening he drove into a campsite, pitching his tent on the perimeter adjacent to the surrounding woodland, then sat outside,

cooked a light meal on his stove, chatted to fellow campers and went to bed.

At 2 a.m., dressed in his stalking clothes, Roddy slipped out of the tent and silently made his way toward where the roe was hidden, a distance of some two miles. Concerned that the roe would have been found and that some keeper might be on the watch, he slipped as silently as he could through the half light until he came to a thicket 100 yards from the hidden buck, then sat down to watch and listen. After 20 minutes sitting silently, he crept forward to the buck, then sat for another 20 minutes beside it, watching and listening. Satisfied that no one was about, he picked it up and hurried back to the sleeping campsite. Wrapping the buck in a plastic sheet he had brought for the purpose, he silently put it in the boot of the hired car then coolly went back into the tent, crawled into his sleeping-bag and went to sleep. Eventually, wakened by the sounds of the stirring camp-site, he dressed in his county threads and casually made breakfast, packed his tent and equipment, placed it in the boot on top of the deer, got in the car, donned a pair of sunglasses and, looking like any other tourist, drove back into Aviemore and turned on the main road south.

He had gone no more than two miles when, rounding a corner, he felt his heart skip several beats. A police car was parked at the side of the road and two officers were flagging down the traffic. Roddy stopped as the car in front was approached by one of the officers who leant in to speak to the driver, then looked into the back of the car for a moment, before waving the car on and walking towards Roddy. Certain that he would be captured, he sat there saying nothing; then the officer leant in the open driver's window and announced that they were looking for an escaped prisoner. Where had Roddy been, where was he going and had he seen anyone of this description? Satisfied with the answers, the police officer waved Roddy on. As he drove away he glanced at the other officer whose attention was on the traffic. It was the very policeman who had found the rifle.

Roddy drove back to Glasgow, left the roe with a friend, and returned the hired car, his mission complete. A few days later he contacted the police to be told to come and collect his rifle. His story about having legal stalking further north had checked out.

Always seeking thrills, Roddy appeared one night at my flat, which was in Sauchiehall Street, close to Kelvingrove Park, the large municipal park in central Glasgow. He announced that he intended to shoot some duck with his bow at the duck pond in the park and invited me to join him, pointing out that it was a full moon and there should be enough visibility. This I was not prepared to do since it was not my idea of sport; besides, if I had been caught I would have lost my job. Since I was not prepared to join him, Roddy asked if he could borrow one of my labradors to retrieve any birds he shot. He remained in the flat watching television and amusing himself until after midnight, then set off for the park with the dog on the lead, his bow and arrows inside a cover. Once in the park, he strung his bow and, with the dog at heel, cautiously approached the pond. He could see the silhouettes of the birds on the water. Coming up to full draw, he picked one silhouette and shot. The bird gave a few flaps then floated dead. Quietly he sent the dog out to retrieve the bird, then shot another which was quickly retrieved by the dog. Seeing two or three more silhouettes, Roddy shot and missed and, though he sent the dog repeatedly back into the water, it failed to return with his arrow. Becoming concerned at the increasing noise being made by the alarmed ducks, he packed bow, arrows and his brace of duck and returned through the park to my flat, where he deposited the dog and related his story.

The following evening, after a day at work, I was on a bus crossing the city going to visit my parents. I was sitting reading the newspaper, the *Evening Citizen*. I turned the page and there was a half-page photograph of two wardens trying to net a goose with an arrow halfway through its neck. The story accompanying the photograph related the strange tale of how some poacher must have shot the bird!

It is a strange irony that Roddy eventually joined the army and, at the time of writing, is a senior officer; his taste for excitement and iron nerve have obviously never left him. His exploits during the Falklands War led to his being decorated. He is today very much a member of the Establishment.

Almost conned

DURING THE 'Swinging Sixties', by a series of lucky coincidences, I was running a small restaurant in the King's Road in Chelsea, called 'The Studio'. Chelsea in the 1960s was paradise for any young dude, particularly one like myself who had never before been further than Glasgow. The whole environment held great excitement and wonder. You need look no further than around you to find a seemingly endless sea of girls! And Chelsea attracted a great variety of people. They all, of course, would visit the various restaurants and we at The Studio had our share.

One of the things you quickly learn when running a restaurant is how to identify those customers who intend to spend little. They would normally order one of the cheaper dishes, particularly spaghetti, and a glass of house red.

One day, the door opened and a most unusual visitor, even for Chelsea, strode in. Tall, bearded and aristocratic, he wore a kilt and brogues, striking a quite splendid figure. He was accompanied by an attractive woman. They selected a table, sat down and with a flourish examined the menu. After some debate he ordered, in a loud upper-crust voice, 'Two plates of bolognese and two glasses of house red.'

When they had finished their meal I approached the table and introduced myself. The gentleman announced that he was the Honourable Charles MacLeod and introduced his wife, Emmanuella. They told me they were in London on business and recruiting staff for their Highland estate. I chatted to them for a bit, then enquired whether they had stalking and was delighted to be told that, yes, indeed, they had lots of stalking and I would be so welcome to come for a stag. I couldn't believe my luck but didn't really except anything to come of it, thinking it another one of those 'oh, do pop in' invitations.

Quite some time later I was surprised to receive a letter, ostentatiously sealed with sealing wax, which invited me to 'come up for some stalking'.

Because of the sealing wax, I kept the letter. I had never seen anything like it before. I telephoned the address on the paper and, having organised a few days off, arranged the trip.

I was collected from Dunkeld station by Charles himself and driven to the estate. I had never experienced anything like this before, so you can imagine what a great thrill it all was for me, but there was more to come.

When we arrived I was surprised to find that the staff of four girls were lined up outside to meet me. They were all the same age as me, but, whilst I was very much a working-class boy, they all spoke with 'Home Counties' accents. I made a few apologetic remarks before being led upstairs to a beautiful room, furnished and decorated with an Oriental theme, and referred to as the Chinese Room. I had never been in a room so opulent. This one room was larger than the whole flat I had been brought up in!

I unpacked and went downstairs for dinner. Charles immediately enquired whether I would like a drink. 'Yes, indeed,' I replied. 'I would like a whisky.'

Over drinks Emmanuella made polite conversation and asked if I had read the little booklet in my room, entitled *How We Run Our Home*. I hadn't, but felt it better to say that I had. A gong rang and I was led into the dining-room. Dinner was served at a long table; Charles sat at one end, Emmanuella at the other, and I, like some umpire, in the middle. Two of the 'debby' girls I had met earlier were serving. The meal portions were so small I felt sure it was a joke. After my tiny dinner I was led to another room for coffee and a few more drinks before retiring to my bed.

Next morning, after a very small breakfast served by one of the young county types, I was introduced to the stalker, a fit, wiry little man with twinkling eyes. His name was Tom Baxter; Charles referred to him simply as 'Baxter'. He and I set off up the hill looking for fallow bucks.

Around midday Tom and I sat down and opened our respective packed lunches. Mine was minuscule. I sat nibbling the delicate, little sandwich, looking longingly at Tom's thick, great sandwiches, stuffed with cheese and other delights. As we made small talk I could tell Tom was sizing me up to judge whether or not I could be trusted.

That afternoon I stalked a buck and after shooting it, I was surprised to find that Tom was going to perform the gralloch. I insisted that I do it myself. I wanted to show off my abilities but, more so, he was much older than I was and, at that age, I was very uncomfortable with the idea of someone acting as a servant.

That night, after yet another ludicrously tiny dinner, served at the long dining-table, Emmanuella enquired whether I liked opera.

'Yes,' I lied, trying to sound more knowledgeable than I was.

'Good,' she said. 'Then I have a treat for you.' As she led me from the room and down the hall she explained that she was an opera singer.

She crossed over to an enormous grand piano and, for the next hour, I endured her renditions. They may have been good; I wouldn't have known. To me it sounded like a hellish, shrieking noise. Eventually she finished and I made my apologies and escaped to my room.

After another tiny breakfast next day, I set off stalking with Tom Baxter. At lunchtime we sat down and opened our packed lunches. I had quickly eaten mine and sat, trying not to watch Tom obviously enjoying his, when, with a little smile, he opened his bag and handed me another lunch box. 'I've brought you some food,' he grinned.

I opened the box. It was full of wonderful, thick sandwiches; some were stuffed with slices of venison, whilst others had thick cheese. As I sat munching in ecstasy, Tom told me that normally when guests came stalking, they were so hungry that he provided them with extra food, once he had realised they could be trusted not to say anything to the Laird.

51

That afternoon, as we were making our way off the hill, I told him how I had met his employers and about the tiny portions at dinner. Swearing me to secrecy he suggested that, after dinner that evening, I make the excuse of going for a walk and come down to his cottage to join him and his wife for a proper feed!

The rest of the week followed the same pattern. I would go out in the morning (by now Tom trusted me to go on my own) and stalk and shoot any poor-quality beasts that I saw, gralloch them and then accompany Tom back on the hill to bring the carcasses to the larder. I would have a tiny dinner, then go to his house for a proper meal.

During my stay I only ever saw the four young serving-girls fleetingly as they were cleaning the house or serving my meals and so had no opportunity to speak to them, though, if the truth be told, I would have been infinitely happier spending my time with them than with Charles and Emmanuella.

On the last evening before I was scheduled to return to London, I was sitting at a root-field not far from the house, waiting for some deer that Tom said were raiding the field. As I sat silently by the side of the track I heard something approaching. I looked cautiously down the track. One of the young housemaids was walking towards me, obviously crying. I caught her attention and she sat down beside me and told me a remarkable story.

My host and hostess visited London once a year to interview applicants

to their advertisement in upper-crust periodicals for 'young ladies of quality to learn housekeeping and Cordon Bleu cookery'. They insisted that
the young ladies attend the interview with their mothers, explaining to
both mother and daughter that the lucky applicant to the post would be
given full tuition in running a smart country house and cooking for guests.
Of course, any young men that they would meet would be 'top-drawer'
and well-heeled. As a further attraction it was added that a mini-car was
provided as transport for the girls and that Charles and Emmanuella took
them out on a regular basis in the evening. The reality was that they were
paid next to nothing, worked like slaves and were restricted to 30 miles
travelling on any personal journey, which prevented them going beyond
the village. As regards the night out, when it did take place it was to the
wrestling in Perth. Why the girls stayed there I have no idea; perhaps they
had signed some contract.

I told the girl it was my intention to return the following evening to
London and she asked me if I would lend her the money for the train fare
until she got home. I was appalled by her story and agreed to lend her the
fare and accompany her south, telling her what time I had arranged the
taxi. We decided to say nothing to her employers.

The next afternoon, I had packed my bag and taken it downstairs when
Charles presented me with an envelope. I opened it and got a shock. It was
an invoice. Carefully itemised, was every drink, every meal and every deer
I had shot. I was embarrassed and annoyed. I couldn't possibly pay for it; I
didn't have the money, and I told him so. He exploded. 'Haven't you read
the little book *How We Run Our Home?*'

I explained that, no, I hadn't read the booklet. Besides, as his guest, I
had specifically shot poor beasts, even hanging them in the larder for the
game-dealer.

'Did that sound like I thought I should be paying?!' I replied.

He told me that he would sue me; then I realised I had him. I pointed
out that I had kept the letter I had received from his wife, sealed with wax,
as a souvenir. It was, clearly, an invitation to 'come up for some stalking'.

He refused to take me to Dunkeld station.

'Never mind,' I said. 'I've already phoned for a taxi.'

I picked up my suitcase and waited outside. When the taxi arrived the
driver opened the boot and put my suitcase in. Charles was standing there,
purple-faced, hurling threats at me. I got into the taxi. But where was the
girl?

As the taxi started to turn in the drive, the door behind Charles suddenly flew open and not one but two girls ran out, carrying their bags,

which they bundled into the taxi. They were obviously frightened and, as one of them was shouting at the driver to move, the other one was holding the door open to tell the speechless Charles they were no longer working for him and were off home.

The taxi sped off, leaving him standing there, open-mouthed, in the middle of the drive. During the journey to London, the girls elaborated on their atrocious working conditions. I, however, was not a little annoyed. I felt that I had narrowly avoided being conned and was worried about the threats of being sued. Thankfully I never heard any more of the affair. I did however retain my friendship with Tom Baxter, who left their employ not long after I had been there, becoming head keeper on a very large and prestigious estate.

Some years later I was visiting him and he told me of his most recent brush with Emmanuella. He had been leaving the bank in Dunkeld when he bumped into her. After they had exchanged a few pleasantries she announced, 'Oh Baxter, I have something for you,' leading him to her car. She opened the back of the car and there was a great pile of LPs. Proudly she told him that she had made a recording of her singing, as she handed him a record. Politely he accepted it. 'Thank you very much ma'am,' he said.

'Oh, that's all right Tom. That'll be £5.00!'

'Oh,' he replied, handing it back. 'I don't have a record player.'

If you go down to the woods at night you could be in for a big surprise!

DURING THE LATTER PART of the 1960s I shared a flat with a chum of mine of many years, just off the King's Road in Chelsea. It was a wonderful time when everything seemed to be so exciting and new: the Beatles, the Stones, Carnaby Street, bistros, parties and girls. He had over the last two or three years been in several, highly successful films and his good fortune and talent had brought him the wealth and recognition that came with being a film star. He bought a country house near the Surrey town of Dorking and I was only too happy to move into a cottage in the grounds. I found that in my fashionable, black Mini-Cooper I could soon be at the film and television studios in London where I worked, yet return home and enjoy living in the country which I had greatly missed.

I was surprised to discover that the south of England had large, wild, wooded areas and an abundance of game. Coming from Scotland I had always gained the impression that the south of England was one great chain of houses, villages and people, with little or no wildlife. I couldn't have been more wrong. It is a beautiful area and I quickly got myself organised with some shooting and, of course, roe stalking. I also discovered the delights of the English country pub, and my chum and I had great fun finding these old, attractive, traditional establishments.

One night we were approached by a large man who obviously recognised my pal. He turned out to be a charming, if a little brusque, North-countryman, obviously proud of his roots. He told us that he had just bought a local estate. Over the next few weeks we became quite friendly; he didn't suffer fools gladly and had no time for affectation of any kind. He had made his fortune out of heavy engineering and plant hire. He had no interest in field sports and declared that he had only bought the estate for his wife's and daughters' horses.

I asked him if I could shoot on his land and to my delight he gave me free run of the place, telling me that I could have all the shooting and stalking; his only request was that I keep the foxes down. As I started to explore the estate I found it quite wonderful. It had originally been laid out entirely for sport, with rich deciduous woodland, thick hedgerows and copses; several little duck ponds were dotted around. There were few fields, the whole emphasis of the place being on sport. There was a network of paths and tracks throughout much of the estate, created by some previous owner so that he could enjoy a lengthy ride around his property, whilst all the time being on different tracks. I enjoyed myself enormously and over the next two years shot several good bucks and a wide variety of mixed game. I found one particular pond fed by a spring, situated in a clearing, deep in the forest. It was heavily overgrown with weeds and surrounding shrubbery. I suggested to the owner that it could be much improved if it were enlarged and cleaned out. His immediate reaction was to arrange for me to be there the following weekend. When I arrived I found that he had had one of his huge earth-movers delivered and, under my guidance, the driver cleared the pond and scraped the surrounding area, creating a much larger and more desirable duck habitat.

As the shooting season approached I watched with great anticipation as the ducks started to use the pond and limited myself to occasional visits at flight time. One night I had been out lamping for foxes in a few fields at the far end of the estate. It was very late and the night was velvety black when I set off on the lengthy walk home through the woods. I had become totally familiar with all the little tracks and paths and have always felt at home in woodland, even at night, when I enjoy walking silently along, listening to the night sounds.

I was deep in the forest when I became aware of a glow in the trees some distance away. Thinking it was poachers I decided to approach them silently to see what was going on. I crept through the woods and as I came closer, I realised the glow was coming from a fire. I crouched in the darkness 100 yards away and peered through the trees. I could make out several figures; they were certainly not poachers. They seemed to be doing some sort of slow dance around the little fire. I could hear them chanting some toneless verses though I could not hear the words. I decided to move closer. With great caution I crept towards them. I could hardly believe my eyes. It was like a scene from a film. They were dressed in long robes. I had obviously come across some sort of black-magic ceremony.

As I sat watching them, wondering what I should do, I suddenly realised that there was a figure standing against a tree about halfway between the people and myself. I decided to leave. I had no sooner turned to go than I heard a shout and the sound of someone running after me. I took off like a scalded cat back to the nearest track and started running as fast as I could. I looked behind me; two or three individuals were chasing me, calling me to stop, one voice shouting 'We only want to speak to you.' I ran on, by now very frightened. I was sure they were gaining on me; then I stopped for a moment and fired my rifle in the air. They didn't chase me any further and as I ran on I could hear no further sounds of pursuit.

Eventually I reached the edge of some fields and sat in a hedgerow, getting my breath, watching and listening. Satisfied no one was following me, I hurried home.

Next morning I phoned a friend of mine, a London detective who happened to live in Dorking, and told him of my experience. Together with the estate owner, the three of us returned to the woodland. It took us a little while to find the exact area. When we did, the marks of the fire and the trampled grass were clear. We also found bloodstains and feathers. I had obviously disturbed a black mass. The stains turned out to be chicken blood and, according to the police officer, devil worship was not uncommon. Indeed he himself had had previous experience of an investigation when the black arts had featured in several crimes.

I found it quite shocking that, in such beautiful surroundings, where the population seemed so civilised, this sort of thing was obviously going on. Though we never found out who had been there or any further details, I often used to wonder what sort of people indulged in these practices and, when I was socialising, whether I was speaking to someone who had been there that night.

Foster

WHEN I LIVED IN SURREY I became friendly with a fellow who, having made a great deal of money in the City, decided to take early retirement and turn himself into a country gentleman. Rupert bought a very smart house near Smallfield, complete with a delightful flight pond surrounded by a reedbed. He bought many of the fixtures and fittings that went with the house and garden. He also discovered that Foster came with the house. Foster was a delightful character. A typical old countryman, it was impossible to tell his age, though I guessed that he was around seventy. He was very fit and had the classic countryman's habit of pacing himself so that he could keep going all day. He lived with his family a few miles distant. He was a fund of local knowledge and a quite excellent gardener, having tended the gardens of the house for many years.

Rupert visited a London tailor and ordered several smart country suits, quite determined in his new role as land-owning field sportsman. He started taking riding lessons, joined the local hunt and bought a library of outdoor books and a nice new Range Rover (they had just come on to the market). He was an instant country gentleman, all achieved with his money. What he could not achieve instantly of course, was knowledge or experience. He took great pleasure in strutting around the garden, accompanied by Foster, to whom he would issue orders to plant a tree here, trim a branch there. It was obvious he regarded Foster as a trusty retainer. Unfortunately, he tended to behave like some medieval monarch.

Rupert didn't shoot but, having happily agreed to me shooting the duck, enjoyed accompanying me at flight time. He was enormously impressed with my dog and questioned me often on its training and commands. I kept suggesting to Rupert that he should have a dog of his own and that I would be happy to help him train it. He kept postponing the idea and I eventually began to wonder if he was secretly afraid of dogs.

At evening flight I would shoot a few duck, which I was happy to share with Rupert. There was no question in his mind that he should ever learn how to clean the birds. This he left to Foster, who was only too willing to pluck the duck for us. I insisted, privately to Foster, that I should pay him for cleaning my birds and was very happy when he charged the princely sum of two shillings a bird. If I'm honest, I must confess that I preferred Foster's company to that of my well-heeled friend. He was a much more interesting man with a treasure trove of country lore and a wonderful way of telling a story.

One morning, Foster didn't arrive. In due course, we found out that he had been arrested for killing a sheep. He was eventually sentenced to three months in prison. I persuaded Rupert to keep his job open for him and, over the months he was away, his son maintained the garden. I missed the familiar figure of Foster. He was an integral part of the house and garden. When he returned I was chatting to him.

'What was prison like?' I enquired.

He thought for a moment, then looking at me said, 'It's a queer old world, sir. Oi got three months for trying to feed me family and shared a cell with a big bastard who got the same for beating up his family. How d'you answer that?' I had no answer. Foster had aged considerably in his time in prison. No longer as fit as he had been, he didn't look well.

Rupert announced to me one day that he had driven into Reigate and bought himself a nice, new shotgun and his tailor had made him a pair of smart shooting-breeks. He also started taking shooting lessons and seemed to be progressing quite well. We had been feeding the flight pond and were looking forward to the opening of the new shooting season with great enthusiasm. Foster greatly admired the new gun and Rupert told me he was constantly trying to borrow it, though this was something Rupert would never agree to do. I had noticed that, since Foster had returned

from prison, Rupert's attitude towards him had changed. He treated him with even more disdain; obviously realising that he desperately needed to keep his job, he acted with no consideration for Foster at all, expecting him to work long hours and paying him a pittance.

We postponed shooting on the pond for four weeks from the beginning of the season to give the flappers time to get better feathered; with anticipation we both looked forward to the first evening we would shoot the pond. I arrived late and, whilst parking my car in the drive, heard shots coming from the direction of the flight pond. Obviously Rupert had decided not to wait for me and the flight had started. Quickly I got gun and dog and hurried towards the pond. It was not quite dusk and a lovely, still evening. As I approached the pond I heard a couple of shots, then the command 'Get on!', followed by 'On, on!'

'Well,' I thought, 'Rupert has obviously got a new dog,' and hurried forward to see the beast. The last thing I heard before I came out of the trees was 'No, no, you stupid bastard, further out!'

Imagine my astonishment. There was my friend Rupert, resplendent in shooting outfit, giving a perfect hand signal to his retriever. And there, waist-deep in the reedbed, was Foster. As I stood watching in incredulity, Foster reached forward, lifted a mallard with his left hand and turning back towards the bank tipped his hat and cried, 'I've got 'im, sir.'

I was visiting one day not long afterwards when a fellow I hadn't seen before appeared in the garden. Rupert announced to me that this was the new gardener.

'Where is Foster?' I enquired.

Rupert looked a bit sheepish. 'I had to let him go. He wasn't up to the job and was a bit impertinent. He treated the garden as his own and was constantly trying to tell me how I should do things.'

A few weeks later Rupert returned home after an evening out to discover the back door had been forced and a burglar had been in the house. But, on inspection, only one thing was missing — the new shotgun.

I heard later, from a farmer friend, of the wonderful job of rabbit and pigeon control being carried out by Foster, who it appeared carried a very smart new gun! It never occurred to me to mention this to Rupert; his insurance had already paid up and, if it was the case that Foster had been naughty, it was perhaps poetic justice.

Who conned who?

I HAD OFTEN TOLD a friend of mine, a keen fisherman, of the wonderful fishing available in some of our Scottish hill lochs and we had decided, since both of us had time off, to make a short expedition to the Highlands. Dave was a film stuntman, whom I had met whilst working at Pinewood Studios. A typical Cockney, Dave had never been north of Birmingham and his fishing experiences had been restricted to chalk streams.

Since I intended to stay in Scotland a week or so longer than his schedule would allow we travelled separately. As we went north in our own cars, I thrashed my humble 1100 desperately trying to keep up with his nifty Porsche. We eventually arrived in the northwest of Scotland and left both cars parked behind a friend's cottage where we spent the night. Next morning my friend drove us further northwest, dropping us off in a lonely, isolated spot. We struck off into the mountains, walking over the range till we reached the spot on the map I had identified as being perfect for our short holiday. The countryside in the area is made up of lots of little, undulating hills and small, hill lochs — ideal countryside for getting close to deer, whilst the lochs are full of trout. We spent several spectacular days stalking and fishing on the land which is all part of a huge estate that belongs to an English aristocrat. I successfully shot a good stag with my bow, whilst the two of us spent many hours fishing, catching many trout. We ate like kings: trout for breakfast, venison fillets and sirloin for dinner, all cooked on our little camping stoves. Our few days over, we packed the venison in our backpacks and set off over the hills to a small, wayside hotel. Leaving our bags hidden in the heather, we phoned from the hotel and arranged to be picked up and driven back to the cottage. Next morning Dave set off back home; I had decided to spend a few days sea fishing, so drove west.

I arrived in Lochinver, the beautiful little West Highland village, situated in a natural harbour facing the Minch. Most of the land around the area belongs to an extremely wealthy English peer, the huge, neighbouring estate being the property of an English duchess. I had decided not to camp, feeling the need for a hot bath and soft bed, so I parked my car in the street outside a house with a 'Bed & Breakfast' sign and carried my bag inside.

Once I had been shown my room, I unloaded my other kit, fishing rod and, of course, my bow and arrows, which were packed neatly inside a bow case. After tea I walked around the harbour, watching the fishing-boats, then went into the local pub. It had a long bar, lino-tiled floor and several tables; a group of men were playing darts whilst a few others stood at the bar. This was obviously the pub most used by the fishermen and local estate workers. I was given a few curious looks, being a stranger, and a few friendly nods. I bought myself a drink and sat at a table in the corner where I could watch the different characters; as a writer I find watching people fascinating.

The bar was starting to fill up, music was playing and there was loud conversation and laughter when I was approached by a large affable-looking man carrying a pint of beer and a glass of whisky. He sat at my table and started to make small talk. He told me he was unemployed and I quickly got the picture that he was a bit of a foxy character. I told him I was there for a spot of sea fishing. We talked for some time about different types of fishing and then the conversation turned to other subjects. I asked him if he ever did any shooting or salmon fishing and he told me that the local estates were regarded as totally private. Actively keepered, it was difficult for a local man to get sport. Though he didn't say too much it was obvious that he disapproved of the situation.

He bought me a drink, I reciprocated and, as the evening wore on, I was enjoying the conversation, when suddenly he turned to me and, in typical Highland fashion, said, 'Yon wouldn't be a bow and arrows you had with you?' This gave me quite a shock. How on earth could anyone know? After all, the bow had been in a bow case and I had only walked across the street and into the bed-and-breakfast.

'Yes,' I replied. 'How did you know?'

'Och, I noticed you carrying it out of your car. It has the name and the wee apple.' I realised my bow bag is emblazoned with the name 'Hoyt' and the apple logo.

'Are you an archer?' I enquired.

'No, no. I just noticed.'

I sat for a moment; the chances of someone recognising a bow bag were remote. How could the fellow have known? I went to the bar and bought another drink for my companion and myself. As I sat down, handing him his drink, he looked at me with a look of feigned innocence. 'What do you shoot with it?'

'Oh, just targets,' I replied. 'But how did you know it was a bow?'

He had by now obviously decided he could trust me and, settling himself back with his glass, he replied, 'Well, well, I'll tell you. A couple of years ago an American fellow came into the bar. Myself and a couple of the lads were having a drink with him when he asked us about getting a licence to shoot deer, telling us that he wanted to shoot one with a bow and arrows. We thought he was bloody daft and decided to take the piss out of him a bit. One of the boys told him that we could arrange a licence for him to shoot a beast and it would cost him twenty quid a beast. He seemed happy about this and, after a few drams, he agreed to meet us in the morning and we'd take him out on the hill. We were just doing it for a bit of a laugh and intended to take him for a "long walk".

'I told him where I lived and he went away off to the hotel where he was staying. I got a hell of a shock the next morning when he turned up carrying a bag just like yours. I got hold of one of the boys and, thinking it would be a bit of a laugh, we set off, as I said, to take him for a long walk. After we'd been walking for some time he stopped and sat down, saying it was time to have a breather. Then out of the wee bag on his back, he produced some sandwiches, a flask and a bottle of whisky. We sat chatting for a while, him drinking coffee from the flask whilst we had a few drams. Then, jumping to his feet, he opened the bow bag and produced a complicated-looking bow with a thing attached to it full of arrows and said he would be back in a wee while and that we should sit where we were till he returned.

'He set off along the hill. We didn't think he could do any harm and lay back enjoying the dram and a smoke. The bugger was away for hours and we were beginning to wonder what the hell he was doing, and whether we should go and look for him or just go back to the village, when he appeared. He sat down beside us, looking hellish pleased with himself, and handed us over six £5 notes, telling us that that was the twenty quid for the beast and a fiver to each of us as a tip. He went on to tell us that he'd shot a stag with his bloody bow and arrows. I nearly shit myself. What the hell were we to do? It's one thing taking a man for a walk. It's entirely another to get caught poaching on that bloody estate.

'He told us he'd gralloched the beast and left it where we could find it easily and that it was up to us to bring the beast off the hill. He only wanted the antlers anyway. We could have the meat. It would've been far too dangerous for us to start dragging the beast in broad daylight. On the other hand, the longer it lay on the hill, the more chance there was of it being found. We went with him and he showed us where he had left it. It was in a wee hollow in some rough ground, a great, big, bloody, heavy ten-pointer. We thought it best to come back later and the three of us went back to the village.

'We decided to tell the Yank to keep his mouth shut, that it had been a

bit of a prank and offer him his money back. He wouldn't hear of it, insisting he just wanted the antlers. We were in a hell of a position. We couldn't leave the beast since it would get found and the bloody Yank might not keep his mouth shut, so we told him to go to his hotel and we'd deal with the beast. That night we got a couple of the boys and walked all the way back in the dark to the stag and brought it in. We cut it up, buried the skin and shared the meat and the thirty quid between us. We wrapped the head in sacks and the next morning managed to get it into the Yank's car without being seen, and told him to bugger off, reminding him to say nothing. So you see, that's how I know about you bow-and-arrow boys.'

As I went up to the bar and bought more drinks I thought of the mysterious American. He couldn't have been as naïve as he was being described. He was most likely a serviceman who had simply decided to have some sport. He was, after all, in a pretty safe position; if he had been caught he could simply have claimed that he had asked for a licence and paid the guide. The foxy Highlander, thinking the American 'bloody daft' had been caught by his own cunning. Indeed, the conman had been conned.

Herbert Fuchs

ONE SPRING EVENING in the late 1960s, I had a telephone call inviting me to visit the Furness Fells and discuss with a Mrs Fuchs the possibility of my cataloguing and setting up a collection of deer and other wildlife memorabilia for display in memory of her late husband.

I travelled to High Haybridge to meet Mrs Fuchs. As I drove through the area I was struck by its beauty. It looked to me to be absolutely perfect as a game- and, more importantly, deer-holding area. I was unfamiliar with that part of the country but was soon to find out that it is a haven for all manner of wildlife, particularly red and roe deer.

I pulled into the drive of the most delightful converted barn, set on a slope overlooking a large enclosure which held a few roe. The door of the house opened and a statuesque, attractive, charismatic lady came forward, introducing herself, and led me into the house. The high, beamed ceiling was covered with many heads of Indian and European game. It was obvious that the principal interest of whoever had been responsible for the collection was deer. Over lunch, Mrs Fuchs told me a remarkable story.

Around the 1920s, the Fuchs family had extensive business interests in India. Young Herbert was entrusted with looking after the family business whilst his father returned to Germany for a business trip and extended holiday. As the ship set sail out of Bombay with father aboard, Herbert, whose abiding passion was hunting, organised a shikar for tiger. He and a chum, accompanied by bearers and the whole panoply of a hunting party of the times, set off into the hinterland. They enjoyed some spectacular hunting and shooting, collecting many trophies which were carefully skinned and preserved for later mounting, as rugs, head-mounts, or whatever was appropriate to the species.

These were the days, of course, when European sportsmen in India were virtual lords of all they surveyed, able to shoot and enjoy a lifestyle equalled only by the extremely wealthy maharajas.

Eventually Herbert stalked and shot a large tiger which he wounded; the tiger disappeared into the long grass. Thinking that climbing a tree would give him a vantage point to see the tiger, Herbert set off up into the branches. It hadn't occurred to him that if he could see the tiger it could obviously see him. There he was, scrambling up the tree, when the tiger came up behind him, grabbing him by the thigh. Fortunately for Herbert,

his friend, an obviously quick-witted man who must have been a fair shot, shot the tiger again. The tiger dropped from the tree, taking with it large chunks of Herbert.

Herbert fell from the tree, his thigh terribly torn. There they were, far from civilisation and deep in the Indian bush, with a man horribly injured. The Indians gathered round. One of the more knowledgeable and experienced bearers wrapped and bound the injured limb with leaves and then, carrying Herbert on a handmade stretcher for several days, relays of men took him to the nearest Western medical help. He would have no doubt died had it not been for the attention of the bearers.

He convalesced and eventually returned to Bombay with a pronounced limp, which was to remain with him all his life. When word eventually reached his father in Germany he was furious at his son's disobedience and a great row ensued, the upshot of which was that Herbert was disinherited from the family fortune and set sail for the UK, where he intended to start a new life. The terms of his father's will stated that Herbert should receive nothing as long as his mother was alive.

When he arrived in the UK he met and married a young American and they enjoyed a long and happy marriage.

I sat listening with fascination to the story, toying absentmindedly with a Turk's head, knotted on the arm of the carver in which I sat. It occurred to me at the time that it was a strange place for anyone to have sat and tied such an intricate leather knot. Next day, as I started to catalogue the enormous collection of skulls and antlers, skins and knives — all the personal memorabilia of a lifetime's shooting and stalking — I became aware of various idiosyncrasies of Herbert. One of his more obvious habits was the tying of Turk's heads in the most unusual places: upon the legs of chairs, bits of wood, walking sticks and antlers. But his habit of initialling and dating everything I can only assume originated with his being disinherited. All manner of things I found had a small H.F. underneath them, even cups and saucers. In fact, *everything* I found had a small H.F. carved or painted on it. He had even carved the stock of his Mannlicher! I found a high seat in the woodland, where he liked to sit in the evening, watching deer. Even there, he had adorned both the seat and rails with Turk's heads and his carved initials.

Eventually, over the weeks, I put everything into place and prepared the exhibits for the museum which Mrs Fuchs wished to establish in his name. In due course, it was opened and the Fuchs Deer Museum proved a fascinating and educational attraction for anyone who travelled to High Haybridge to visit it.

The final irony of the story of Herbert Fuchs was that, despite having lived a long life, he never received his inheritance because of the terms of his father's will; his mother died two weeks after he passed away.

The people you meet when buying dogs

IN OCTOBER 1971 I travelled down to Ayrshire to see a fellow who was selling black labrador puppies. He had a reputation for breeding quality dogs. I was shown both dog and bitch, the dog being a Field Trials Champion, and was greatly impressed, picking out a small, black, 8-week-old puppy that resembled a little black bear. Buying a puppy is always a gamble. After a long period of feeding and training, it may well turn out to

be useless, dashing your hopes. On the other hand it may turn out to be wonderful. This puppy was destined to have a spectacular career, being one of the truly greatest dogs I have ever owned. So it was a memorable visit to Ayrshire as it turned out in more ways than one.

The fellow, whose name was John Patterson, suggested that, prior to my drive back to Glasgow, I should go round to his local pub and join him for a drink, to wet the puppy's head.

It was a typical, Scottish, working-class pub with few comforts. After we had bought ourselves a drink I looked around. The place was full of folky types: fellows with beards, Arran sweaters and sandals, and girls with long, straight hair and Indian skirts. At the end of the bar there was a small, raised platform, some 18 inches high. As I stood talking to John, a folk-singer got up on the platform and started his act. After a few mournful songs he went off, to be replaced by another hippy-looking folk-singer who began talking to the audience in a thick Glasgow accent. I wasn't paying much attention until I heard him make reference to a news item that had been in all the headlines. Three policemen had been shot dead in a Glasgow tenement. The folky-type on stage said to the audience, 'I was watching the news on television last night with the wife, about these three polis that were shot. She said, "That's terrible." I said, "Aye, it's f---in' murder!"' At which point both he and the audience howled with laughter.

I thought the joke was in extremely bad taste, but something about the fellow made me go up to him afterwards, introduce myself, explaining that I worked in theatrical management and that I might be interested in talking with him further. A few days later I visited his home — a room and kitchen in a condemned building in a slum part of Maryhill. There he lived with his wife, small boy Jamies, and black labrador bitch, Corab, in conditions of squalor.

A few days later he came into my office and, after discussion, I agreed to handle his affairs. Little did I realise that I would spend much time in the future working on his timing, nurturing him, building his confidence, retrieving him when he ran off in terror at the prospect of a concert, teaching him about the business he was in, going to enormous lengths to create opportunities for him and building him up from being a Glaswegian folk-singer earning £30 per week. Something about him that night in the Ayrshire pub had made me recognise the potential that would eventually make Billy Connolly internationally popular.

Goose shooting

MY FIRST INTRODUCTION to goose shooting was as a teenager, when I discovered that the farming community all over Perthshire, where the grey geese annually wintered from Iceland, were only too glad of some enthusiastic shooter prepared to shoot the geese and generally keep them on the move. In those days goose shooting was nothing like as popular as we know today. That was to come later, with the increasing cost of game shooting, the increasing number of shooters, easier transport and the popular shooting-press publicising the attractions of goose shooting. But in those days farmers were only too happy to let an individual on his land for the geese, expecting no payment, though a token bottle of whisky was always appreciated. I soon became addicted to the sport and spent many long hours watching, studying and shooting these fascinating birds.

It was during the early 1980s that I first met Sir William Murray of Ochtertyre Estate in Perthshire. Willie, as he was known to his friends, had

one abiding passion, the theatre, and had established a delightful little theatre in the grounds of his beautiful country house. There he mounted several, highly ambitious theatrical and musical productions. I, at that time,
worked in the entertainment industry and was looking for a cottage in the
country where I could live and concentrate on developing my work as a
writer. Willie agreed to sell me a cottage and rent me the shooting of the
land on his estate. I had already become friendly with several of the local
farmers and landowners and quickly accumulated more and more goose
shooting facilities. Rents were beginning to creep up and my work as a
writer was not bringing in the amount of money I needed to live on,
never mind pay the rents, so I decided to advertise for goose shooters.
There certainly were professional goose guides on the Solway and other
fowling areas, but I must have been one of the first to start to commer-
cialise the sport inland over decoys. For the few years that I took out
shooters for the geese, before finding myself in a position where I no
longer had to, I gained a rare insight into the different attitudes of field
sportsmen. They range from the stupidly greedy to the totally sporting,
from the man who wants to shoot a sackload to the individual who is more
than happy with a couple of birds.

Something strange

DURING THE WINTER OF 1979 I experienced the strangest series of occurrences. I had no explanation for them then and, to this day, still cannot
explain what happened. The number of occasions I am about to recount
will show that simple coincidence cannot be the answer.

A bookmaker from Portsmouth by the name of Don Symonds booked a
week's goose shooting with me. So determined was he to get my undi-
vided attention that he insisted that he have the full week on his own and
that I should not take any other bookings to share the shoot. When he
arrived Don turned out to be a charming, middle-aged man who was
obviously a keen shooter but had never shot geese. Full of anticipation for
the coming morning, he went early to bed in preparation for the 5-a.m.
start.

Next morning, whilst it was still dark, I erected a small single hide in a field I knew to be used by hundreds of pinkfooted geese. I set out the decoys and sat in the hide with Don. As the light began to increase, the first skein of geese appeared, coming towards our field. As they came into the wind they set their wings and started in. I glanced at Don. He was almost trembling with excitement. Everything was going perfectly until, suddenly, when the birds were 50 to 60 yards away, they started calling in alarm. Breaking their glide, flapping their wings, they turned and flew away.

Feeling rather silly, I hurriedly checked the decoy pattern and the hide. Everything was perfect; besides, I had done this hundreds of times. Then more birds were in the air. I sat in the hide beside Don and watched the birds come in. They turned into the wind, crossed the end of the field, set their wings and started to drop their paddles. Then 50 to 60 yards away, panic — they turned and fled. I couldn't understand this. I checked everything again. Perhaps Don had moved. I sat beside him, put my hand on the back of his neck and held his head down as the next skein started to come in to the decoys, only to repeat, exactly, the pattern of the earlier two flights.

Eventually, without firing a shot, the morning flight was over and, making my excuses, we returned to the house for breakfast. Everything would be fine, I assured him. The flight pond in the evening was bristling with greylags. We would soon get amongst them. That evening we sat by the flight pond. The cover was fine. I had been there many times over the years with great success. In the early dark I heard the first calls of approaching geese. The geese were talking to each other as they came in towards us. I could see them clearly. They would come straight over our heads. Then, at some 50 or 60 yards away, the leading birds suddenly started to call in alarm and turn frantically away from where we sat. Several times more that evening the geese repeated exactly these actions.

Over the next five days I became increasingly frustrated as I tried desperately to put Don under some geese. Every morning I would take him to different areas and always the pattern was the same. Eventually, we both realised we had one final flight left — Saturday night. There was a field near my house where over a thousand greylags had been grazing undisturbed for over a week. To one side of the field there is a six-foot-high stone wall. On the field side of the wall is a sparse line of stunted oak trees. The norm for geese leaving that field is to gather and lift and stream straight towards the trees, some of the birds so low that they come between the trees. Then, they glide downhill to the loch less than half a mile distant.

I parked the car in plenty of time and we walked in a crouch behind the wall to the place which I knew from the experience of years of observation would be the centre of the area the geese crossed on their way to the loch. By now, I had become convinced that the reason for the bizarre events of the last five and a half days had something to do with the tension and excitement that almost seemed to radiate from Don, such was his enthusiasm. We sat behind the wall and I quietly shared a flask of coffee with him, insisting that he relax. Through a tiny chink in the wall I could check the birds in the field some 150 yards distant. Around 5.15 p.m. the note of the goose-talk audibly changed and, through my tiny vantage point, I could see the birds starting to gather together. I had insisted that Don remain seated on the grass, leaving his gun to one side. He was not to move until I told him to do so.

The goose-talk seemed to increase and change again. Then, at 25 minutes past the hour, they lifted and came straight towards us in a long line. I knew we should succeed this time. Then to my utter astonishment, when the front line of birds was some 60 yards distant, and with a few cries of alarm, they started to part. The whole field full of birds, probably a thousand greylags, split in two and flew round us at a range of some 60 yards, regrouping behind us at about the same magical distance, then flew on towards the loch.

In the course of the week's shooting from Monday morning to Saturday night, Don had many potentially good flights, yet on each occasion the birds behaved as I have described. I have no logical answer — perhaps the only clue was his vibrant excitement and anticipation, almost as though he was emitting a 'force field'. Perhaps he was!

Harry

A FRIEND OF MINE, Harry, a chicken farmer from the north of England, used to come shooting with me every winter during the early 1980s. Although we were basically rough shooting, Harry primarily came to shoot geese.

A remarkable man, he and his wife, were foster-parents and took in several children from broken homes, mainly from the Liverpool area, often having as many as half-a-dozen foster-children at any one time. On his extensive holding at the chicken farm, Harry had established a kennels from where he ran the local dog pound for the Council. Strays would be brought to his kennel, where they would remain for a short period to give them the opportunity of being either collected by their owners or taken by someone looking for a pet. If this did not happen in the allotted time the dogs were then put down. He once told me, with sadness, that he received more money weekly per dog than he did per child. Harry was a true countryman, very fit; he enjoyed following the fell hounds on foot and had wonderful stories of pursuing hill foxes.

As a wildfowler with an enormous love and affection for grey geese, the highlight of his sporting year was his annual foray with me in Scotland. On any occasion when he pricked a bird in the wing, he would take the greatest care in cleaning and dressing the wound; keeping the bird alive, he would take it back south where, over the years, he had established a small population of greylags and pinkfoots on a large pond close to his house. Even the coldest, wettest, winter weather could do nothing to discourage Harry's enthusiasm.

One Sunday, knowing Harry was due to arrive that evening, I toured the whole area where I shoot, checking which fields the geese were currently using. Geese move constantly looking for food. Once they find a field to their liking, they will use the field until either they have picked it clean or repeated disturbance moves them on. Weather also plays its part. High gales, heavy rains and snow will all influence the direction the birds take when leaving their roost. After having visited several areas, making notes on which fields held geese and the direction from which they were coming in, I eventually found a field near the village of Dunning with approximately 3,000 pinkfoots. As I sat in my vehicle watching them through my glasses I noticed, right in the centre of the vast number of birds, a barnacle goose. As I studied the bird I saw two more. I thoroughly checked the great, grey, goose army. I was certain there were only three barnacles right in the midst of the sea of pinkfoots. This was highly unusual; I had never known of barnacles in the area. Apart from the normal greylags and pinkfoots all that I had on rare occasions spotted were one or two white-fronted geese.

That night, when Harry arrived, he phoned me from his hotel to invite me to join him for a drink and general fill-in so that both of us could catch up on each others news. I told him of the vast number of pinkfoots and where I intended we should shoot in the morning. Of course, I mentioned the barnacles. He looked at me with obvious scepticism and wondered whether I could have been mistaken — there were no barnacles in the area. I assured him that I was not mistaken and felt reasonably confident that, if they had been there that day, I could probably find them again. He bet me £25 that I could not put him under a barnacle.

Next morning, after loading hides, decoys and, of course, my dog in the vehicle, I collected Harry from his hotel and we set off in the dark. There had been, overnight, a dramatic change in the weather; a strong wind was blowing and I thought it best that we build our hides several fields away from where I had seen the birds, feeling sure that the gales would bring them over us and that the field they had been using the previous day would probably be too exposed in the prevailing weather. Having parked the vehicle in a farmyard, we carried all our gear across the dark fields. We built our hides against a thin hedge, staking them down to prevent them flapping. Then I started to lay out the decoy pattern, having to anchor the decoys to prevent them blowing away in the bitter wind. There was still

some time before flight time. I had just put out the decoys and was hurrying back to my hide for that first hot coffee from my flask. Harry was completing the hide when he started to whisper frantically that he could hear some early geese approaching and, grabbing his gun, quickly loaded it and squatted down, watching the dark sky.

As we peered into the sky a few silhouettes appeared coming straight towards him. He resisted the temptation to mount his gun too soon and waited until the birds were almost overhead; then, in one fluid motion, he stood up, swung through and fired two shots, a beautiful left and right. Two of the silhouettes crumpled and dropped like stones, hitting the ground with a loud thump. I lifted the net of my hide and sent Bracken, my black labrador, bounding out into the darkness. He was quickly back holding a pinkfoot. I took it from him and immediately sent him racing off for the other bird. As he ran back with the bird into the hide I took it from him. Imagine our surprise when we realised that he had returned with a barnacle. Harry carefully laid the bird out and, producing some tissues, dabbed the few bloodstains, smoothed down the feathers and laid it to one side. The bird was an adult in perfect plumage. It was the first barnacle that Harry had ever shot and he intended to have it mounted. He was overjoyed — so was I. I won my £25!

The following year I watched carefully for the appearance of the barnacles. Eventually, in late December, in the same area as the previous year, I spotted seven barnacles in a group amongst a large army of pinkfoots. Over the following three years the barnacle numbers in that small area increased to about 30 birds, always in the company of pinkfoots. Then one year they had disappeared and, although I looked carefully, I never saw them again.

White hare shooting

WHITE HARE SHOOTING as we know it today, when mainly foreign guests pay substantial sums to shoot on the high tops of Scotland, is very different from the hare shoots of only a few years ago, when an estate regarded the hares as a pest and was grateful to anyone prepared to assist in the cull. My first experience of one of these events was in the early 1970s when I was invited to a 'hare drive' in northern Perthshire. I arrived at 9 a.m. and met with my fellow guns, some 20 individuals made up of local sportsmen and estate workers. We stood around chatting as the head keeper organised things before calling us over to the back of his Land Rover to pour us all a liberal glass of whisky before distributing two boxes of cartridges to each of us. We were then directed to load ourselves into a variety of estate vehicles. I climbed into the back of a Land Rover and a fresh-faced fellow, a few years younger than myself, dressed in Barbours with a deerstalker on his head, started to climb in. I reached forward and took his gun for him, which I noticed was a rather smart Boss. The fellow sat beside me and, as the cavalcade of vehicles started off up the rough track, I chatted idly about shooting, the weather and other minor topics. We stopped for a short time whilst the line of walking guns dismounted, then continued our upward, bumpy journey. Our elderly Land Rover was last in the line and, by the time that it finally chugged its way to the top of the mountain, the other vehicles had already disgorged their passengers. I stepped down into the biting-cold wind and continued the idle chat with my new chum. Most of the other guns in my party seemed to have drifted over to the left behind a vehicle with a trailer and, prompted by the cold wind, most of them were relieving themselves. I found myself somehow seeming to drift with my new companion in the other direction. After a few yards I stopped, the demands of my bladder becoming urgent. As I stood there, making patterns on the light covering of frost on the ground, I turned to my companion and enquired why the cold didn't make him want to pee. My companion looked me in the eye and, removing the deerstalker to reveal an abundance of hair tied up in what I think is referred to as a French plait, SHE said, 'I will when you go away!'

I was one of the standing guns; we walked a short distance, then, under the direction of the keepers formed a line. I was standing just below the top of a small hillock. After a wait of some 20 minutes a few hares started appearing over the rise. The guns had started shooting. I noticed that several hares were allowed to run past the guns unscathed and assumed that my fellow guns were either not seeing them or were just bad shots. I, on the other hand, whilst picking my shots, started to shoot the hares as they came towards me in my area of fire. At first they were just a trickle but very quickly they increased in number until they were more like a white wall of running, jinking, furry bodies. Then a whistle blew, shooting stopped and, shortly afterwards, the walking guns came over the hill. Following the example of my fellow guns I had started gathering together the bodies of the hares I had shot, putting them in a neat pile. I felt quite pleased with myself; it was obvious, looking down the line of collected little white mounds of bodies, that I had shot many more than the other guns. Indeed I had shot over 30! This was when I discovered that the guns were expected to carry what they had shot to a trailer behind a tractor at the nearest access track, which for us was a considerable distance downhill. As I staggered along, laden with some 15 hares tied together, I quickly regretted having shot so many. Having deposited them in the trailer, and while my fellow guns enjoyed both a rest and a quick drink from a flask, I had to toddle all the way back uphill to the distant little white pile.

The party of guns of which I was one was then led uphill and on to the next section of moorland, where we were strung out by the keepers and then walked in line, driving the hares in front of us and shooting the occasional one which could be carried in a game bag; obviously it made sense not to shoot too many. Very soon the hares in front of us increased until, right across the moor in front of the walking guns, I could see several dozen running white bodies. I could hear firing in the distance and, as we approached the standing guns, the shooting increased; then the whistle blew to alert the standing guns to our presence and shooting stopped. The bodies were collected and carried to the nearest cart. There was time for one more drive before lunch, which was provided by the estate and was a hot-pot of venison stew.

The afternoon drives took the same form as those of the morning. Slowly the party of guns made its way in a circular route around the high moorland area of the estate, all the time taking a downward direction, so that the last drive found us fairly near where we had started out from that morning. I became increasingly disillusioned with the 'sport' as the day progressed. It was really not my cup of tea. There was no difficulty in shooting these animals, no challenge. We were simply culling them. Eventually the shooting was over and, loading ourselves into the vehicles, we were transported back downhill to the larder where the hares were sorted and counted prior to hanging for collection by the game-dealer. We had shot an astonishing 1,100.

Although I was invited several times over the next few years to white hare shoots, I never attended any. They were not my idea of sport. In those days the hares multiplied at an enormous speed, the only predators they had to deal with being hill foxes, wild cats and, of course, eagles. Their populations were allowed to build until they reached enormous proportions and threatened the hill-grazing for sheep, whereupon the estate would organise a hare shoot to reduce the number. In most areas these shoots were no more frequent than every two or three years. With a combination of the foreign sportsman prepared to pay substantial sums to shoot them and the occurrence of several bad winters, mountain-hare populations have generally decreased in most areas to a fraction of their former number.

A lucky escape

I ONCE RAN a small deer-stalking syndicate. A vacancy arose and we advertised for someone to fill it. A fellow from Chelmsford in Essex seemed to fit the bill in every way. Small of stature, he was very fit and a very keen shooter. He had wide experience of game shooting, but admitted that he had little knowledge of stalking and asked, if he were allowed to join, would I teach him?

I agreed and over the next few months he was a willing pupil, journeying from the south to Scotland on a regular basis. I soon had him stalking quite well, shooting accurately and caring for the carcasses. He eventually came to the stage when he wanted to buy his own rifle. I suggested a well-known make which was reasonably inexpensive and would last him a lifetime. Imagine my surprise when a few weeks later he telephoned to tell me he had bought a secondhand rifle, made by one of England's premier rifle-makers. The rifle had been originally made for a woman and therefore was small enough to fit my little friend. The only problem was that it had been made for the original lady owner to take to Africa and was in a large obscure calibre. When he told me what he had paid for the rifle I was horrified. He had paid the price of a small family car!

I asked him why he had bought the rifle, pointing out to him that none of the proprietary cartridge-manufacturers made ammunition in the calibre and therefore he would find it extremely difficult to obtain cartridges.

'No, no,' he said. 'I will have no difficulty. The chap I bought the rifle from owns a gun shop and is expert in loading his own ammunition. He has assured me of an adequate supply.'

'Well,' I countered, 'with such a large calibre, it will be fine for stags, but far too large for roe.'

'No, you don't understand,' he said. 'In the home loads I can buy from him he can provide 160-grain bullets for red and 100-grain bullets for roe.'

'All very fine,' I said, 'but what about your point of aim? You'll have to re-zero your scope every time you change ammunition.'

'No, he has assured me that he can balance the charge so that I have the same point of aim with two different bullets.'

I tried to tell my friend that he was talking through his hat but he wouldn't hear of it. His new chum had obviously convinced him, no doubt surrounded by the trappings of the gunmaker's art, that he knew what he was talking about.

He then went on to tell me that he had successfully managed to obtain some good-quality roe stalking in the south of England. I congratulated him and heard no more of him for some months until he telephoned me one night to tell me of his experience.

He had gone out stalking for roe early one morning. Knowing his rifle was already zeroed, he opened a new box of home loads and loaded the magazine. He had crept through the woodland, looking for roe until he eventually spotted a shootable buck and stalked it. Finally getting himself into position, he lifted the rifle, resting it on his shooting stick, took careful aim and squeezed the trigger.

There was an enormous explosion and the rifle flew from his hands. Shocked, he checked himself for injury and finding none picked up the rifle. He couldn't believe his eyes. The barrel had gone and so had the bolt.

After a careful search the bolt was found many yards behind him and the barrel to one side. When he had fired the gun the bolt must have come straight up and over. it was a miracle that it didn't pass through his head and that the barrel had flown away without damaging or removing his hand.

The reason it happened? His 'expert' friend, who had more enthusiasm than knowledge, had confused pistol and rifle powder, compacted it down too vigorously and then, for good measure, added a few extra grains of powder. He had created a lethal concoction which could have had tragic results.

A little learning is a dangerous thing!

If you've got to go, you've got to go!

I USED TO SHARE a deer forest with a media celebrity, whose public persona is one of aesthetic, intellectual excellence. A very fit man, two of his interests were hill-walking and climbing, of the more ambitious kind. He took annual holidays during which he would climb in the Alps or cross the mountain ranges of Corsica and he had climbed Mount McKinlay. He had decided to take up deer-stalking and asked me to teach him. We became firm friends, though as a deer-stalker he was quite dreadful. His was the classic case of a little learning being a dangerous thing. He was also, while excellent on the target, a shockingly bad shot at anything other than paper and I constantly had to nursemaid him on the hill, an intrusion which he greatly resented.

He had various other quirks, but certainly the most bizarre was his uncanny ability to wish to defecate at the wrong time. During the roe-stalking season we would stay in a little cottage, get up at 4.30 a.m., have a quick coffee, visit the loo and set out. There was one small wood that he seemed to find impossible to walk past without suddenly announcing, 'I need a jobby!'

As he disappeared into the trees I would hurry to the other end of the wood. Inevitably, as he squatted at one end of the wood, relieving himself, any deer in the wood would come out from the other end and I shot many good bucks, thanks to my friend's toilet requirements.

Over the three or four years we stalked together I became so used to his constant bowel demands that I began not to notice, but one classic case bears telling.

As I have said, he was a dreadful shot. It was the last day of the hind season and he hadn't shot a beast all year. I was quite anxious to help him get at least one. I knew that there would be hinds at the bottom of a long escarpment on our ground and started cautiously along the slope with him looking for beasts. The ground here was easy stalking, being made up of grassy, heathery areas peppered with huge boulders from some prehistoric landslide.

It occurred to me that he might stalk better on his own and, if I were to go to the top of the escarpment, there would be only one way the deer would take. In the unfortunate event of him wounding one I would be there to prevent its escape. I made my way up to the top of the ridge where there is a large, flat rock overlooking everything below. I crawled out on the rock and cautiously looked over. There below me, within easy range, was a party of hinds, with some shootable beasts among them. 'Perfect,' I thought. 'How can he fail?'

I lay watching for my friend's appearance and the expected shot. But nothing happened. I noticed the deer had started to get restless, yet there was still no shot, nor sign of my friend. Little did I know, though I should have guessed, that he had stopped for the inevitable!

I decided I couldn't wait any longer. The deer, I knew, were ready to go. Carefully, I lined up on an old hind and squeezed the trigger. She went down as I swung on to another and fired. The deer had started to run

along the slope. I swung on to a particularly old beast, held on her shoulder and fired. Three shots, three hinds down. I lay for a moment watching the three beasts when suddenly, to my great surprise, a hat on the end of a stick came round one of these enormous boulders, not 30 yards from the third hind I had shot.

I gave a shout and my friend's head appeared around the rock. I made my way down toward him to discover him, toilet paper in hand, cleaning the back of his legs and buttocks. He told me his version of the events.

He had been coming along the escarpment when he was struck by the call of nature. Putting his rifle down, he had dropped his trousers and squatted. Suddenly there was a loud shot, followed by another. In crab-like fashion, trousers around his ankles, he scuttled around the rock to be confronted with a group of deer, running towards him. Simultaneously to a third shot, one of the beasts went down. Desperately scrabbling backwards for his rifle, he had tripped and sat down. Imagine where!

The stag that would not die!

I LEASED a deer forest at one time with a friend, a man who had the classic symptoms of recurring buck fever. At a target he was an excellent shot, able to group his bullets tightly together, yet the instant the target became a living deer he went to pieces. His lack of marksmanship was so bad that I 'mother-henned' him, always insisting that I accompany him to make sure that any animals shot did not get away.

The owner of the deer forest had complained to us that a large stag and a party of four hinds were inside the forestry fence of the plantation and that they were causing considerable damage to the young trees. I glassed the area and seeing the five deer lying just above the tree-line inside the deer fence decided it would be best to try to stalk them coming in from above. I led my friend in a wide, circular route and eventually we found ourselves on a little knoll, just above the deer. It was a bright, sunny, winter's day and, though the stag was out of season, we realised we should have to shoot it to get it out of the trees. Since my friend had not shot a stag that year I suggested to him that he take the first shot at it before I turned my attention to the hinds. Lying side by side, I watched the stag through my rifle 'scope, ready to shoot it should he miss. On the sound of his shot the stag fell pole-axed and rolled out of sight. Assuming it to be dead I turned my attention to the four hinds and shot them all.

Standing up and reloading my rifle as I walked downhill towards them, a sixth sense made me look up to the right at the deer fence and there, to my surprise, I saw a large stag run uphill and jump right over the fence. I suddenly realised what had happened. This was not another stag; it was the one my friend had shot. I ran uphill as fast as I could and climbed over the deer fence, expecting to see the stag in the wide basin stretched in front of me. He was not there. Yet I could not understand how he could possibly have disappeared. He couldn't have run out of my line of sight in the time and I assumed he had fallen, wounded, into some hollow. I proceeded to search the wide basin where I thought he should be. My friend appeared and I sent him back to gralloch the hinds before joining me. We searched until darkness fell, then returned home. I was furious at myself for ever having allowed him to take the shot and for my haste to shoot the four hinds. Next day I went back to the area with my dogs and spent the day searching. I never found the stag and and had to assume that he had got away.

The following summer I was out on the hill with another friend, Roger Hale. We were lying on top of a rise, counting the hinds and calves just below us on the valley floor. As we lay there in the warm sun, overlooking the beasts, I noticed a deer grazing into sight below us. It had an obvious stag's hindquarters and I thought it odd that a stag should be down so low at this time of the year and among the hinds. When he lifted his head I could see that he had only one antler. He looked dreadfully thin and was walking with a pronounced limp.

I asked Roger, an exceptionally good shot, to shoot the beast. He took careful aim at the base of the stag's neck and squeezed the trigger. The stag collapsed instantly and rolled out of sight; as the hinds gathered together and made off, Roger and I stood up and started walking downhill towards the stag. We couldn't see it until we were very close. Imagine our feelings when we saw the stag standing, head down, obviously mortally wounded. Roger wanted to shoot it again. I countermanded this as unnecessary. The animal was obviously in a bad way and it was easier and quieter to use my knife. I walked over to the stag and, taking him by his one antler, pushed him down and cut his throat. Stepping back I looked at the beast. Roger's bullet, aimed at the spinal cord in his neck, had struck low; missing the bone, the bullet had gone through his neck, making an enormous exit wound in his throat. The stag continued to breathe, the gurgling air making a deep, throaty gasp through the exit wound. As I watched, the stag started to lift his head and try to struggle on to his knees. Roger asked me to kill it. Telling him that I already had, I put my knife behind its shoulder and pushed it up to the hilt and again made sure I had cut the throat properly. I stepped back from the stag and couldn't believe my eyes. The beast kept breathing this hellish sound through its shattered throat and several times made increasingly failing efforts to get on to its knees. Then it died.

I looked at Roger. He seemed as shocked as I felt. I have never seen anything like that. The stag had seemed determined not to die. When I examined him, the horror increased. This was surely the same stag shot the previous winter. He had an entrance wound on his side and a correspondingly larger exit wound on the other side. Both of them had healed over. The entrance was about the size and texture of a walnut, the exit about the size of a tangerine and made up of granulated scar tissue. The bullet, on passing through him, had disintegrated. One piece, turning and passing between his legs, had destroyed one testicle and ripped his scrotum. This piece of shrapnel had then continued into his knee, shattering the joint. His broken leg had healed with the joint fused into a great calcinated mass and his hoof, no longer able to touch the ground, had grown like a long, curved, Indian slipper.

The bullet, on passing through his stomach, had obviously destroyed much of his digestive capabilities and though when I gralloched him his stomach was packed full, his body was so painfully thin that I can only assume that he was able to extract only a minimum of nourishment.

I have no explanation for the facts I have related. I can only guess that this beast had undergone such misery that he had developed a determination to live. I am only sorry that I didn't find him sooner, or that he ever had the misfortune to be the target of an incompetent.

Beware of the wind

A NUMBER OF YEARS AGO I was visiting one of the television stations in London. At lunchtime I went with the programme director to the canteen, where I joined the queue for some food. I suddenly realised that the fellow next to me was a well-known pop-singer. I acknowledged him with a friendly hello, which he returned. Getting my food I followed the director over to a table and sat down; a few minutes later the pop-singer approached me and asked if he could join us. We introduced ourselves and he told me that he wanted to ask me a few questions about one of his dogs. He then went on to tell me that he had most of my field-sports videos. I was obviously flattered, though I tried to appear 'cool', and found myself greatly amused when I told him that I had most of his albums. He asked me not to reveal that he was a field sportsman, being concerned about attracting unwelcome publicity. I understood his concerns since the media would quickly make a meal of such news. We sat for a while chatting about field sports. I found him to be a really nice guy, completely different to what I would have expected him to be.

Not long after that meeting the telephone rang at home one morning and, on answering it, I recognized the voice of my new friend. He told me that he had a German short-haired pointer which was destroying some of the expensive furnishings in the fabulous house he has in the south of England. Would I be prepared to take it on for training and, if so, how soon? I told him I could take it straight away and that he should send it to me. 'Great,' he said. 'You'll get it today.' I fully expected him to send it with one of his roadies or various assistants so it was a considerable surprise to me when later that afternoon a beautiful Ferrari Testarossa pulled into my drive and out jumped my friend. He had just driven all the way with the pointer on the front seat. I took him into the house, introduced him to my wife and we sat having coffee. Then I heard a commotion at the front door and my two teenage daughters, home from school, came rushing in to enquire who owned the fabulous car. The look on their faces when they saw who was sitting on the settee was priceless. He stayed the night and, during dinner, had the two girls completely captivated with amazing stories of making records, world travel and life as a pop-singer.

I had invited my friend stalking and it was the following year before his busy schedule allowed him sufficient time to take advantage of my offer. We decided to have a few days stalking hinds in early January. When he arrived he proudly showed me his newest bit of stalking clothing. It was beautiful, being made by a Norwegian company that specialises in warm, wool clothing. The garment, originally designed, I believe, for North Sea divers to wear under their diving-suits, is referred to by them as a 'woolly bear'. It looked exactly like a large Baby-Gro, covering the wearer from ankles to neck to wrists. There was a zip down the front from throat to crutch. With the little bootees supplied, it was so warm that it was necessary to wear only a waterproof overgarment in even the coldest weather.

Since we were going to be stalking in snow, I lent him a white suit. I have found the cheapest and best to be the type of suits available from agricultural suppliers and made for tractor-drivers when spraying chemicals. We drove to the deer forest, donned our white suits and set off up the snow-covered glen. We walked for some considerable distance and were glassing the ground in front of us when snow started to fall gently. I spotted a party of hinds containing several animals that fell into the category of shootable beasts. After carefully studying the ground in front of us, we worked out the best line of approach to stalk the deer, which involved a wide, circular route, and set off, walking at first, keeping to folds in the ground, then crawling through the snow until we got ourselves into position within 100 yards. My friend shot two hinds, I shot one and, as the remaining animals made their way out of the glen, we walked over to begin the gralloch. That done, we roped the beasts and started dragging them downhill towards the nearest track where I could get in with the estate's Argocat.

By the time we had dragged the hinds down to the track the falling snow had thickened as the wind got up. Eventually we found ourselves walking through snow which was blowing horizontally, when my friend suddenly announced that he simply had to answer the call of nature. I gave him a wedge of toilet paper which I always carry in a little plastic bag and

suggested he try and find some shelter behind some large boulders nearby. As I waited for him I thought with amusement how he would facilitate the task; since the only openings in both the white suit and his nifty, woolly undergarment were zips from neck to crutch, he would obviously have to strip himself naked to the knees whilst trying to hold all the garments in both hands between his legs as he squatted over — and all this in the midst of a freezing blizzard. Suddenly I heard a cry of 'Aaaahhhh' and a few moments later he appeared adjusting his white suit. What was the cry I enquired? He looked at me sheepishly, then admitted he hadn't quite realised the wind was holding his woolly suit out like a parachute behind him; so great was his haste to perform the task in hand that, having completed it, he had quickly struggled back into his suit only to realise that there was a warm object on the small of his back. He had removed as much of it as he could but I noticed the first thing he did when we got back to the house was rush off and have a bath.

Ever since that day, whenever I see my friend on television portraying himself as the ultimate in 'cool', I cannot help but think of the anguished shriek coming from behind the rocks, or the picture it conjures up, so very different from his public persona.

Texas bow hunt

MY FRIEND IN THE MUSIC BUSINESS spends much of his time in the USA and has a house in Los Angeles. He had invited me to visit the States and go hunting with him. I jumped at the chance and flew out on a direct flight from the UK.

The plane landed at Los Angeles airport and, after I had collected my luggage and cleared Customs, I walked through into the Arrivals Hall looking for a familiar face. He spotted me before I saw him: Stan, my host's driver and general assistant. We carried my luggage out and walked a short distance to the car park where I loaded it into the trunk of the large saloon. Then we set off to drive into the city.

My friend lives in Beverley Hills and Stan drove me the full length of Sunset Boulevard, pointing out various sights. At first the Boulevard, which is several miles in length, is fairly downmarket: shops, fast-food bars, hookers at every corner and dotted along both sides of the road. They all dress in variations of short skirts and skimpy tops. The whole effect is one of sleaze. Then, as you journey down the Strip, the hookers thin out, the shops change and, suddenly, after you have crossed an intersection, the whole effect starts to get richer and more exclusive. It is a known fact that the police turn a blind eye to the girls as far as a particular intersection; thereafter, they are not tolerated and are quickly taken off the street. The result is an immediate transformation. Further down the Boulevard toward Beverley Hills the exclusivity is tangible: fabulous houses, many of them behind large ornate walls. Stan pointed out one large house, sitting on a hill, with some splendid gardens, decorated with several white marble statues of nudes. The house was a burnt-out shell. The story was that some rich Arab had bought the house and put the statues in the garden then, for a wheeze, had painted dark pubic hair on the appropriate parts of the statues. Some unknown individuals had burnt the house down.

As we travelled further on we turned up into the Hills. Here the homes are even more exclusive. You can't see them, each one being set behind high walls. The streets are spotless and shiny; expensive cars are everywhere; even the police cars are gleaming. Eventually we turned into a large entrance. Stan lifted a little transmitter from a tray in the front of the car, pointed it at the gate and pressed a button. The electric gates swung open, closing behind us as we passed through. The garden was immaculate as we drove round a curved drive and stopped in front of a large house which gave me the immediate impression of a garish wedding-cake.

A Filipino maid opened the door and showed me to my room, explaining that my friend wasn't at home. After I had unpacked, I wandered around the garden, then jumped into the swimming-pool and had a short swim. As I was sitting by the pool, sipping an iced tea brought to me by the Filipino girl, I reflected on the sheer luxury of this lifestyle. When my friend finally appeared late that afternoon, he explained that he would be busy for the next two days, before we set off on our hunting trip.

That night, telling me he had booked a table, we set off with his wife to the restaurant. I had heard of it and knew it to be very exclusive. Spagos is one of these fashionable restaurants where money alone does not guarantee you one of the best tables; that privilege is reserved for the famous. When we arrived we were shown to our table and hadn't been sitting there long before we were joined by another couple that my friend had invited.

The food was great and I enjoyed looking around for famous faces but, when it arrived, the bill, which fortunately I was not paying, was horrifying.

Next day, left to my own devices, I decided to have a look around and set off to walk around the area. I was dressed in slacks and a light, short-sleeved shirt with a tiny PC embroidered on the breast pocket; over the shirt I wore a light sports jacket. I intended to find my way down toward the main drag where I could find a taxi. I had only walked a short distance when a police car pulled up beside me. What, the officer wanted to know, was I doing and where was I going? When I told him and produced my identification, he explained that nobody walked around the area and that anyone doing so was naturally regarded with suspicion. He then offered to run me the mile or so to a taxi rank, where I found a cab to take me to Sunset Boulevard.

I got out of the taxi outside Rex's Fish Market, a fish restaurant, and set off walking along the Strip. I was enjoying the sights, window-shopping and looking at the people. I bought a street map showing the location of various landmarks and decided to go as far as Gromin's Chinese Restaurant before turning back. I had walked quite a distance and was enjoying the sunshine and the sights when I was suddenly confronted by a young Hispanic girl in tiny hotpants and a thin T-shirt. It was obvious that that was all she was wearing. She stood in front of me on the pavement and offered her services.

'Thank you,' I smiled. 'But I'm not interested.'

The girl was determined. 'Only $40.'

'Oh, I can't afford it,' I said, trying to walk round her. Quick as a flash she retorted:

'Anybody wearing a Pierre Cardin shirt can afford $40.'

I walked on, incredulous. I had just been given a perfect example of the strange malaise of this part of America, where there seems to be an all-pervasive emphasis on money and an individual's worth. Even an Hispanic hooker, who couldn't have been more than eighteen, has you assessed on sight. There can be few places in the world where the significance of a tiny set of initials on the pocket of a casual shirt could have any meaning. And that was whilst I was wearing a jacket!

My friend, when I told him later that I had been walking around, was horrified. Jogging's fine in certain areas but nobody walks; it is a car community.

Next morning we set off for the airport and flew to Dallas where we were met by a courtesy vehicle from the ranch at which we were going to stay. We drove west towards Abilene. I had been invited to join my friend hunting on an enormous private hunting ranch which has over 100,000 acres with high-quality mule deer and aoudad and mouflon sheep. When we arrived we were shown to our rooms which were on the first floor of the large, purpose-built ranch-house, a misleading term for what was more like a small, 12-bedroomed, five-star private hotel, complete with swimming-pool and outdoor dining-area.

The idea behind these ranches, which are to be found dotted across the USA, is little different from any large sporting estate in the UK that specialises in shooting and stalking holidays. The only difference is that, instead of simply relying on indigenous species, some ranches go further, introducing interesting species for the hunter, generally referred to as 'exotics'. Fallow and other species of deer, wild boar and, on some ranches, antelope can be hunted. The animals are as wild as they would be in their country of origin. Another advantage of these ranches is that they are highly organised. An individual can go there and enjoy all aspects of shooting and hunting with a high degree of efficiency. The animals are there; you need only find them since, as I have said, they are wild.

We met the other hunters who were staying at the ranch: a party of four and one of two. Some of them recognised my friend but, apart from a few complimentary remarks to him about his music on their first meeting, they didn't make any fuss and we all quickly got to know each other in the relaxed atmosphere. Both of us were there to try for a mule deer, my chum with a rifle, I taking advantage of being in a country where bow hunting is legal and widely popular, had preferred to use my bow, which was once the way that all deer were hunted in the UK!

I had brought with me a Browning Compound bow with a peak weight of 80 pounds, fitted with a five-pin hunting sight and a quantity of XX 75 2317s shafts with five-inch plastic fletches. Each shaft was fitted with broadheads. I had also brought with me a camouflage suit, in the pocket of which I carried a face net.

Next morning, after a light early breakfast, my friend set off in a jeep driven by a guide to the area he was to stalk. I was taken about a mile from the ranch-house and shown to a tree-stand over an obvious deer path. I didn't really want to shoot from a tree-stand. This method of shooting is to me entirely false and is little different from legalised and relatively unskilled meat collecting. All you have to do is sit there quietly until an animal of the size and type you wish to shoot is unfortunate enough to come along; then the only skill required is that you make an accurate shot. However, I agreed to sit in the high seat for a few hours, assuring my guide that I would find my own way back to the base.

I sat there watching the birds and generally enjoying the morning feeling. I had hung my bow close to hand on the side of the tree-stand rather than sit holding it, since I had little intention of trying to shoot a deer from this position. I had probably been there for about an hour when, without warning, I realised there was a deer standing along the track; it was on the edge of my vision, through the leafy screen about 50 yards away. I sat quietly watching. I could only see its legs and belly but from its slow, stepping movements it was obviously browsing. Then it started to walk towards me, a mature doe. She had the characteristic, huge ears of a mule deer. I sat motionless, watching her as she picked her way without the slightest suspicion along the track, passing me at the closest point on the track of 15 yards. She carried on along the track and disappeared.

About 20 minutes later a tiny movement caught my eye at the end of the track where the doe had first appeared. As I watched, a nice, young buck appeared. Too young to shoot even had I wanted to, he walked slowly along the track without stopping and disappeared from sight. Having seen two deer in such a short time, I sat full of expectation. Nothing else appeared and eventually it was time for me to walk back to the ranch.

I arrived back in the early afternoon and, since all the parties were still out, I showered and sat around relaxing. I was joined by the hunt manager who ran all the shooting on the ranch. He was concerned that I was enjoying myself, which I assured him I was. I explained to him that I did not wish to hunt from a tree-stand and would rather take pot-luck stalking on the ground, on my own without a guide, assuring him that I understood that, by turning down the chance to sit over a trail, I could dramatically reduce my chances of success. He eventually agreed, since safety was not a consideration; being on a private ranch, each hunter is assigned an area, unlike the general hunting areas where it is wise to wear bright clothing to avoid the risk of being accidentally shot by some overzealous, inexperienced hunter.

The other parties started to drift in about mid-afternoon; several of them reported success, having shot either deer or sheep, which had been hung at the larder after numerous photographs had been taken. My chum arrived last, just as I was getting ready to set out again. He told me he had shot a nice buck after a long and interesting stalk and that he had seen several, top-quality, trophy animals. The best times to hunt deer anywhere are early morning and evening. This is particularly relevant if you are a bow hunter, since by necessity you must move slowly and quietly, and it is obviously an advantage if the deer are active and moving about, rather than couched in cover.

I persuaded one of the guides to drive me down towards where I had been that morning, then set off walking over the rolling countryside, which is covered with lots of light tree growth — perfect terrain for stalking. Probably the best advice for any deer-hunter was given to Howard Hill, the legendary American bow hunter, by a Seminole Indian when he asked him the key to successful hunting. The Indian simply replied that the good hunter should 'walk little and look much'.

The technique I used was to move as silently as I could into a vantage point overlooking a grassy area surrounded by thin tree-cover, then sit quietly watching and listening. Once sure that no animals are in the area, you move quietly on to the next likely spot then sit, watching and listening. I find that, when stalking alone and employing this technique, all my senses become greatly heightened and that I enjoy a feeling of sharp exhilaration.

After I had travelled about half a mile, sat overlooking three different areas, and seen only one doe, I was moving quietly through some trees at the edge of a long, shallow gully when I had that feeling I get occasionally. I knew there were deer very close. I stood motionless looking down into the patch of cover. In one dense area, not 60 yards from me, several fallen trees created a dense thicket; then, as I watched, out from the other side sneaked a nice mature buck. How long he had been aware of me I don't know. After he had gone I gave him a few moments then continued along the side of the gully. As I passed above the thickest part of the windblows from which the buck had appeared, I heard a little sound behind me. I turned my head and there he was, a big, heavy buck, slipping away silently; he had obviously allowed me to walk right past him. I could have kicked myself, but then again deer-stalking and bow hunting in particular are all about the thrill of stalking and, whilst it might sound perverse, I actually get an enormous kick, albeit tinged with frustration, from being that close to a deer which then slips away. It is the many occasions on which I don't succeed that make the occasional successes so worthwhile.

The light had started to fade. I realised I had been out much longer than I thought and started back towards the ranch. When I arrived, there was a party atmosphere. Everyone was enjoying themselves, chatting excitedly about their various experiences, both that day and on previous hunting trips. After a short break for showers and change of clothing, we all sat down to dinner which was a quite spectacular barbecue featuring several different meats — venison, beef, chicken and the chops from one of the sheep shot a few days previous — huge salads, sweetcorn, baked potatoes and black-eyed peas, all served outdoors with lots of good-quality Californian wine and, of course, the most delightful apple pie.

Next morning I reluctantly struggled out of my bed at first light, greatly regretting having eaten and drunk so much and sitting up late the previous evening. I quickly dressed, grabbed my equipment and hurried downstairs. The cook was already in the kitchen with the coffee brewing and I quickly swallowed a cup of the hot, strong liquid before hurrying outside.

It was a beautiful, clear morning with a slight chill in the air and, after I had walked a few hundred yards. I began to feel better at the prospect of trying for a good buck. I intended to go back to the area where I had been the previous day. I was walking purposefully along, intent on getting to the hunting area, when I walked over a little rise in the ground. There in front of me, already aware of my presence, were two bucks and a doe bounding off. I felt rather silly and determined to concentrate on keeping my eyes open.

I walked back to the track where I had sat the previous morning in the tree-stand and started to walk silently along the path. From the tracks in a wet patch in front of the tree-stand, I could see that the path was obviously heavily used. I had walked only a short distance past the tree-stand when I came to the edge of a long, natural meadow and squatted down against the front of a tree to watch and listen. I had been there only a few minutes when I realised that there were two deer under the trees on the left side of the meadow about 200 yards away. I examined them through my binoculars. Both bucks: one with an average head, the other a good mature animal. I decided to try to make my way towards them and set off around the edge of the trees, moving as silently as I could.

The first 100 yards were quite easy. Both the deer were relaxed, unaware of my presence and moving slowly away from me at a slight angle into the meadow, walking a few yards then stopping to graze. I watched the bigger of the two bucks. He would take a few nervous nibbles then jerk his head up, looking around. The light breeze was blowing across in front of me and I felt confident that, if I took my time, I could make the distance to the buck unobserved. As their heads went down I moved forwards a few yards and froze; then I repeated the exercise. About 50 yards from the deer, I squatted down against the trees and carefully ran my eye over my bow, checking that my arrow was sitting on the rest, then started forward. Suddenly there was a little noise to my left in the trees. A deer bounded away; I didn't see it but it must have got my wind. The two bucks jerked their heads up and in a few bounds were into the trees and gone. I stood up slowly.

There was little point in continuing in the direction which they had taken so I turned across the meadow with the wind in my face and started climbing up the tree-covered slope towards the little ridge before the ground dropped into the next shallow valley. On the ridge I sat down and started to glass the ground below me. I could see several deer on the opposite slope but couldn't work out how I could silently make my way across to them. The cover on my side was dense. To have tried to go down through it would have announced my presence to every animal in the area, so I decided to go back and sit in the tree-stand. It was, I reasoned, perhaps not such a bad idea in this sort of country and little different from a high seat in any forested area in the UK.

I had been in the tree-stand for about half an hour; nothing had passed and I was beginning to feel drowsy and to contemplate a little snooze when a young buck came along the track. This perked me up and I sat for the next hour or so but no other animals appeared. Realising that the morning was wearing on, I climbed down and walked back to the ranch. By the time I got there, all the other hunters had eaten their breakfast and set out for the day.

That afternoon I set out again, earlier than I had the previous day. My plan was to go back to the area where I had been the day before. I cautiously made my way to the edge of the long, shallow gully and started to move silently along the rim; squatting down every 50 yards or so, I would sit for lengthy periods watching and listening. As I approached the heavy, windblown thicket where I had seen the two bucks previously, I moved into the trees away from the edge of the little ravine; reappearing above the densest bit of the cover I sat and studied the thicket. There were lots of signs of deer: droppings, tracks and quite clearly defined paths. I sat with my back against a steep part of the bank and decided to wait. I slipped the face net over my head; now, unless I moved, or the wind gave my scent away, I would be very difficult to see.

After about an hour I was beginning to wonder whether I was doing the right thing, when, as I slowly turned my head to my left, I realised a deer was on the other side of the thicket. I could hear tiny movements. I strained my eyes but couldn't see anything; then I realised that the little patches of browny-grey visible through tiny gaps in the thicket were hair. I had no idea where the deer had come from, whether it had been there all the time or had walked along the gully unseen by me. I didn't know whether it was aware of my presence and ready to bound away. There was a little light breeze but it was drifting towards me. I couldn't move to get more comfortable or into a better shooting position since I knew the deer would hear me, so I sat there hardly daring to breathe, watching where I knew it was. It could have been a buck or a doe. Then it took a few steps forward and I saw the head; it was the big, mature buck from the previous day and obviously unaware of my presence. He was only 25 yards away.

Slowly I started to draw my bow until I felt my index finger anchoring in the corner of my mouth. I held my position at full draw, wondering how long it would be before he took the next few steps; then he moved. His head passed across a narrow gap, then his neck, then his shoulder. I held the pin sight behind his shoulder and low, right on his heart, and released the arrow. The arrow struck him on the spot where I was aiming and passed completely through him. In one bound, the buck disappeared.

I sat there aware that I was trembling with nerves and excitement. Stalking with a rifle isn't remotely as thrilling as this. Whilst I knew that I had hit the animal in the heart-and-lung area, and was certain that it would die swiftly, I decided to give it a full 15 minutes to be doubly sure. Deer, if wounded, will not run unless they are being pursued; intead they lie down and the haemorrhage caused by the arrow or shot will continue. If, on the other hand, you panic a deer by chasing it, it can run a long distance, which makes finding it very difficult. My caution was unnecessary. The deer had run less than 30 yards before collapsing.

When I gralloched it, I found that the arrow had passed through the top of his heart, the four razor-sharp blades creating awesome damage. The deer had felt nothing and had died in seconds.

It was dark by the time I reached the ranch. I found two of the guides and we went back in a vehicle towards the spot where I had left the deer. I led them along the side of the darkened gully and we dragged the buck back to the jeep before setting off on the short drive to the ranch-house. They dropped me off and carried on to the larder. I walked in to the same party atmosphere as the previous day. Everyone had had a successful hunt and were already on their second or third drink. My chum came forward; he could see from my expression that I had been successful.

The next day we flew back to Los Angeles where I spent a couple of days being shown the sights. One great highlight for me was Sea World in San Diego on the southern tip of California. Then reluctantly I flew back to the UK and to the realities of earning my living.

The Spanish lady

ONE DAY I RECEIVED A LETTER on very expensive notepaper, set at the top with an elaborate crest. The letter invited me to meet the writer on matters pertaining to deer, sika in particular, on the writer's estate; it was signed, with a flourish, 'The Marquesa del Torres Hermana Hermosa'.

I was both flattered and delighted to receive the letter. I wrote back saying I would be happy to visit and, over the next two weeks, viewed the coming meeting with great anticipation. I managed to persuade myself that the Marquesa would look like the girl in the Doncella cigar advertisement. She would be beautiful and single, living in some Scottish castle surrounded by thousands of acres. She would be disgustingly rich and, of course, longing to share her estate, her fortune and her bed with me.

When I eventually set off to meet her I had my smartest suit in the back of the car, together with a well-ironed shirt — in fact a complete change of clothing. I arrived in the vicinity of her estate and went into a roadside Highland hotel. In the toilet I washed and changed, emerging dressed for the smartest company and reeking of expensive aftershave. I obtained directions from the hotelier and drove towards her house. I turned into the

only possible drive that the directions would allow and drove up the rutted track — I was sure I must be on the servants' entrance — and then arrived at a large, run-down house.

This I assumed must be the under factor's, or under keeper's, abode. I rapped on the door and stood back. A hunched-up, dirty, little figure, of great age, hobbled round the corner of the building. I viewed with distaste the cropped, thin hair, the lapels of the ancient jacket encrusted with dandruff, egg and God-knows-what other proteins, the dirty trousers and the turned-down wellies. Things would certainly change once I got my hands on my Spanish lovely.

I enquired in my most superior and laird-like voice, 'Where will I find the Marquesa del Torres Hermana Hermosa?'

The little person looked at me. 'Good afternoon, I am she.'

Marga

HAVING OVER THE YEARS KEPT SEVERAL of the lesser birds of prey, which I enjoyed training and flying, I finally applied to the Department of the Environment for a licence to keep a goshawk. Three of my friends, all enthusiastic falconers, had also applied and, when the licences came through, we sat down to decide how we could procure these magnificent birds of prey. Getting the licence was at that time difficult. Getting a bird was a much harder proposition. Almost all of the birds that came to the UK for falconers originated from Germany and, unless you had extremely good contacts there, it was virtually hopeless. On an impulse, I telephoned a friend of mine, the head of a large company, who I knew marketed his goods in Germany, and asked him if he had any contacts there who might know a falconer. He phoned back the next day to tell me that his German distributor had a good friend, a Herr Echart Shaumeir, who was the president of the Deutschland Falcon Club. My friend had spoken to Herr Schaumeir, who was awaiting my call. I immediately telephoned and, after a lengthy conversation, was invited to Germany and told to bring with me all four DoE licences. Ideally, the birds I was looking for should be female; in common with all birds of prey, they are one-third larger than the males and are much more versatile birds when flying at a variety of game. A large female, once trained, can take prey up to the size of a brown hare, the smaller males generally being restricted to rabbits. A heavy cock pheasant, whilst manageable by a male gos, is just so much more easily handled by the larger female.

Echart met me at the airport and drove me to his home, a splendid, converted, 800-year-old farmhouse. We immediately discovered a rapport, having many common interests, particularly stalking and, of course, falconry. Echart explained to me that this was the right time of the year to collect birds of passage, immature young hawks migrating south from the north of the European continent. Next day we drove a short distance from his home, entering a large forest where I was to be shown how the birds I had come to collect would be trapped. Several elaborate cage traps had been built at strategic points throughout the forest. In a little compartment in each one, a live pigeon sat with a supply of food and water. A hunting gos, seeing the bird, comes down into the top of the trap to grab the pigeon, whereupon the pigeon drops, by an ingenious little trapdoor, into another section of the cage, whilst the gos finds itself unharmed but imprisoned. The first trap we arrived at held a huge, adult female, her deep-red eyes staring at us with rage. Goshawk eyes slowly change colour as they mature from yellow to a deep red. It was probably largely their red eyes and, of course, their aggressive, unbreakable spirit that convinced many medieval northern Europeans that they were devil's birds. Indeed, in some areas of Germany, it was the custom to crucify a gos on a barn door to warn off evil spirits. Echart explained that the adult gos was most likely a local bird and, opening the cage, let her fly free.

We moved on. The next pen hadn't been touched. When we arrived at the third, I could see a large, brown-coloured bird trapped in the upper compartment. On examination it turned out to be an immature, female gos. Her piercing, yellow eyes stared back, full of aggression, as Echart, wearing heavy, leather gloves, carefully removed her and held her whilst I quickly fitted a pair of leather jesses to her legs, before putting her into a purpose-built carrying-box in the back of the car. After we had driven back to Echart's house, we tethered the bird to a perch under the oak trees in the garden; then after dinner I fetched the bird to start the long, slow process of encouraging her to eat from my fist. As I approached the bird she baited frantically, trying to escape, but I carefully lifted her on to my gloved hand and carried her inside. On examination we noticed she had broken the last inch and a half of her second primary; Echart immediately suggested that we must find it so that I could imp it. Calling his young son, Wolfe, he asked him to go and find the feather. Immediately Wolfe left. I looked out of the window to the darkening garden, thick with oak leaves.

'How,' I asked Echart, 'do you expect the boy to find a brown feather in the dark, amongst a pile of brown leaves?'

Echart looked at me and simply replied, 'With a torch!'

This was my first introduction to the attitude of parental discipline and respect that was obviously the norm in Germany, yet to my British ears sounded extremely strange, knowing the attitude of a typical British teenager. Eventually Wolfe appeared with the feather and I started to imp it. Shaping a small, plastic cocktail stick, I fitted it inside the hollow quill with glue and repaired the feather so necessary for perfect flight. Next day I was looking at Echart's peregrine tiercel, 'Pan', sitting on his screen perch in his place of honour in a corner of the enormous hall.

Noticing a large, antique cabinet against the wall, I crossed to admire it. Echart asked me if I would care to see his gun collection and, taking the key from a little drawer, opened the cabinet. A row of shotguns and rifles stood in the rack, whilst a few handguns sat on the shelf. After I had admired the weapons, Echart turned the key in the lock and dropped it back in the little drawer.

'Aren't you concerned with three young sons in the house, that they will be tempted to open the cupboard and play with one of the guns?' I enquired.

Echart merely shrugged his shoulders. 'No, of course not. They are told not to.'

Over the next few days we successfully collected three more immature, female goshawks and, packing them all into a regulation bird-carrying-box, complete with airholes, I flew back to the UK. Landing at Glasgow airport I had to go through the Customs shed. A Customs Officer, on hearing I had four goshawks, began to study a large book of rules. Not finding what he was looking for he closed the book and asked the value of the birds, no doubt having been influenced by media reports of the alleged many thousands of pounds some birds of prey were worth. I declared that the birds had no value; the Customs Officer was insistent; everything had a value.

'No,' I replied. 'They have no value and I didn't pay for them.' Indeed I went on to point out to him that it was at that time illegal to sell birds of prey and, if it was illegal, how could he expect me to attribute a value? Furthermore they were widely regarded in some parts of Europe as vermin.

'Why do you want them then?'

'For falconry.'

'Then they have a value.'

'No, only intrinsic value.'

'Look,' I said. 'Imagine I was importing a bucket of shit. It would have no value, yet it could well be of use to me. I would not have to pay duty on that.'

The Customs Officer smiled. 'Oh yes you would, sir.' He patted his books of rules. 'That would be categorised as fertiliser.' I refused to weaken and the Customs Officer was obviously enjoying the small, unusual dispute.

'Right,' he said. 'Can I see the birds?'

'Yes, if you can take me into a small, lock-fast room. Since the birds have not yet passed quarantine and it is illegal for me to remove them from this box until they reach the quarantine facility, you must also supply me with a heavy, leather glove.'

We had reached an impasse. The Customs Officer started trying to peer into the airholes, then, to my surprise, poke his finger through several of the holes. Before I could stop him he let out a shriek and jerked his hand back from the box. A long, black talon had made a jagged rip in his finger. Holding the bleeding finger in a hanky he waved me through with the comment, 'I like birds anyway, I just wanted to hear your argument.'

I called my bird 'Marga' and, after many long, patient months of getting her manned, fit and coming to my fist, entered her at her first prey, a small rabbit. She enjoyed two years of spectacular hawking, taking a range of prey, mainly pheasants and rabbits. On one memorable occasion when I had her very fit (she was in 'yaroch', the term used when a bird's flying weight is perfect) I took her out in the early morning, built a hide exactly as though I was going to shoot geese and sat in the hide with Marga hooded. I waited until some pinkfoots had landed amongst my decoys then, carefully removing the hood, lifted her above the net. Seeing the movement, the geese started to jump, Marga rocketed from my fist, covered the 20 yards like a bullet and grabbed a pinkfoot by the back and neck. The goose fell back the two or three yards to the ground and the two birds rolled about, struggling. The large, beating wings of the goose couldn't reach her; then the goose lay on its belly as Marga sat on top of her, her wings half open as she mantled her prey.

Another morning whilst being flown, she missed a pheasant and landed in a tree. Before I could call her down, her keen eyes caught movement in another tree and she rocketed forward, catching a grey squirrel. I stood helpless, watching her perched high up in the oak as she proceeded to kill, then eat it. Your relationship with a bird of prey is based only on food. When a bird is not hungry it has no reason to come to your fist. Gorged on squirrel, her crop swollen, she sat gazing impassively down at me as darkness fell.

I was out at first light, listening for the sound of the bells on her legs. Eventually I spotted her but could not lure her down and, though I tried over the next few days, I knew I had lost her. The abundance of rabbits and other game would provide a ready supply of food. I visited all the local keepers, explaining a simple way of trapping her, offering a large reward and trying to convince them that a gos, like all other creatures, is essentially lazy and, in countryside over-run with rabbits, many of them suffering from myxomatosis, their pheasants were safe.

Although I received reports of her being seen and her bells being heard in the area, I never saw her again. Then, one evening, a young gamekeeper friend of mine came to my house. He produced a small scrap of paper. On it were written a line of numbers. 'Is this your DoE licence number?' he enquired. It was.

'Where did you get it?' I asked.

'Her leg and DoE ring are sitting as an ornament on the mantleshelf of a gamekeeper I know. He heard bells and found her sitting eating a myxy rabbit so he shot her and removed her leg and ring as a souvenir.'

Though I tried every inducement, the young keeper refused to tell me where he had seen the number. His job and future would have been finished had he broken the code. Whenever I think of Marga I feel sure that some day, someone will talk, boast about killing the giant, grey hawk; then I will know who did it.

The eagle's revenge

IT IS A SAD FACT OF LIFE that many of our wonderful predatory birds are shot purposely by those few, dreadful individuals who blight field sports. They are not sportsmen and, in my opinion, their actions should be prosecuted. Certainly, caring sportsmen should not stand by and say nothing. I myself have always advocated a policy of standing up and being counted and, on more than one occasion, whilst in the midst of a pheasant drive, have shouted out a warning when a sparrowhawk has come over the guns. I have even occasionally remonstrated with individuals for shooting at these birds. On one particular occasion I became so incensed after calling a warning of 'Sparrowhawk, don't shoot' to the gun next to me in line, whereupon he swung through and shot the bird, that immediately after the drive, I approached him, telling him what I thought of him. He laughed and, in the ensuing argument, received an extremely bloody nose! The other group of individuals, some of whose members kill our predatory birds, are, of course, gamekeepers.

I am not saying that all gamekeepers are guilty of this crime; far from it. Indeed, I believe that, generally, wildlife is in the most responsible hands when under the care of a modern keeper. However, where I live, I know of several gamekeepers who kill everything with a hooked beak, whether by shooting, the use of poisons or destroying their nests. I had applied to the Department of the Environment for Licenced Registered Keeper status. This simply means that any Schedule 4 birds found injured in the area where I live should come to me for care, prior to my hacking them back to the wild. Word spread that I would be the recipient of any birds brought to me and I lost count of the number of birds of prey I rescued and released.

I once had a telephone call late at night from a man whose voice I recognised, a friend of mine, a retired gamekeeper. He phoned me to ask

me if I wanted two of 'they birds'. I knew he was referring to two peregrine falcon chicks. He told me they were in a box, in a shed, at a head
keeper's house so, asking him to ring me back in half an hour, I phoned
another friend, an eminent falconer, and explained the delicacy of the situation. I could not expose to the authorities the source of the birds since my
elderly friend who was offering the birds was in a particularly vulnerable
position, and his life within the area would have been hellish had the word
got out that he had blown the whistle on the head keeper. My falconer
friend told me that unless I was prepared to phone the police or the Royal
Society for the Protection of Birds, I should do nothing, since my idea of
taking the birds then declaring the following day that they had been left
anonymously at my door was so fraught with danger that I could find
myself being charged with the theft of the birds. I thought carefully about
the implications of my actions, then phoned a friend of mine, a senior
policeman in the City, and told him that I intended to take the birds
secretly, then to declare them the following day. If in the interim I was
apprehended, then he was prepared to vouch for the fact that I had already
spoken to him. By the time my friend phoned back I had the plan
arranged. Sadly, when he went to collect them, the head keeper had
already wrung their necks and 'put them down a hole'.

The only difference between the attitude of years ago, when keepers
could do as they pleased and freely slaughtered all predatory birds to preserve the game, and now, is that keepers must be a great deal more careful.
The laws are strict and many more members of the public are aware of the
environment and enjoy walking in the countryside. In addition to the legal
implications, keepers caught and prosecuted are now more likely to lose
their jobs. Fear of discovery and prosecution are therefore having the
desired effect whilst other gamekeepers and countrymen are certainly
changing in their attitudes and appreciation of our predators. Nevertheless,
it is a rare person living amongst them who would have the nerve to report
one of these individuals for fear of the repercussions.

A friend, who lives in a Highland glen, rather than report the killing of
a protected bird tries to cultivate an appreciation of the birds. He is a
wildlife-painter of international reputation and popular with the other
inhabitants of the area, particularly the stalkers, shepherds and gamekeepers.

The glen is one of the longest in Scotland, made up of several estates. It
was there, during the summer of 1990, that an incident took place that has
an ironic twist. A gamekeeper from the glen, who, according to my friend,
is a cold and callous individual, was far out on the hill, remote for even this
isolated area. As he sat between some rocks taking a breather and eating a

sandwich, he noticed a golden eagle coming along the ridge above him. The huge bird was not particularly high and had probably not spotted the keeper as it patrolled the ground below, searching for some suitable meal. The man settled himself down into a comfortable firing position, took careful aim at the eagle with his rifle and fired. The rifle boomed across the hills, but the eagle was unscathed. Again the man took aim and fired. Another miss. The third time he fired, the bird, obviously hit, started to tumble earthwards. The man jumped to his feet and started making his way towards where he had seen the bird fall, some distance away, to find and ensure its body was stuffed down some hole where it could never be found.

As he walked across the hill, no doubt congratulating himself on a good shot and ridding the area of a bird that might eat some grouse, he suddenly heard a shout from below. The man looked downhill. Four figures had appeared a quarter of a mile away over a ridge and were moving quickly uphill towards him. Hill-walkers or climbers, they had obviously witnessed the whole incident and the man knew well the repercussions, both physical and legal, if he were to be caught. Putting his rifle on his back he set off across the heather as fast as he could run. It was imperative that he get the eagle's body and take it with him. Realising that the individuals in the anoraks were gaining on him, he bounded along not a little concerned. Eventually he came to the great bird lying in the heather, gathered it up quickly into his arms and ran on.

Suddenly the man became shockingly, painfully aware that the eagle was far from dead. It had been stunned in its tumble to the ground. His bullet had broken its wing. As the bird became conscious it sunk both feet, equipped with huge talons, deep into his guts and hung on. Each great, hooked talon would have, in the flutes on the underside, a quantity of bacteria introduced by morsels of rotting flesh and blood from the bird's prey. In enormous pain the man ran on, trying desperately to kill the bird but unable to stop for fear of his pursuers. Knowing the ground, and having the advantage of height and being very fit, the keeper amazingly made good his escape, eventually managing to kill the bird and hide it deep under some rocks.

The matter was, naturally, reported to the authorities but the time-lag and lack of evidence made it impossible for them to have a successful prosecution. I have no idea how the keeper explained the injuries to his stomach. He must have suffered excruciating pain from the resulting septi-caemia which, of course, required medical attention. It is, in the opinion of many who hear the story, a less than fitting penalty.

The lady of the manor

THE TELEPHONE RANG. It was Rick Wilson, the editor of the *Scotsman* colour magazine. Would I cover the story of a Scottish lady who had written a cookery book, he enquired. He had thought of me because I lived near the area and, whilst I knew little of cooking, he thought I could give a good pen-portrait of the authoress.

He gave me the address — Lady Gleneck, Gleneck, Inverness-shire — and a telephone number. I phoned Lady Gleneck, introduced myself and, in my most charming voice, told her I would like to visit her home to conduct the interview and take photographs because the magazine intended to do a several-page spread. It would be ideal, I suggested, if she could arrange a small dinner-party for herself and a few friends in her no doubt splendid dining-room; the theme of the story would then take the form of a glimpse into this rarefied atmosphere. The meal set on the table should reflect her culinary prowess and her new book.

She arranged a suitable date with me, stating she would invite a few

guests and that I, of course, should number myself as one of those fortunate few diners. Since the evening promised to have great potential, and
because I intended to exploit fully the possibilities of both the wonderful
dinner and the stalking and shooting potential of their estate, I enlisted a
photographer to take the photographs rather than do them myself, which
would have been more usual.

On the appointed day, with great anticipation, we drove up the A9
heading for the Highlands, through the glen and into the drive up to
Gleneck House. We bumped our way up a rutted drive, to be faced by an
inauspicious, slightly dilapidated, grey house.

I knocked at the door and a kilted, bearded figure opened it, introducing himself as 'Gleneck'. He led us into the house; the whole place had a
decidedly run-down and seedy atmosphere. We sat in the drawing-room,
awaiting the appearance of Lady Gleneck. Eventually, the door opened and
a fairly attractive woman in a hideous, pink party-frock came through the
door. Introductions made, Gleneck tried to insist that nothing should be
written about his wife without his having read and approved the copy. I
told him that this was out of the question and, after some argument, he
agreed.

The photographer suggested a photograph of Lady Gleneck in the gardens with her dog. 'Do you have one?' he enquired. Gleneck left, returning with a horrid-looking, liver-coloured beast that vaguely resembled a
labrador. It entered the room wagging its tail. As I reached forward to
acknowledge the dog, Gleneck gave a sudden cry. 'Careful, have a caution!
He goes straight for the throat!'

I was beginning to have the tiniest suspicion that things were not quite
right. However, by the time we had taken some photographs, had a few
drinks and I had interviewed and taken notes of the background of Lady
Gleneck, the guests had started to arrive. I knew the first fellow through
the door who was introduced to me. Indeed, he is a shooting agent I had
previously described in print as a one-man ecological disaster unit.

After a further few drinks we were led into the dining-room. An enormous expanse of lobsters had been laid out: some halved and ready for eating, others intact and used for display. We sat down. The photographer
suggested that Lady Gleneck slip the shoulder-straps of her party-frock
over her shoulders; she did, instantly giving a more elegant appearance.
Gleneck leapt to his feet and bounded round the table with a cry of 'No,
no, cover your shoulders!' At that he yanked the shoulder-straps back to
their original position. As he walked back to his seat, Lady Gleneck slipped
them down again. Gleneck turned and, seeing the offending shoulders,

walked quickly back and yanked them up again. As he turned toward his seat for the second time, Lady Gleneck once more slid the straps over her shoulders. The photographer pressed the shutter and took the shot and, as Gleneck turned, she replaced them. We proceeded to eat the lobsters whilst the photographer busily took pictures of the diners. Lobsters finished, I sat expectantly awaiting the second course. Lady Gleneck stood up and started to thank me for coming. Then I realised that was it. One course, no coffee, off you go!

The photographer and I thanked our hostess and made our escape. As we were loading ourselves and our equipment into the car, Lady Gleneck came bounding out of the house carrying several whole lobsters in her hands and insisted we take them with us. We put them on some newspapers in the boot and waving our goodbyes set off down the drive. We had no sooner reached the main road than we had to pull in whilst I was violently sick on the grass verge. Obviously, the lobsters had been lobsters a long time. Indeed, when we returned home and had a chance to examine those in the car we realised that they were all 'off'.

A few days later, having written the story, I phoned Lady Gleneck to check on her husband's correct title. Was he a Lord I enquired, or a Sir?

'No,' came her reply. 'He is referred to simply as "Gleneck".'

'But, surely,' I persisted, 'if your title is Lady Gleneck, it must follow that he was Lord.'

'No, no,' she corrected me. 'Simply Gleneck.'

I decided to push. 'Tell me, Lady Gleneck, are you a real Lady?'

'You're mispronouncing my title. I am "The Lady, Gleneck".'

'You mean,' I replied, 'your title is the same as anyone whose house has a name, like "The Lady, Dunroamin"?'

There was silence at the end of the phone. . . .

Do unto others

WHEN I WAS TRYING to establish myself as a field-sports author, I experienced some success and felt that I had a contribution to make to field sports. I had served my apprenticeship, written in several magazines and national newspapers, published a book and presented a television series. I felt justified in writing to the editor of one of the premier field-sports magazines in the UK. It was a simple request: to write occasional pieces for the magazine and I outlined my areas of expertise. I awaited the reply with anticipation. It never came. Assuming my letter may have been lost in the post I wrote again. There was no reply. I phoned the editor on several occasions. He was always at 'meetings'. I left messages; he never had the courtesy to reply. Eventually I gave up.

I wrote to the editor of a second magazine, received an immediate reply and started writing a regular column. I still continued to buy the first magazine I had written to and, over the next two years, began to form an opinion of the editor who had never replied. He seemed to use the magazine to publicise and promote himself and his own interests. He obviously regarded himself as a Very Important Person and the voice of the field-sports establishment.

On one occasion the magazine I worked for was asked by a manufacturer to review a very expensive hunting-knife. The magazine gave the manufacturer my telephone number. He called me and I agreed to review the knife; he simply had to send it to me.

'Well,' he said, 'there we have a problem. They're so expensive that we only have one for Press purposes and we are having difficulty getting it back.'

He went on to give me the name of the very editor who had never returned my calls. A few days later he called to say that the knife was being sent directly to me by the editor's office. When it arrived I was horrified. It had been quite obviously used for throwing. The tip was broken and someone had obviously tried to buff off the matt finish.

Then one day it was announced in the field-sports media that the editor had resigned. I couldn't believe how anyone could give up such a job and assumed he must have moved to a better position. Meanwhile, I had been asked to write and present some field-sports videos and they had received considerable media exposure. Imagine my surprise when I received a letter from the ex-editor enquiring whether I would be interested in employing him in a video. I wrote him a courteous letter thanking him, turning down his offer.

The following year I was asked by the Irish Tourist Board if I would be interested in looking into the feasibility of making a video on shark fishing off the south coast of Ireland. The Tourist Board invited me to travel to Ireland to visit various locations and, naturally, to sample some shark fishing. I flew to Dublin and met their representative, who briefed me over lunch then ran me to the airport where I was to catch a flight south to Limerick.

As I was walking through the airport the representative suddenly announced to me that I would be travelling around the south in a car provided by them. I would be accompained by a journalist from England, and he went on to mention the name of the ex-editor. During the short flight down to Limerick I decided to say nothing about all those unanswered letters and telephone calls. It was, after all, in the past and I had no intention of being petty. So it was a smiling and affable me who met the ex-editor at Limerick and, after introductions, we set off together in a little car for what promised to be a pleasant few days.

The first hotel we stayed in was decidedly downmarket. The boat that took us out had no life-preservers, was dirty and stank of diesel. The fishing 14 miles off the coast was fairly uneventful. My companion caught a shark, I produced my camera and took lots of photographs, then I caught one. After I had played it for a bit I passed him the rod and concentrated on taking photographs.

Next day we moved on. I was navigating as we drove south to Kinsale. I had heard quite a lot about Kinsale. Situated off the south coast, it is a pretty place where the hotels and restaurants, working admirably together, run a delightful, annual food festival, the principal influence being sea food.

The address we had been given for our accommodation had the romantic name of 'The Lighthouse' and, as we drove south through the pretty, Irish countryside, we both visualised staying in some converted lighthouse on a jagged finger of rock, jutting into the sea. It would be run by some splendid Irish 'character' and we would eat fresh fish at every meal.

Eventually we arrived in Kinsale. It was as pretty as we had expected, with lots of attractive little hotels.

'Where is The Lighthouse?' we enquired of locals as we read out the address.

We were directed up various streets, amongst houses on the hill above the town. Then we found it, an inauspicious-looking little house surrounded by others. As we stopped in the street, a little man came out and addressed us in an American accent. Which one of us, he enquired, was the ex-editor?

'That is me,' he replied.

'Well,' said the American. 'Your office has phoned several times, it must be important. Let me show you to your rooms.'

He led us into the house and my nostrils were immediately assailed by that unpleasant, marzipany-smell that some houses seem to have. I was led through to a little room on the ground floor. The walls were liberally decorated with religious paraphernalia and little corn dollies. I put my suitcase down and walked up the stairs to my companion's room. I opened the door and started to laugh. It was so small that he and his suitcase filled the floor; the rest of the room was taken up by a tiny four-poster and the walls were decorated like mine with religious pictures and corn dollies. The house resembled a set from some old black-and-white film.

'You'd better phone your office,' I said as we started down the stairs.

I went into the sitting-room to be confronted by numerous china dolls sitting on the furniture. I turned to the right; there a woman sat on the couch with more china dolls, her bare feet tucked up on the couch. She looked to me exactly like Bette Davis.

'Oh, your office has been calling. You've to call them straight away,' she addressed us both in an American accent.

'Thank you. Where is the phone? I will reverse the charges,' said my companion.

The woman turned to him and said, 'We don't allow private calls. You'll have to use a phone in the town.'

111

That was enough. 'Get your bag,' I said as I turned, walked through to my room and lifted my suitcase.

I told our American host and hostess we were leaving and walked out. We drove back down the hill into town and booked into a smart hotel, explaining that the Tourist Board would be paying the bill. That night we had a splendid meal and the following morning moved on to our next shark-fishing location.

Again we travelled some 14 miles off-shore. The boat was clean, the weather delightful, as we sat with the rubby-dubby bag full of minced mackerel over the side, spreading a trail of blood and fish oil in the sea. We had put out baited hooks and sat watching the drift of our lines. Eventually we hooked a shark which, after a fight of some 15 minutes, was brought to the boat where the boatman tailed it and lifted it on board. I photographed it and put it back in the sea. During the afternoon we caught five more sharks, which made three each. I took several photographs of the playing and landing of each one before we released it, unharmed.

Next day we followed the directions we had been given and drove to meet Mr Brian Byrn, who was to take us fishing for conger eel. His purpose-built boat was spotless, completely outfitted with every conceivable fish-finding device and fully equipped with life-preservers. We travelled a short distance down an estuary, then dropped anchor and proceeded to drop our baited lines over the side. In the course of the afternoon we caught over 20 conger eels which, once we had brought them to the boat, Brian de-hooked and released. There is no question that, for a sea angler, the fish were there, both conger and shark, but try as I might I couldn't convince myself that there was sufficient action to warrant making a video.

I returned home next day and wrote my various letters of thanks. The photographs which I had taken I forwarded to the ex-editor and thought I would hear no more. Then several months later I was in Italy. My host had several British field-sports magazines, including a recently launched, new title. As I idly flicked through it I came upon a photograph of myself. There was a large feature written by my companion from Ireland, fully illustrated with the photographs I had taken. Nowhere was I credited for them.

When I returned to the British Isles I sent an invoice for the photographs to the ex-editor. I eventually received a cheque for £25.

Newfoundland adventure

WHEN I WAS ASKED to make the video *Training the Labrador Retriever* I decided to give the programme a lift and broaden its scope by including sequences filmed on location on the island of Newfoundland, where the labrador retriever was developed from the original dogs taken to the island by English timber-workers. Situated off the northeast coast of Canada, Newfoundland enjoys pleasant summers and arctic winters. Its inhabitants gain much of their income from fishing and timber.

The plane landed in the capital, St John, an attractive, small city built around a wonderful, natural harbour. We met our guide, supplied by the Newfoundland Government to assist us in finding locations, and set off to visit various parts of the island where I wished to film the remote communities.

After several days, the crew and I were beginning really to enjoy the very different scenery and people and we filmed some fascinating, traditional, fishing communities. The language spoken there is English, but must be unique to the island. It is a fascinating mix of eighteenth-century English, Scots and Irish words and phrases spoken with a distinctive accent, yet is obviously Canadian.

We were fortunate to be on Newfoundland at the time of the capelin run, that great natural phenomenon when countless millions of small fish, some six to eight inches long, run on to the shore with the high tide to lay their eggs in the sand, before dying in the shallows. To stand on a headland and watch the shoals of capelin running towards the beach, so dense in the water that it seems to turn black, gives little idea of the real scale of fish numbers and movement.

Frequently we would come across signs at the side of the road warning drivers to beware of moose, though we never saw any. Yet you needed to look no further than around you for startling sights. I stood on a bridge in one small community looking down along the sea loch and counted no fewer than 20 sea eagles. And, from the side of the main highway, we were able to film three ospreys fishing. Indeed, we were fortunate enough to get all three in the frame simultaneously.

But, the one species I really wanted to try and film was the whale. I felt these wonderful creatures perfectly embodied the immense, icy, arctic waters which had developed the Labrador.

113

We travelled to the north of the island, visiting one small community after another, looking for the sort of scenic views that would combine modern and traditional Newfoundland. We eventually arrived at a village that was perfect. We parked the vehicle overlooking the small harbour. I noticed our guide was decidedly uncomfortable. Indeed, he suggested he could find a better location than this one. I didn't agree and, telling the crew to remain with the vehicle, I walked down the jetty towards two men working together at a table, removing the roe from lumpfish.

As I came towards them I was aware that the older of the two was studying me as much as I was studying him. He was a great bear of a man with an open, pleasant face and enormous shoulders. I introduced myself to the man, whose name was Winston, and he introduced me to his son, Randy. It turned out that Winston was the spokesman for the village, a sort of headman. I told them what I was there to do and asked if they could assist me in filming whales and that I would like to hire his boat. He thought for a moment then suggested a very modest sum, adding that he would be delighted to assist us in filming whales.

I had gained the distinct impression that the small Newfoundland communities, and this one in particular, were sea-going, northern versions of 'good old boys'. As I looked at Winston and Randy I kept thinking of the words in the country-and-western song that described them perfectly — 'broad at the shoulder, narrow at the hip, everybody knew you didn't give no lip to Big John'.

We arranged to go out looking for whales the next morning. When we arrived it was bright and sunny. As we started to load the cameras and equipment on to Winston's boat our guide came walking down the jetty. I can only assume Winston recognised him as someone from officialdom, for he looked at the guide and said, 'Numbnuts — don't come on my boat!' The guide got the message and said he would wait by the vehicle.

We had a wonderful time, filming whales all day long. Some of them came within a few yards of our boat. One memorable cow and calf passed under the boat, clearly visible. Then the cow lifted her head completely out of the water, a few feet from where I sat on the gunwhale and looked at us. We returned, at the end of the day, with a feeling of total exhilaration.

As we came back in along the coast towards the harbour, I noticed an enormous bull moose in the trees at the water's edge. Winston came out of the wheelhouse and watched the moose with me. 'He'd be good eating,' he commented.

Winston had invited the crew and me to dinner that night at his home, a wooden building overlooking the harbour. We were served Fisherman's Brew, their traditional dish: cod, boiled and mashed (minus bones) with cubes of pork crackling seasoned with salt and pepper. Delicious! After dinner we were having a few drinks in the den when I noticed a bow hanging on the wall beside the rifles and shotguns.

As the evening wore on Winston, Randy and I discovered we had many common interests. The conversation quickly got round to shooting. I asked about the bow; it belonged to Randy who had acquired it when he spent some time on the mainland. He took it down from the wall and handed it to me. It was a Bear Alaskan Compound, set at 70 pounds and with a 31-inch draw. I drew it back, anchoring at the corner of my mouth. Randy was obviously impressed. I told him I'd been shooting a bow since I was a teenager. Indeed, I had one exactly like his back home.

It was Winston who suggested that we should try for a moose the following day. Not having a licence I felt this might be looking for trouble. I asked what would happen if the Mounties or Game Rangers found out. Winston shrugged; he had a licence and besides, 'They won't come here, and they won't find out. Our community don't talk!'

Next morning the three of us went round the coast by boat and landed at a little inlet on the estuary of a river, near where I had seen the bull the previous day. The countryside was wooded and broken up with boggy, swampy land and small, grassy clearings. The trees, typical of the island, were short conifers. I was to stalk one side of the little valley and Winston and Randy would take the other. They were carrying a rifle, I the 70-pound Compound with a bow quiver with six, five-inch, plastic-fletched Easton shafts, tipped with Bear razorheads.

I made my way along the low ground, then started up the steep slope of an intersecting valley. Walking was fairly easy, the ground being covered with a short heather-like plant. After I had gone about a mile I sat down on a little vantage point to glass the slope on the other side of the valley. I sat for some time, then I saw a good-sized bull moose, grazing out of the trees below me. I started cautiously down, having worked out the best route to make the stalk. Having studied the terrain it appeared that, if I was extremely careful, I could actually remain out of sight whilst I covered most of the distance to the moose. If I was right and didn't spook him I should be within 100 yards of the moose. I would then have to stalk closer — the effective range of a bow is 30 yards — and whilst I had never shot moose before, I kept telling myself it was just a big deer.

Everything went according to plan and I found myself in the cover of a windfall. Cautiously I looked for the animal. He wasn't there. I sat and

looked carefully at every possible thicket. He had vanished. Whether he was warned of my presence or he simply moved on I will never know. Though I searched for other animals for the rest of the afternoon I saw nothing and returned to the boat.

Next morning, having given the film crew the day off, the three of us returned round the coast to the same area. Winston dropped Randy and me off at the estuary. The wind had changed and Randy suggested we should 'still hunt' the watery meadowland, half a mile or so up the estuary. 'Still hunting' means that you sit at a vantage point over a game trail until you spot an animal which you hope will come within range. Together we sat at the edge of some trees, watching the ground out in front which contained lots of little ponds, surrounded by reeds, and a few trees on either side of the little river. We sat in silence for hours and, although we saw many different species of wildlife and had a grandstand view of what I had come to realise were the commonplace osprey, fishing in one of the ponds, no moose appeared. I was acutely aware of the stiffness in both my legs and bottom and started to change my position when Randy signalled to keep still. At the far end of the long reedbeds a moose had appeared out of the trees. We had a whispered conversation. I was sure Randy would want to shoot the bull with his rifle, but he insisted I should try for it.

I studied the terrain in front of me and, having planned the stalk, set off. It was relatively easy getting to about 100 yards from the bull; then I started inching my way closer. No responsible bow hunter would dream of shooting at a range greater than the recommended 30 yards. Eventually I had made my way to the cover of a windfall. The bull was no more than 40 yards away, but I couldn't get a clear shot. I squatted in the grass, hardly daring to breathe. The bull was munching on some water plants, his great head dipping down for a few choice leaves, his bell swinging as he raised his head. He was so close I could hear the occasional, gurgling rumbles in his gut. He took a few steps and disappeared behind some thick bushes. I squatted there, every muscle in my legs aching.

Suddenly, he reappeared. He was closer, yet still I couldn't shoot through the screen of undergrowth. He started to walk forward. I came up to full draw and watched the clearing between the bushes. His huge shoulder filled the clearing. I concentrated on the spot behind his shoulder. He moved forward a few inches and I released the arrow. It struck him on exactly the spot I had been aiming for, the arrow disappearing up to the fletch. He rocketed forward and charged towards the trees. After some 80 to 90 yards, he stumbled, staggered and went down on his knees. I sat quietly for 30 minutes, hardly daring to breathe, shaking with excitement and nerves, then went cautiously forward. The bull was dead. He was so large we couldn't roll him over to do the gralloch. Quickly Randy went back to where the boat was to pick us up. I sat there beside the moose expecting a Mountie to leap out from behind every tree. I was convinced I would end up in some Newfy jail.

After some considerable time waiting for Winston and Randy, they appeared. We turned the bull over and gralloched him. Far too large for us to move, we covered him with undergrowth and left him, returned to the boat and went back to the village. Winston organised a few men and they set off to retrieve the bull. There was enough meat on his carcass to ensure the whole community could top up their freezers!

A few days later, our filming finished, we were ready to leave. Winston invited us to a local dance, giving us directions to a roadside bar and dance-hall some miles away, near the main highway. When we arrived the car park was crowded with pick-ups and the dance was already in full swing. We walked into the darkened interior, so dark you could see only silhouettes of bodies. Country music was playing and the air was full of smoke and the smell of drink. We stood around for a moment, then out of the darkness loomed the enormous shape of Winston. He gave me a great bear-hug and led the crew and myself to a table by the edge of the dance-floor. The drinks flowed as we joined the dancing, which went on until breakfast was served, prior to the crew and I leaving.

I cannot think of that wonderful community with their simple and honest way of life, without feeling the desire to return again for another adventure.

Difficult stalking

OF ALL THE SPECIES of deer found in the British Isles, my favourite is the beautiful and fascinating roe. These little deer are found throughout most of the country and can be difficult and challenging stalking. Undoubtedly the most difficult roe stalking I have ever taken part in was during the making of the programme *Roebuck Stalking*. The story of the making of that film is one of excitement and frustration. It was with a great deal of enthusiasm that I accepted the challenge of making the programme. Little did I know when we started quite what I had taken on.

The static pieces of presentation when I was speaking to the camera were of course quite easy and were quickly accomplished and 'in the can'. However, it was necessary for us to shoot bucks on camera; not just any bucks, but animals that represented the correct categories of deer that should be shot — poor-quality heads, old animals and, of course, as a highlight for the film, it was most desirable that we should stalk and shoot a really good, representative trophy head. All this had to be accomplished whilst I was accompanied by a cameraman carrying a large camera. I also felt that, to be truly representative, we should stalk bucks in locations from the south of England to the north of Scotland.

Whilst the recording of ambient sound, that is the normal sounds of the countryside, was comparatively easy, the actual sounds of the stalk provided another challenge. The sound engineer, after much experimentation, rigged me with a highly sensitive throat mike, a tiny black button with a cable running under my shirt to a small transmitter on my belt. In this way I would be able to give a whispered commentary whilst I was actually stalking, which would be recorded by the engineer who would follow some 150 yards behind the cameraman and myself.

Our first location was arranged for May in Inverness-shire. I and the crew journeyed to the estate and, after carefully explaining to the stalker what I required, we set out at 4 o'clock on the first morning. There were plenty of roe about but no animals that were either of shootable quality or in the right position, and before we had shot a frame it was 9 a.m. The bucks had all disappeared into the thickets.

I and the crew then returned to our hotel where we sat around until late afternoon when we set out again for an early-evening stalk. I spotted one buck that was perfect for the job and with Alastair, the cameraman, I set off on a long stalk across a heathery moor fringed with Scots pines. Eventually we got outselves into position in the gathering dusk and, as I lay there in the heather, the buck no more than 60 yards away, I stole a glance over my shoulder at Alastair to make sure the camera was running and everything perfect. We had arranged a series of signals since there was no point in my shooting an animal before the camera was in perfect focus. I glanced at Alastair, waiting for the signal, and he brought his eye down from the eye-piece and waved his hand. There was insufficient light for quality film.

The events of that first day were to be repeated for the rest of the week: we either saw deer that were not what we were looking for or, when we found them, the conditions were not right. During the week, while out walking one day, I had noticed an area where I felt sure there was a real chance of seeing a big buck. I told the stalker this was where I wanted to film; he was quite adamant that there would be no roe in that area.

However, I insisted and that afternoon, with plenty of time, Alastair and I positioned ourselves in a beautiful scenic spot amongst some large, mature Scots pines, which were well separated and gave us a wonderful view through the trees to a solid wall of conifers of a plantation not more than 80 yards away. Since we were sitting in one position, Alastair had brought the large tripod and erected it with its legs down and spread so that it was low. In this position he could kneel behind it and swivel it around to cover the area. I sat beside and just in front of him and there we remained motionless as the early evening wore on. Nothing appeared but I knew from the signs I had observed and from that instinctive feeling I have developed over the years that this was where I would find a big buck.

Then, as the sinking sun behind us gave a beautiful, golden light effect, without any warning I realised a roe deer had appeared out of the dense plantation 80 yards away. I could see its body from the shoulders back. I signalled Alastair but he had already seen it and started the camera. As I sat motionless, watching the deer, it took a few steps and revealed its head and neck. Through my glasses I examined him carefully. He was one of the largest bucks I had ever seen in Scotland. His antlers were long and thick. From where I sat I judged him to be old and certainly eminently shootable.

As I watched, he walked a few more steps, nibbling here and there, then stopped, giving me a perfect shot. I turned to Alastair, who had his eye against the eyepiece, and gently touched his knee. His hand made a thumbs-down signal. I turned back to the buck, which had taken a few steps so that I could no longer see his neck and shoulder. Then I felt Alastair gently tap me to go ahead. I couldn't. I didn't have a clear shot. Then, as he took another few steps, I had a perfect view of his shoulder and neck; I lifted the rifle and again glanced at Alastair; his eye fixed to the eyepiece, he was holding his hand thumb down.

For the next 20 minutes we sat there being eaten by midges, unable to move as the magnificent, grandfather buck wandered around in front of us. Each time I raised my rifle Alastair had his thumb down; each time he slowly turned his hand thumb up I didn't have a clear shot of the buck. Then, undisturbed as the light was beginning to fade, the buck turned and casually walked back into the plantation. We both turned to each other to discuss what had happened. Due to the position of the trees, Alastair, though he was sitting close to me, had only been able to get a perfect view of the buck when the trees obscured my view.

Next morning I spotted a roe grazing in a ride. Carefully I stalked the buck with Alastair at my shoulder. When I had got within some 80 yards I stopped and, glancing at Alastair, received the thumb up. I lifted my rifle, put the crossed reticules perfectly on the buck's heart and squeezed the trigger. In large bounds, he rocketed forwards towards us at an angle across the ride and collapsed dead at its edge — a perfect shot. I turned to Alastair who looked worried as he took his eye from the camera. On screen it was useless. The buck appeared to have run off straight into the woodland, for whilst he had actually collapsed dead, the camera had not seen him do so. We couldn't use the film of an apparently wounding shot. Later that day we tried again and, in the failing light, we finally succeeded, after a long stalk on our knees, in shooting one, very poor-quality cull buck. The week over, we returned to base with what amounted to a very few moments of usable film.

We had scheduled our next location in Perthshire. On the first morning the crew assembled in heavy rain and we then sat for several days looking out at unseasonable weather, unable to film anything. Then one morning we got up at 4 o'clock in perfect summer weather. We set off up the hill through the woodland and there, at the edge of the wood, in perfect conditions, were two roe. We stalked and successfully filmed the shooting of another cull buck. We had no sooner completed the filming of my piece to camera, discussing the beast, than the heavens opened with rain that would stay with us for the rest of the week.

Moving to another location in Perthshire the following week, we had several more days of frustration before one morning, at about half past five we spotted an excellent buck grazing at the edge of a field, bordered on one side by a small country road. Carefully Alastair and I started the stalk, eventually finding ourselves lying on a little hillock with the buck in front of us not more than 70 yards away. Everything was perfect. Alastair kept the camera running on the beautiful animal and we obtained lots of film that we could use. He signalled to me that I could shoot the animal at any time but, confident of what I was doing and wanting more film of the grazing animal, I signalled to him that I would wait a little longer. Finally the buck, having grazed closer to us, was no more than 50 yards away and standing in perfect broadside. I signalled that I would take the shot and, lying in the lush grass, quietly lifted my rifle, settling the reticules on the base of his neck, my fingers gently starting to take the pressure on the trigger. Suddenly the buck raised his head and started to run towards us; seeing us lying in the grass he swerved and bounded off. The cause of his disturbance came bouncing down the small country road — a large delivery van. We finished the third week with little to show for all our efforts and constantly escalating costs with crew wages, transport and accommodation.

We set off for our next location, Petworth, Lord Egremont's beautiful Sussex estate. The game management of the estate is under the control of David Whitby, one of Britain's foremost stalking and shooting authorities. I explained to David the series of frustrating disappointments we had experienced and of my uncompromising determination not to take the easy route and shoot just any buck. I wanted one more cull buck, then a really splendid trophy, to complete the programme. The light had to be good, the scenery pleasant and there must be no foreign noises. Noise can be a problem in the south of England; there are many more people, vehicles and, of course, aircraft. However, if we stuck to filming in the early mornings and evenings, disturbance should be minimal.

On our second evening at Petworth, at the edge of a wheatfield, I decided to try the calling sequence I wanted to film. I produced my little German call and made a tiny squeak of a roe kid in alarm. After a few calls a doe appeared, moving towards me through the long vegetation, followed by a buck — a poor, thin, little head with one antler more pronounced than the other. Alastair had adjusted the camera to the extreme of its

121

capabilities and, in the gathering dusk, I quietly called again. The buck came bounding towards me, then stopped no more than 50 yards away, lifting his head and neck clear of the surrounding plants. I shot him perfectly through the neck. We now had only one buck left to shoot.

We then started on the most difficult period of our filming, searching for a really excellent trophy buck to give the film a highlight. Our routine was exhausting. We got up every morning at 3.30 a.m., showered and dressed, loaded all our equipment, had a quick coffee, set out to meet David at 4.30 a.m. then started to search for a buck to stalk. Time seemed to fly and it was soon 8 o'clock, with the sounds of cars moving in the distance and of the general, early-morning disturbance as the local inhabitants started their daily routine.

We would return to the attractive farmhouse where we were staying and, after breakfast, would sit about, try and sleep, normally unsuccessfully, and spend the day amusing ourselves before preparing for the evening stalking session. In this way we spent the next week. Not once did we see a buck that fitted the criteria demanded.

Finally, on our second to last morning in Sussex, I saw the perfect buck. He had long, thick antlers and fitted in every way the starring role I had cast for him. He was with a doe at the bottom of a large field surrounded by trees. As I watched, the buck lay down at the field edge in a patch of thistles, the doe lying near him. Through my glasses I could

clearly see their ears moving, disturbed by flies. It looked an impossible stalk. The only way to approach the buck would be to go right down the full length of the field at the field edge within sight of him all the time. If he was to turn his head and look in our direction he would surely see us.

I decided that we should try to stalk him and set off down the edge of the field, walking with the utmost care, carefully putting each foot down, feeling the ground before gently transferring my weight forward. Slowly Alastair and myself crept towards the buck. Alastair kept the heavy camera running as he took the various sequences we would later edit together. I was almost afraid to breathe as we moved ever closer. I felt sure that at any minute one of the roe would turn, raise its head and see us.

We moved on. We were about 80 yards from the buck and I could clearly see the tips of his ears waggling and his antlers protruding above the thistle patch. Then suddenly a fox stepped out of the long grass in front of us no more than 15 yards away. It ran a few steps forward, then stopped and looked back at us over his shoulder. We had frozen. Alastair filmed the fox as I whispered into my mike, 'There's a fox.' Then he slipped silently into the wood.

We went on. I was sure at any minute the buck would jump and with a bark, bound away. We were only 40 yards away from the buck, but I was now presented with another problem: how would I shoot him? I could only see the top of his head. Then the doe stood up and turned toward us; we instantly froze. She looked at us, bobbing her head to focus her eyes, then urinated, probably with nerves, I risked a whisper into my mike, 'Don't run doe.'

Then she turned and started walking casually down the field. I lifted my rifle to my shoulder waiting for the next move. Suddenly the buck stood up and started walking after her. I made a kissing sound with my pursed lips. He stopped. I put the cross on his heart and squeezed the trigger.

As the buck fell dead instantly and the doe bounded away, Alastair and I relaxed. The tension of the stalk had been tangible. Alastair put the heavy camera down and started flexing his hands and shoulders. He had been so caught up in the long, careful creep of at least 200 yards down the field that he had been totally unaware of the weight of the camera, which suddenly seemed extremely heavy. I gralloched the buck, giving a commentary to the camera. As we switched the power off, we realised all the filming sequences were complete. Now all we had to do was edit the programme.

Our determination and patience were well rewarded. The finished film was warmly received, not only throughout the UK, but also in Europe, where it received wide acclaim from both roe stalkers and field sportsmen.

Dented ego

In 1989 I was in Italy to see about the Italian distribution of some of my field-sports video series. Massimo, my Italian distributor, had arranged numerous meetings during the day, whilst in the evenings I was entertained in some of the splendid restaurants in Milan. He told me that he had arranged to take me at the weekend to a gun-dog test. We drove south from Milan to an estate near the mighty River Po and, turning off the road, drove through some low-lying fields with lots of plantations of those wonderful, tall, thin trees which the Italians grow for making paper. Eventually we arrived at a typical Italian farmhouse with an attractive, red-tiled roof. As we pulled into the yard I saw a large number of people, all with labradors, milling about, drinking coffee and chatting. When I got out of the car and walked towards them with Massimo, several of them started gesturing towards me and speaking excitedly. I didn't realise that their enthusiasm for the breed was fairly recent and that all of them had been using my videos for training. I was introduced and treated like some famous personality and I must say, whilst I was slightly embarrassed, I certainly enjoyed all the attention.

Once all the competitors had arrived we walked down to a wooded area where they lined three dogs out. Then, at a signal, a cock pheasant would be released from a hidden position and, as it flew up over the trees, one of the two guns would shoot it prior to a retriever being sent out. To me, being used to testing in the UK, it seemed strange and not quite what we British would think of as sporting, but I am a great believer in the maxim 'when in Rome . . .' and I was certainly not about to start being critical. It was, after all, little different from pulling a chicken's neck.

After the test was over I was invited to join the party for dinner, during which I was asked if I would consider coming to Italy and giving lessons in dog training. I readily agreed.

The following summer I flew to Milan to be met by Candy Baroni and driven south to a large farm just north of Genoa. This farm is the perfect example of agriculture and field sports working hand in hand to increase both land use and income. It is dominated by the *casa*, or farmhouse, and buildings situated on top of the hill where they enjoy the breezes. Large cattle courts full of healthy Charollais are set to one side then, as the land drops away into a series of undulating hills, every square inch has been put

to good use. Large areas of sweetcorn are grown, as both human and animal food; other areas are rich grassland, whilst the slopes are planted with vines. Fitted in neatly to what is an obviously highly successful agricultural unit are the shooting interests. Pheasants are reared and released, whilst in some low, boggy ground several enormous ponds have been created, which are stocked with fish as a secondary crop, but whose real purpose is for rearing the thousands of duck released for sport. The sporting facility was under the direct control of Giorgio.

After I had been allocated a room in the *casa* I was shown over the farm to decide which facilities I wished to use for the dog-training sessions to be held over the next week. It was obvious that I would use the grass fields, the cover and, of course, the large ponds. I couldn't, however, find any fences and so asked that a small enclosure 10 yards square by a yard and a half high should be built, so that I had an area into which I could ask the dogs to jump. Next morning, after an early breakfast, the people with their dogs started to arrive. I couldn't believe my eyes: over 100 dogs and handlers and another 100 individuals as spectators. How was I ever going to conduct meaningful training sessions with so many pupils, particularly when they ranged in age from puppies to mature dogs, and in standard from overweight show puppies to imported, British trialling stock, even the best of which was trained to only the most elementary level? The only thing to do was to split all the dogs and handlers into groups by age, then ask each individual to give me a quick demonstration of what they and their dog were capable of, if anything. I then assessed that the majority should simply concentrate on basic discipline: walking to heel, sitting and other simple and basic tasks. Once I had the different groups working in the areas allotted to them, I then found myself running from group to group, giving instruction. There was one obvious group of dogs that shone in their potential and I decided to concentrate on them. One dog, handled by a Swiss lady by the name of Francesca, showed great potential. Candy Baroni was handling an older, yellow dog that was good, but the dog that for me stood out above all others was Bullet, owned and handled by a particularly handsome young man by the name of Stefano. He was the epitomy of the 'Italian Stallion'; not only did he drive a fancy car but in conversation was quick to tell me that his family had given him a small farmhouse, where he could live on his own with his various dogs, plus his pets — a wolf and a cougar.

I concentrated on the older and better dogs, giving the handlers and dogs individual instruction and, while Francesca and Candy listened to everything I said, I noticed that Stefano was so self-opinionated that he wasn't listening. That night over a splendid dinner I was constantly bombarded by the various owners for comment on the potential of their dogs. Finally Stefano asked me in front of his friends, in the most casual fashion, what I thought of Bullet. I sat thinking for a few moments of what I should say and, being aware of the enormous ego of the good-looking and obviously well-heeled Stefano, I said to him that it was a great shame that Bullet belonged to such a clown as him. His face darkened with a look of incredulity at my insult but I went on, explaining to him, in the harshest terms I could muster, that, whilst the dog had wonderful potential, anyone as obviously opinionated and big-headed as he could only create a disaster. I did, however, finish my insults by saying that if he had the sense and ability to listen to what I said, rather than playing to the gallery, he could really make something special of his dog. Looking around at his friends, his dark eyes full of controlled anger, he said simply, 'I will listen.'

Over the next few days, whilst I concentrated on training and instructing the different groups, I found it amusing that Stefano stuck to me like glue; his whole attitude had changed. Several of the other people there, who had obviously heard of my insults, remarked on the change in him. Then one day at lunch-time, as everyone was enjoying a wonderful alfresco lunch outside the *casa*, a large limousine pulled up. One of the most beautiful girls I had ever seen got out, accompanied by a dignified, grey-haired man. His jacket was loosely draped over his shoulders and he looked like either a captain of industry or a Mafia Don. He radiated authority as he came towards me. One or two of my friends nudged me excitedly, telling me that they were Stefano's father and sister. I was introduced and, after exchanging pleasantries, the gentleman said to me, 'I heard of the things you said to Stefano.' I didn't know what to say in reply. I was embarrassed and concerned that I might be thought of as bad-mannered. Then he added: 'I hope it works.' I gave an embarrassed smile and said nothing.

Near the end of the week, casually over dinner one evening, it was announced to me that the Italian Labrador Working Championship was to be held and then, to my even greater surprise, I was told that I was to be the judge. I explained that it was not possible for me to judge a test when I had just spent the last week intensively training both dogs and handlers and insisted that other judges should be brought in. After a few hasty telephone calls, two judges were arranged, one travelling up from Tuscany, the other from France.

Under my instruction, a whole series of tests had been devised, utilising the cover, the water and a nice, long retrieve from the fenced-in enclosure. The tests were designed for the three levels of dog that would enter and specifically tailored to examine the handlers' control of the dogs to a high standard. Nevertheless the demands were no more than any competent trainer anywhere would be able to meet with confidence. On the day of the test the judges arrived. The French judge was a young man and very knowledgeable. The Italian, an elderly woman, was the epitome of an English county lady and obviously knowledgeable and experienced. As the various handlers and their dogs assembled, even more surprises were in store. Competitors arrived from Germany, France and the Netherlands, some of whom were professional dog-trainers. The first test run had some 20 entrants and was won by one of the Italians with a young dog. The second test, more advanced, was easily won by Francesca.

The third test was really quite difficult and involved two blind retrieves over long distance, a blind retrieve across the widest pond, a swim of at least 300 yards, then several more retrieves involving both water, cover and the fenced-in area. The standard of the dogs was quite high but all of them showed wide gaps in their training. The Dutch professional couldn't manage to get his dogs across the water any more than a short distance before they turned back. The German and French dogs were good and I waited with baited breath for Candy and Stefano. Candy's dog did well. Finally I watched as Stefano was called forward with Bullet. Quietly he handled the big dog effortlessly through every task. Bullet didn't put a foot wrong and his unmarked retrieves across the water were quite splendid. The test over, we all went back to the *casa* and, whilst the judges conferred with each other, I and the competitors sat drinking some of the wonderful local wine. Then the results were announced. Like all good competitions they were in reverse order. Third was a dog from France, second was Candy's yellow dog. Then they announced the winner of the Italian Retriever Working Championship, Bullet.

That night over dinner, Stefano quietly thanked me for my help and I thought the matter closed. Next morning the Retriever Club, taking advantage of all the competitors being there, had organised a dog show at the *casa*. This was of course nothing to do with me and show judges had been organised. I was walking round the courtyard with Giorgio, admiring some of the dogs, when the limousine appeared. I watched as the beautiful girl and her father walked toward me. 'Buongiorno' I greeted them. 'Buongiorno, James,' the gentleman said with a smile. 'Thank you for teaching my son.'

Stefano and I have since become good friends. At the time of writing this story, Bullet is firmly established as the top trialling dog in Italy.

Dog training Southern-style

THE FIRST CONTACT I ever had with Peter was when the postman delivered a fancy envelope emblazoned with a stamp of the USA. It wasn't the stamp, however, that drew my attention, but the illustration of the labrador in the bottom left corner of the envelope and the logo 'from one of the world's great dog trainers'.

I opened the envelope full of curiosity. Who could it be that could make such a claim? The letter started off 'Hi! James', then went on to explain that the fellow had some of the videos I had made on dog training and shooting, that he was a professional gun-dog trainer in the USA and was intending to visit the UK for an extended vacation and would like to visit and meet me. The letter was signed 'Yours, Peter'.

I was curious and not a little flattered, so promptly wrote back inviting

Peter to contact me when he arrived in the UK and saying that, yes indeed, he would be most welcome to visit my home.

A few weeks later Peter phoned me from London, telling me that he and his wife, having arrived, were spending a few days in the city, then planned to travel north and that he intended to arrive at my door on Friday morning.

When his hired car drove into the drive, I went forward to greet them. A fit-looking fellow got out, dressed head to toe in new, British, country clothing: shining brogues, natty twills, smart hacking-jacket over checked shirt, a yellow cravat with little fox-head motifs around his neck and, to complete the outfit, a nifty, flat cap of tweed to match the jacket. Surely some mistake, I thought. This cannot be my American guest. He, in turn, was looking at me with obvious surprise, since I was dressed in cowboy boots, jeans and casual shirt. The illusion of an English county gent was shattered when he opened his mouth with the greeting 'Well it's real nice to meet you, James,' spoken in a thick southern accent. He turned to introduce me to his wife Connie, who had got out the car, a very attractive woman in her early thirties, dressed in a similar county style. She was I soon discovered, a real Southern Belle, sounding as though she had just stepped off the set of *Gone with the Wind*. Connie was obviously greatly attracted to British styles and our British way of life, thoroughly enjoying the world of horse trials and driven shooting at our large country houses, and was quick to declare how she would have liked to live here.

As I led them into the house, Peter produced a book with a flourish telling me this was his latest publication on dog training and was a gift for me. He had already written in the flyleaf a flowery little message. Over coffee we chatted. Peter was very keen to talk dogs. He told me of some of the astonishing prices that he was paid for dogs that he described as 'dogs for duck hunters', going on to explain that his customers preferred their labradors to be very large, tall and broad. He said that some of his customers wouldn't even consider one of our small British animals and that size seemed to be more important than either breeding or brains. Indeed, I gained the distinct impression that, like some men's fascination with large calibre weapons, this desire to have enormous labradors had something to do with their macho image, what I describe as the 'Big Ball Syndrome'.

I was interested in finding out more of how and where they lived, particularly after he told me they lived near Memphis. Had he ever seen Gracelands, Elvis's home? What was it like in the deep south? Was it anything like *In the Heat of the Night*? Did he like country music?

They were staying in a small, local hotel and intended to spend two or three days in the area. Peter was particularly keen on seeing my training techniques and I invited him to return the following day and spend some time with me. After they had gone that first day, I flicked through his book. Some of the photographs caught my eye. 'Goodness me,' I thought. 'Can this be for real?' I sat down and read the book from cover to cover, my incredulity seeming to increase by the page.

Next morning when Peter arrived, almost the first thing he asked was had I had time to look at his book.

'Yes,' I said, trying to change the subject.

What did I think of it, he persisted? I tried to busy myself showing him round.

'Interesting,' I replied. He obviously detected my reluctance to say more.

'Come on, James, don't bullshit me. Just tell it as it is. I really wanna know what you think of it.'

I turned to him and looked him in the eye. 'It's difficult for me to comment. Your book obviously reflects how you do things at your kennels back home. We do things differently here.'

He persisted, 'Yeah, but what did you really think of it?'

'Tell me, Peter, would you like me to tell you the truth or would you like me to tell you something else?'

'Hell! I can take it, I guess you don't like it.'

How could I tell him I thought it the biggest load of rubbish I had ever read? Not only did it go into great length to explain the most bizarre and stupid details, but parts of it advocated cruelty that would never be tolerated in the UK.

When I showed him how we trained our young dogs he was full of questions. How did I manage to train them when they were so free to run away? Didn't I use long lines? Did I simply rely on a natural instinct to retrieve? Then, when I brought out several of my own experienced dogs and started to give a demonstration, he asked how I managed to work several dogs simultaneously. When I tried to explain I realised that, whilst he undoubtedly was a professional dog trainer, his approach was in such contrast to mine that he just couldn't understand how I did it.

I took Peter for a night's duck and goose shooting on my flight pond and he proved to be a good sporting shot, accounting for several birds.

Eventually Peter and Connie returned to the USA, inviting me to visit them in Tennessee.

The following year I was going to the USA during their shooting season and, having a few days to spare, decided to fly down to Memphis and visit Peter and Connie. The plane that brought me from New York landed around midday at Memphis airport. Peter was there to meet me and, as he gave me a short tour round Memphis, I was struck by how big and brash everything seemed to be.

His home was a good hour's drive down the highway through the flat countryside. As soon as I had unpacked I was keen to be shown round. The kennel layout was similar to kennels anywhere. Where they differed dramatically was in two additions that I had never seen before.

Inside a long shed there was a built-in cupboard running the full length of one wall, approximately 20 yards long. In depth, the cupboard was a good yard and a half. The top of the cupboard had been designed to give the effect of a long work surface. Stretched from one end of the room to the other was a wire, set a yard and a quarter above the centre of the cupboard.

This, incredibly, is how Peter advocated teaching a dog to retrieve. The dog is placed on top of the cupboard and fitted with a collar, which is linked by a chain to a running loop attached to the wire. The dog is then made to run down the length of the work surface. In addition, there is what Peter describes as a 'magic string' — a length of string tied in a clove-hitch around the dog's wrist joint and running down to a half-hitch around the dog's two middle toes; the free end, about 20 inches in length, is held in one hand. In the other is held a piece of dowelling or a dummy. Simply by pulling the string you can pinch the dog's toes, causing pain and discomfort. As soon as you pull the string and the dog opens its mouth to protest about the pain, you shove either the dowelling or the dummy into its mouth, at the same time releasing the string and thus stopping the pain immediately. In this crazy fashion, he then goes on in his book to explain in great length how you should teach your dog to retrieve.

I was astonished when I read it. I was incredulous when I saw it in operation.

Outside he had a large, square pond, approximately 100 by 50 yards for water work. Fitted on both sides were tall straining posts; attached to one was a rope with a block-and-tackle and, running across the pond, a double-rope system which was attached to a pulley on the other straining post. This alarming device, which looked as though it had been designed in medieval times for the purposes of drowning witches, had a highly novel use. It was, in fact, Peter's idea of the way you introduce the dog to water. The idea is to attach a rope to the dog's collar, then no matter how reluctant the dog might be, by simply standing back and pulling the rope, the pulley system yanks the dog into the water. You can then haul the dog, whether it wishes to swim or not, out into the water and, when you wish it to return, you simply pull the other rope and the pulley does the work.

I asked why it was necessary to go to such lengths to encourage retrieving and swimming, rather than just to develop the dog's natural instincts willingly to perform these tasks. Peter couldn't understand my dislike of his methods.

'Why,' he reasoned, 'not give a little scientific assistance to nature?', insisting that he could get the job done much more quickly using his mechanical aids.

However, there was one mechanical aid that Peter used in his training which I did find both interesting and highly sensible. This was an electric collar. Snakebites can be a real problem in the southern United States. It is entirely possible for a dog-owner and his dog to go shooting for many years and never encounter a snake. It is, however, equally possible to encounter several snakes in one day, so if there is the slightest chance that a dog being trained by Peter might be in an area where it is likely to come across a snake, he snake-proofs them, a simple technique using aversion therapy. The dog is fitted with an electric collar and is worked in a pen where Peter has released a de-fanged rattlesnake. Inevitably the dog, when it comes across the snake, approaches it out of curiosity. As the snake strikes, the dog is given a small electric shock. This ensures the dog will associate the snake with the unpleasant sensation and give all serpents a wide berth thereafter.

Next day I felt that I couldn't be in Memphis without visiting Gracelands. I needn't have bothered. Such a display of bad taste, designed to milk the emotions, is almost an affront to the music of the house's former occupant.

Peter had organised a couple of days' duck hunting for which I was to join him and two friends. We loaded two of Peter's dogs and two shotguns plus our luggage into his pick-up and drove south. After we had been driving for some time, Peter suggested we stop for something to eat, pulling into a Howard Johnson establishment. As we sat down, I looked at the incredible array of ice-creams available: 75 different flavours, some of the flavour combinations almost defying belief. Replenished, though I must admit without ice-cream, we continued our journey.

We were to meet up with his friends at a small cabin which one of them owned, near the wetlands where they intended to shoot. We arrived at the cabin in mid-afternoon and I was introduced. Brandon, the cabin owner, was in his forties. A huge man, he looked like a football player or a heavyweight boxer. I was surprised to learn he was a dentist. The other, whose name was Clyde, worked as a pilot; he was Brandon's brother-in-law.

The land we were to shoot on belonged to their family. They were real southern gentlemen and proud of their family history. The land had been in their family for several generations, their ancestors having been in the Confederate Army.

After introductions everyone was anxious to set off and try for some duck.

In this area, which lies around the estuary of a small river that flows into the mighty Mississippi, the land is very flat and swampy. The vegetation reminded me of films I had seen; *Southern Comfort* sprang to mind, the image of the everglades. We loaded ourselves and our equipment into one pick-up — four men and four dogs, the other two having brought one each — then drove about a mile on a rough track through the trees and long grasses, arriving at a little jetty where two aluminium, flat-bottomed boats were tied. The boats belonged to Brandon.

We had brought outboard engines with us from the cabin and, these fitted, we quickly loaded the boats and set off, each boat carrying a cargo of two men, guns, decoys, flasks, snack-boxes and, of course, two large labradors.

As we pulled out from the jetty, Brandon and Clyde turned left, down-river, Peter and I following. After a short journey of no more than a quarter of a mile, we came to a large reed-covered island about half a mile long. Brandon pointed in towards a little bay where we were to shoot. They intended to shoot further downriver.

We tied the boat up at a little jetty then, with Peter leading the way, we walked through the lush vegetation to the edge of a small bay, where I was shown to a duck blind. Peter was to sit in another, set 80 yards away on the other side of the little bay. As Peter set out the strings of decoys, I examined the blind. Built of a wood frame and slats, it was obviously a permanent fixture. The vegetation had been allowed to grow up around the blind so that it blended in as a natural feature. Inside the blind a bench seat had been fitted. It was the most comfortable hide I had ever experienced. Peter told me that there were several of them dotted over the shooting-area.

Peter disappeared into his blind followed by his two dogs and I sat in the still, late afternoon watching for duck. I was in the midst of pouring myself a coffee from my vacuum flask when a party of mallard skimmed in past my hide, passing over the decoys. They had started to turn when two shots rang out from Peter's hide. One duck fell as the rest climbed away. I watched as one of Peter's dogs, Duke, appeared through the reeds in front of his hide and swam out to retrieve the duck. Duke was on his way back with the duck when another party of mallard came past. This time I was paying more attention and, swinging through, shot one drake. The bird folded and dropped into the water with a splash. The other dog, Lee, appeared from the reeds in front of Peter's hide and swam out, passing Duke closely, the dogs ignoring each other. Lee swam out then seemed to tread water as he looked back for direction. Peter stood up, gave him a hand signal and Lee turned, following the direction perfectly; picking the drake, he turned back towards the bank. Though I had seen only two retrieves it was obvious that these dogs were both very fit, powerful individuals who were thoroughly enjoying their water work.

Over the next hour, I heard occasional distant shots. Obviously Brandon and Clyde were having some sport. Many parties of duck appeared in our area. Though several of them were out of shot, those that did come into range of Peter and myself gave us good sport.

Then the darkness seemed suddenly to fall. Peter gave me a shout to stop shooting and I walked around toward his blind to help carry the duck. All mallard, mainly drakes, they were large, well-fed, healthy birds. Between us we had shot nine duck. We walked back in silence toward the boat, loading our equipment in the bow where I sat. Both dogs got in the centre section whilst Peter sat in the stern by the little outboard.

We set off for the short journey back to the pick-up. We had just unloaded all the equipment and were tying the boat firmly when our two companions arrived. They also had had several duck.

Back at the cabin we hung the duck in a cool-box. The dogs fed, we cleaned the guns, then sat down to a light meal before climbing into our bunks.

Next morning we had a morning flight, restricting ourselves to a brace of duck each. Then, after breakfast, Peter and Clyde set out to an area about ten miles drive away, where they thought they might have a chance for some wild turkey. I elected to stay with Brandon and we spent part of the day exploring the reedbeds, looking at the wildlife. Brandon, a self-declared occasional angler, fished for a bit without any luck, then in quick succession caught two, large catfish, which he declared he would prepare that night for a real southern meal.

When Peter and Clyde returned they told us that, whilst there were turkey in the area, only Clyde had been successful shooting one small gobbler.

We set out for the evening flight in late afternoon. It was the same form as the previous evening. This time I accompanied Clyde and, by the evening's end, each of us had shot another brace of mallard plus I had shot a wood duck. That night I sat down in great anticipation to the catfish. It was, to my palate, barely edible and I contented myself with the much more tasty gumbo and, of course, bowls of crawfish which the boys had brought with them. The addition of some roast duck to this southern banquet made it a most memorable meal.

Next morning Peter and I set off back north toward Memphis, leaving Brandon and Clyde who intended to spend two more days at the cabin. We drove north without stopping, arriving back at Peter's base in late afternoon.

I could have happily spent more time in the area. I had been shown a different approach to shooting and to gun-dog training. In the main it was not what I myself would have done, but certain aspects were valid and I had learnt some valuable lessons. I had, however, a schedule to keep to and so, thanking Peter and Connie for their hospitality, I set off in a hired car, driving west.

Stand up and be counted

WHEN I WAS INVITED to a particularly smart shoot in October 1991, run by a wealthy farmer, I was delighted. It promised to be a splendid day out. I knew the land, it had lots of cover and any time you passed there were always plenty of pheasants in evidence. I was sure I had only been invited because I had sold the farmer a dog. I mentioned the invitation to some of my friends who were obviously impressed. The shoot was regarded as highly desirable. The syndicate was largely made up of professional city men and none of my friends had ever heard of invitations being issued.

I arrived early, dressed in my smartest shooting suit, car washed, my best dog at heel. I was introduced to the other guns and, over coffee and biscuits in the palatial kitchen, my host explained to the party how the day would be run. It would be a mixture of driven and high-quality walked-up. We set off for the first drive. The presentation of the pheasants was splendid — high, curling birds that were the essence of testing sport. I was in my element, on my best behaviour, shooting well and, after the drive, working the dog on the most difficult runners. Three further drives were fitted in before we broke for lunch, served in the kitchen, a delicious game hot-pot. I sat there enjoying the conversation, hoping that I could become a part of this enjoyable company.

After lunch we had two further drives then started on a long sweep across arable fields, bordered with overgrown ditches and, to my delight, wonderful, thick hedgerows. The intention was to work the ground for game, which we would leave at strategic points for later collection. In this manner we would walk the fields all the way back to the house.

I was walking in the line when a hare got up 40 yards in front of the gun nearest to me. The fellow lifted his fun as the hare sped off and fired both barrels. The hare ran on, apparently unscathed. Then another hare jumped from its couch and sped away. The fellow, having reloaded, raised his gun at the hare, which was well out of sporting range, and again fired. I saw the hare go down momentarily on its back legs, then run on. I didn't approve and was unsure what to do. As the line continued across the grass fields, several hares go up, some in range being shot cleanly, whilst others were obviously being fired at out of range. As we walked on, another hare jumped in front of the gun next to me only to be shot at extreme range and, wounded, run on. I called to the fellow as politely as I could that he was shooting them out of range and should restrict himself to sporting shots. A short time later another hare jumped, again to be fired at out of range.

This was enough, I was not prepared to continue to be a silent witness to such behaviour. Opening my gun, I looked down the line for my host. He was out of sight so, turning, I walked over to the fellow, asking him to calm down, act like a sportsman and, if he couldn't restrict himself to animals within range, not to shoot. Obviously embarrassed, he tried to shrug off my comments saying that they were certainly in range, it was just unfortunate that he had 'legged it' and, if I had any further complaints, to address them to the host. I resumed my place in the line as we moved forward, aware that the others had witnessed the incident. For the rest of the drive the fellow didn't shoot. The drive over, we were having a bowl of soup, a drink and chatting about the day. The fellow I had spoken to, and his friend, didn't join us, and none of the other guns mentioned the incident. Then my host left the room. Away some time, he was obviously in conversation with the fellow outside.

Eventually everyone started to leave, shouting farewells as they drove out of the yard. As I thanked my host and got in the car he came over to me. 'I understand you don't approve of how we do things here,' he said. 'I don't think you'll be invited back.'

I looked at him, then replied 'Some of us are prepared to stand up and be counted for what we believe in. If that's how you do things I wouldn't wish another invitation.' It never came.

An eventful journey

DURING THE SUMMER OF 1992 I was invited back to Italy by the Retriever Club for a two-week period. A few days before I was due to leave I slipped coming down a steep part of the hill above my house, tumbled through the bracken and crashed on top of a large rock. I broke several ribs on my right side and endured the most dreadful pain every time I moved. However, I was determined not to miss my Italian trip. Besides I knew everything had been arranged and I could not possibly let them down.

I arrived at Linate airport in Milan to be collected by Stefano. He had his super, black labrador, Bullet, in the car and had also brought with him a new, young dog to work with in the training sessions. When I arrived I met once again many of the friends I had made during my previous visits. People had travelled from all over Italy, making a holiday out of the trip. I saw a dramatic improvement in the standards of both dogs and handlers. Following my advice, the numbers in the classes had been greatly reduced; there were no more than 20 individuals with their dogs. What I had been attempting was to instil a standard of knowledge sufficient for the Italians to develop a pool of expertise of their own, so that they could train themselves rather than be dependent on bringing in visiting trainers. Once they have achieved this self-sufficiency and independence, they will be in a better position to increase the standard of training throughout the country.

Being midsummer I soon discovered it was only possible to work in the cool of the early mornings and evenings. We stopped at about 10 a.m., not restarting till 5.30 p.m. This meant that we had the major part of the day to relax, sunbathe, tour the area and have delicious, long, alfresco lunches, accompanied by lots of local wine.

One morning after breakfast one of my hosts, Carlo, an eminent banker from Rome, announced to me that he had arranged a tour of the area then a visit to a gun club, where he intended to take part in a clay shoot. The banker, a small, neat, dapper man, no doubt, when dressed in his banking attire of fashionable suit, shirt, tie, etc. looked extremely smart and was probably the height of chic, respondent with his neatly tied pony-tail and enormous moustache. He was not, however, dressed so smartly when we left, wearing light leather slip-ons, no socks, jeans, a T-shirt emblazoned with 'Guns 'n' Roses' and dark sunglasses. His huge moustache gave him the appearance of a 1960s' hippy. It was his hairstyle, however, that put the seal on his strange appearance: with a dramatic, receding hairline over a high, domed forehead, his hair was swept straight back, hanging loose and fully shoulder-length. I towered over him, with my bushy hair and a full beard, dressed in jeans, trainers and T-shirt and, of course, sunglasses. We no doubt looked like two ageing hippies. Carlo drove a little, white Fiat Uno with Rome number plates. Having loaded his shotgun on the back seat, I gingerly sat in the front of the little car. My ribs were slowly improving; only when I tried to turn or move quickly did I get the sharp jagged pain.

We set off in the bright sunshine, driving through the beautiful, hilly countryside with the windows wound down, enjoying the breeze. The sides of the hills were planted with vines, the low ground was rich with fields of maize and delightful, small farmhouses with red-tiled roofs dotted the countryside, whilst occasionally we would come to ancient, little churches perched on hilltops. We visited a village of great antiquity and several vineyards, where we enjoyed a glass of wine and bought a few bottles. Everything was idyllic.

As we drove down a narrow country road, the lush, heavy vegetation overhanging the verges, Carlo suddenly exclaimed, 'Shit, shit, shit!' as he frantically tried to fit his seat-belt while glancing in his rear-view mirror. Then, with a very Latin shrug of his shoulder and gesture with his free hand, he pulled into the grass verge. Looking in his mirror, he again said, 'Shit, shit, the police,' then turning to me said, 'Sit there, James. I speak to them.' He jumped out of the car and I heard him talking excitedly in Italian as he disappeared behind the vehicle.

I was aware of a figure on the other side of the car at the rear side-window. Unable to turn around because of my ribs, I wondered what was going on behind me. I didn't have my seat-belt fastened either and thought to myself that at the worst it would be a fine. As I sat there I could hear Carlo's voice becoming increasingly agitated, then a curt voice snapped, 'Silenzio!', then 'Signore, Signore.' I was obviously being called.

I tried to open the door. We were parked so close to the verge that it would only open a short distance and I started to squeeze out slowly, aware of my painful ribs. Finally out of the car, I turned and got the shock of my life. Standing behind the car some three yards from me, in a wide-legged, combat position, his machine pistol held in both hands, aiming at the ground at my feet, was an olive-skinned sergeant of the carabiniere. To his left a policeman stood poised for action, his machine-gun pointing somewhere at my feet, whilst behind the police car Carlo was standing, feet straddled, his hands on the roof, with a third officer, gun drawn, standing beside him. Carlo was calling in a loud voice, 'Professore scozzese esperto di cane.' He was obviously referring to me; translated it means 'a Scottish dog trainer'.

The carabiniere were quickly satisfied as to our identity. Visibly relaxed, and putting their guns away, they explained the reason for their actions. Several terrorist incidents had recently taken place in the region and the terrorists were apparently using a white Fiat Uno. The previous day a policeman had been murdered in a distant city and the police were in a high state of alert. They had seen us drive past and the combination of our appearance, the little car and the fact that it had number plates issues 500 miles away in Rome was sufficient reason for them to stop us. Add to that the gun case on the back seat and their actions were entirely understandable. Taking their advice, we removed the gun, put it in the boot out of sight and continued our journey to the gun club.

How big are your balls, Mr Douglas?

WHEN I WAS ASKED to make a video programme on the shooting of wild boar I had a choice of Europe or Tunisia. For several reasons, principally weather, we chose Tunisia and, after several months of negotiation with the Tunisian authorities for the various permissions required to allow the camera crew to enter the country and film, we prepared to leave. Some countries get highly suspicious of anything out of the ordinary. Television crews, after all, can be filming a variety of forbidden installations or perhaps wish to expose aspects of a country which the government would rather were kept under wraps. Therefore there is a set procedure which must be gone through to acquire the necessary documentation, without which travel and filming within a country can be extremely difficult. In our case there was an additional requirement, that we would be bringing in guns. Also, since we intended to film Tunisian boar shooting, which generates considerable income for the Government, we felt justified in insisting that we would get access to areas where we had a real chance of seeing quality animals.

I set off a few days before the crew was due to join me. Arriving in Tunis, I met a Government representative who whisked me through Customs and into a waiting car and off we set in the gathering dusk into the town. I noticed an obvious police and military presence in one area and, on enquiry, was told that Yasser Arafat and various other dignitaries were holding a summit meeting. I was deposited in a large, tourist hotel where I was told that my driver and vehicle would collect me in the morning.

The car turned out to be an elderly Renault, driven by a young Tunisian who made Nigel Mansell look positively sluggish. We hurtled out of Tunis and sped off to the distant Atlas Mountains. Our journey took us across typical Tunisian countryside of fairly flat, red soil with a variety of crops. We raced through numerous little villages where the people had to leap nimbly out of the way of the speeding Renault or risk being run over. Chickens and donkeys the driver swerved round. I was not at all happy with his driving and several times asked him to slow down, politely but forcefully, at which he laughed and pretended he didn't understand. Finally, as we narrowly missed colliding with a huge truck, I told the driver in language which even he could understand to slow down. He did. The rest of the journey went without incident. We eventually started to climb higher and higher into the foot-hills until I was eventually deposited at a hotel overlooking the small community of An Drahan.

The hotel was relatively sparse, with bare floors and few of the luxurious trappings of the coastal hotels for tourists. This hotel's principle business came from European sportsmen, mainly French and Italians. After a typical dinner of French bread, a not quite recognisable part of a chicken, and salad served with bottles of local wine, I was sitting eating fruit when the hotel patron approached me and introduced Mohammed, our hunter–guide. He sat beside me, drank coffee and explained to me how boar were hunted in Tunisia. All the time he sat there I was assailed by a pungent aroma of armpit.

I retired for the night, looking forward to the following day when I hoped to find lots of local colour to give me ideas for filming. Was I in for a surprise!

Next morning I walked down into the village of An Drahan to have a look around. A few pieces of fly-dotted meat hung from hooks in an open-fronted shop which was obviously the local butcher's. From what I could see their total meat display consisted of one goat, complete with head. Men lounged everywhere, particularly around the café. The whole community lived in dirt and poverty and I soon realised there was little of interest to film. I spent the next four days in drizzling rain, awaiting the arrival of the crew. They arrived as expected, in the afternoon, with a long story to tell of great delays at the airport whilst a seemingly endless chain of uniformed individuals checked their authority to bring in our camera and sound equipment before letting them into the country. That night, as we were having dinner, we were approached by a very smart and obviously educated fellow who introduced himself as Nadim. He was to be our Government liaison, a general term covering many tasks. It was his job to make sure everything went well and that we didn't misbehave or end up embarrassing the Government.

We met up with Mohammed again, over breakfast the following morning, and we set off, all of us crammed into a Shogun. This was not a journey for the faint-hearted since Mohammed smelled so disgustingly strongly of sweat you could almost taste it. Neither he nor his clothing could have been washed for God knows how long. In spite of the stench I found it slightly amusing, our P.A., a young lady of startling good looks and enormous ego, dressed in designer jeans and T-shirt, sat pale-faced, squashed against Mohammed who obviously fancied her, the smell emanating from him easily overpowering her expensive perfume. We all put the windows down as we drove to an area some ten miles from the hotel where we were to meet the *rabatteurs* (beaters).

When we arrived I was confronted with some 30 extremely thin, ragged men — local hill people earning a tiny pittance daily as beaters. Nadim made a speech which seemed, as I stood watching and listening to him, to be very earnest, almost threatening. I found out later that he did this every day and was explaining to them that they had to work hard since the film would show Tunisia in a good light, bring more visitors and result in more employment.

Some of them had with them small mongrel dogs with which to drive the boar. The men with dogs get paid an extra few pence daily for the dog. We set off walking along a series of paths. The countryside was hilly and covered with a variety of trees, primarily dense cork forests. As we walked along I was acutely aware of the constant, chattering conversation amongst the *rabatteurs* and it came as some surprise when, eventually Mohammed pointed out where I should stand and went off leading the *rabatteurs* to put them in position. All the while, they chattered and shouted excitedly to

each other and, as they walked off to get into position, I could easily follow their progression from the noise they were making. I couldn't understand how they expected any boar other than the profoundly deaf to be so
foolish as not to have slipped away from the noise.

How a drive works in any country for any species is basically the same.
The guns stand downwind on one side of a square. The main line of beaters starts on the opposite side of the square facing the guns. Other beaters
stand down the other two sides of the square. The principle line of beaters
starts forward, whilst the side-beaters keep the animals contained within
the square. The only area of quiet is where the guns are waiting. Not in
Tunisia!

Here they did not seem to understand the first rudiments of ambush or
caution as everywhere they went they kept up their constant shouting and
chattering. Once the guns were in position, the *rabatteurs* would all walk
down one side of the square, shouting until they all got into position, then
come forward, making a ferocious noise. It never occurred to them as they
were getting into position to be quiet. I cannot say how many boar there
really were in these thickets, since, although some of them stayed until the
beaters moved forward and then came towards the guns, obviously a considerable number must have already gone.

I stood there holding my double-barrelled shotgun, the only weapon
allowed into Tunisia (rifles are banned). It was loaded with Brenica slug. I
had positioned the camera crew where I thought they would get an excellent view. The practice in Tunisia is to stand with your back to the beaters,
shooting the animals after they have passed you so that the slugs have no
danger of continuing on and bagging a *rabatteur*. This rule had been
brought out a few years previously after the demise of several of those
unfortunate individuals.

I kept my ears strained for the noise of oncoming boar. Several little
jackals slipped across the ride and then I heard a distinct movement coming
towards me. I was standing to one side of a little path, looking at the dense
thicket. I suddenly noticed a large sow standing in the thicket, less than
three yards from me. She was obviously watching the clearing and me. The
noise of the little dogs got closer. The sow, followed by a smaller boar,
crossed the clearing in front of me, travelling so fast they caught me completely unawares and the best I could do, as I swung hopelessly after them,
was to fell two little trees behind them as they disappeared. The drive was
soon over, with no further animals appearing, and we went back to the
vehicles and moved on.

Two further drives were fitted in. On each occasion no boar came past

me within range and none of the others was particularly large. After eating our packed lunch, we moved on for the first drive of the afternoon. Again the *rabatteurs* made a fiendish noise as they got themselves into position and started the drive. I stood poised for action, then heard huge excitement as the constant noise of shrieks and roars grew distinctly louder, followed by excited yapping coming straight towards me. This time I was ready and, as the large dark brown boar rocketed across the clearing, I swung through and shot it through the point of the shoulder. It crashed dead instantly, to be covered immediately by some 15 little dogs that had been chasing it, each one darting forward for a quick nip at its rear end. Mohammed and the *rabatteurs* gathered around, making even more noise, as they dragged the boar unceremoniously from the thicket and we set off back to the vehicles.

We moved on to another drive. Once we were in position, with the camera ready, the drive commenced. Little foxes and an occasional jackal passed, but any boar that came out were out of sensible shooting range. The day over, we returned to the hotel, where I took the opportunity of examining my boar. I measured his tusks and felt certain he would make a silver medal. Mohammed supervised his removal to the larder. Back at the hotel the word had already spread amongst the French and German

shooting parties who were staying there and we were bought several cele-
bratory drinks in the bar that night.

Although we saw several boar next day, I only managed to fire one shot,
killing a large sow. The constraints put on anyone making a film of such an
activity is, I believe, a great deal more difficult than most people would
credit. Not only do you have to wear a microphone and give commentary
to the camera, which cannot be scripted since no one knows quite what
will happen, but you must constantly keep in mind camera angles whilst
simultaneously concentrating your mind on the job in hand — shooting.
There is after all a saying in show business, 'Never work with children or
animals.'

On day three, Nadim joined me and the crew for breakfast and suddenly
made a startling announcement. He had taken it upon himself to organise
a party of what he referred to as 'important men' to come from Tunis and
join in the shooting, in an effort to help kill more boar. I tried in vain to
explain to him that simply killing boar was not the object of the exercise.
We wanted to film them being shot correctly in front of the camera.
However, realising that Nadim had made a great effort and would lose
enormous status by any climb-down, I agreed to see how things went. I
cannot describe my consternation when I went out of the hotel after
breakfast to meet my 'fellow sportsmen'.

Resembling more the sort of individuals you hear calling for your attention as you pass strip clubs, they were generally fairly 'smooth' in appearance, looking more as though they were going on a 'hit' than on a sporting
day out. All of them were armed with automatic shotguns which they
waved about with casual indifference. They had their own 4×4 into which
they had packed food and a large amount of wine. We set off, the camera
vehicle in front, followed by my new chums.

We arrived at an area in the foot-hills and the whole countryside was
covered with a heather-like plant, growing up to ten feet tall in places.
Mohammed positioned us across a ride and the drive began. A large sow
broke cover to my left, going very fast and, judging it to be unsafe, I didn't
lift my gun. A Tunisian sportsman, next in line, obviously felt more confident and swung through and fired. I saw the sow's face snap to the side and
she ran on shaking her head. When the drive was over I walked over to
where I had seen the sow struck and picked up teeth and bits of jaw bone.
I was very angry and turned to the fellow, holding out the teeth and bone,
and said, 'What do we do now? It's wounded. We've got to get it.'

He turned to his fellow Tunisians who were gathering round, shrugged,
laughed and said to me, 'Ha, ha, it has been to the dentist.' They all turned

away back towards the vehicles, anxious to get on to the next drive. There was nothing I could do.

During the next drive I watched these men. They were all obviously trigger-happy and any animal that came out remotely in range was guaranteed to be shot at. During the drive another animal was wounded but allowed to run on. I was in a very difficult position. I had never been afraid to stand up and be counted, but there was literally nothing I could do and I was convinced that to have insulted them would have caused problems for the crew.

After lunch we started another drive. I was standing under some trees when a very large sow crossed the ride, travelling at speed. It was not safe to shoot and I held my fire, but the next fellow in line fired. I saw the animal hump its back, obviously shot in the stomach and run on down a boar tunnel in the tall heather. I was very angry. This was not sport — it wasn't even shooting. These individuals had no right to be carrying a gun. The drive over, I asked them how they intended to follow up the wounded boar. They shrugged and laughed.

'Where I come from we follow our wounded game,' I said. 'Wait here.' With that I entered the tunnel. These tunnels are runs used only by the boar. Some are part of a large network, others are merely short runs through thickets. In the tunnel it was cool, with only a dappled light penetrating the shrubs. For the first 200 yards I followed the blood spotted every few paces or so. I had to move with extreme caution. I was half-crouched, carrying my gun in front of me at half-mount, ready to snap into action.

With the twists and turns of the tunnel, at no time was visibility any more than 10 yards. The thicket on either side of the tunnel was virtually impenetrable. Then, after another 100 yards, the tunnel became lower and I found myself crouched right down as I moved forward. Occasionally there were larger splashes of blood where the boar had obviously stopped. I followed the trail for several hundred more yards, with the tunnel at times becoming so low that I was forced into almost a crawling position. I had begun to realise that, in the close confines of a tunnel so tight, if I encountered the boar coming towards me there could be no possibility of error. I would have to get it first time, for if I missed there was nowhere for me to go.

I was also beginning to question the wisdom my actions. Like any family man I have responsibilities and which one of my family would thank me for coming off worst in an encounter with a boar? I decided to go a few yards further and, if there was still no sight of the animal, to turn and go back. The ground started to drop down into a dry riverbed. The tunnel roof became slightly higher and I was able to half-stand. Creeping forwards I saw her. Standing in the centre of the dry stream, facing me, head down, she was badly wounded. I lifted my gun as she started to turn and shot her through the base of the neck. I cannot tell you the relief I felt. Suddenly the tunnel became oppressive and I wanted out. I realised I had come well over half a mile into the thicket and lost no time in starting back.

Approaching the entrance to the tunnel I stopped and composed myself. Running my hands through my hair and straightening my clothing, I casually walked out into the bright sunlight. The crew, Mohammed, Nadim, *rabatteurs* and hunters were all standing about in groups watching and waiting anxiously. They had heard the shot but were quite sure I must have been gored. As casually as I could, I called Mohammed over and, as though I were indicating to a picker-up where I had seen a pheasant fall, I said, 'Send some of your boys down the tunnel, Mohammed. She's quite a big animal.' The *rabatteurs* refused to enter the tunnel, obviously afraid of what they might meet, but I did gain the impression that they started looking at me differently.

The last drive of the day took place and, though I heard some shooting, I saw no boar. As I walked down the ride, followed by the crew some 60 yards behind me, I could hear a commotion ahead. I came to a steep bank down to the road where the vehicles were parked. There were the *rabatteurs* standing around, howling with laughter and watching some of the hunters playing with the object of their enormous merriment. They had a little boar piglet which had either been hurt by the dogs or shot with birdshot. One of the hunters was holding its hind legs up like the handles of a wheelbarrow. The little pig was running with its forelegs, squealing in terror as the man guided it on a zigzag course through the legs of his friends.

I could take no more. I lifted my empty gun and closed it as though to shoot, and shouted down to them, 'Stand out of the way!' There was a great scatter, accompanied by shrieks of terror as men dashed in all directions. I walked down the bank to the little pig, which was crawling about on its forelegs. I produced my skinning-knife and cut its throat. Calling Mohammed and the nearest *rabatteurs* I indicated the now dead piglet and told them to skin and clean it, for tonight I intended to eat it for dinner.

On the way back to the hotel, Nadim, who had witnessed the day's adventures, explained to me the Tunisians' attitude towards the boar. As Muslims, he said, they do not eat pork. They had no respect for these animals which gobble up their crops and breed as only pigs can. They were of no value whatever except that European sportsmen were prepared to pay to shoot them and, whilst they were happy to take their money, it was obviously difficult for them to understand sporting ethics.

Nadim agreed with me that I and the crew would get on better alone and that the Tunisian sportsmen should shoot in a different area.

Next day, Mohammad had chosen yet another area. We walked into position with the *rabatteurs* making their usual fiendish noise, chattering, laughing and, to my mind, chasing everything for miles around. After the first, two, non-productive drives I was getting rather short-tempered with Mohammed and his noisy crew. When we arrived at the area for the third drive, not realising the camera was already running and the sound engineer recording, I called to Mohammed as he set off with the *rabatteurs*, 'Mohammed try and explain to them it isn't boar we're hunting. Try and make them pretend that instead of boar it's Russian soldiers and if they alert them they might get shot.'

Mohammed looked at me mystified. 'But why should I say that Mr Douglas? The Russians are our friends.' He turned away.

I thought for a moment and called, 'Then, Mohammed, tell them it's Israelis. Oh, but wait a minute, Mohammed. You'd better say there's only one of them, or they'll all run away!' By the end of this day we had no success.

That night it was obvious that much of the conversation amongst many of the Tunisians was about that day's lack of success, so it was with a degree of determined resolve that we all set out the next day to an area I was told had not been hunted for several years. We drove for some time, eventually climbing up into the mountains, where we came to a small community. I was introduced to the headman — a tiny little man with such nobility radiating from him that I realised I was in the presence of a man I could respect. He had already positioned his *rabatteurs*, who I discovered were all the men of the community, by having them march silently into positions which he had chosen. He accompanied me and the crew for a walk of some half mile. Indicating that I should stand in a clearing, he pointed to a sharp outcrop of rock several hundred yards away and, pointing at himself, produced a little hunting horn from under his long Arab dress. As he disappeared I quickly organised the camera positions with the crew. As I was doing so, Nadim, always trying to be helpful and amenable, was standing around. Suddenly he said to me, 'What size of bullets do you use, Mr Douglas?' I was concentrating on the crew and aware that we didn't have time for chat.

I turned to him and said curtly, 'I'm not using bullets, I'm using a spherical ball.' I then turned away to pick myself a good spot to stand, leaving Nadim standing with the crew.

As I stood in the morning sunlight, the only sounds one could hear were a few birds and the distant, occasional yipping of a dog. Then I saw the little man appear on the point of rock. I watched as he raised the horn to his lips and the notes sailed out over the hills. As the sound died away in the valley below me, a great noise of men shouting and beating tins started. I stood listening to the noises slowly coming closer. I became aware of the growing insistence in the yapping of the dogs. The noise was gradually getting louder and more frantic. I stood listening. Then, as I heard a noise behind me, I looked cautiously down the slope through the bushes.

An enormous boar was coming at a lumbering trot up the hill towards me. I could clearly see his huge, gleaming tusks. A group of little dogs was yapping at his heels, being careful to stay well clear of his jaws and tusks. In pace to his trot he swung his great head from side to side, obviously willing his tormentors to come forward in range of his tusks. As he came up past me, no more than five yards away, I stood motionless, then started to mount the gun. In the action of lifting the gun, the boar accelerated like a rocket. I swung through and put one shot through the base of his neck. He somersaulted and lay still as the little dogs rushed in, biting at his dense coat. I approached the boar. It was obvious he was of spectacular size. As the *rabatteurs*, Mohammed and the little headman appeared out of the trees the crew and Nadim gathered around.

I was examining the boar and unaware that Alistair, the cameraman, was still filming when Nadim pushed his way importantly up to me and said, 'What size are your balls, Mr Douglas?'

I stood up, looked at my huge, gold-medal boar, which I had killed with one shot, turned to Nadim and said, 'Bloody enormous!'

When we returned to An Drahan I was curious to see where my big boar would be stored, since his tusks were of great value to me and I didn't fancy the idea of some Arab or one of my Latin fellow guns having it away on his toes with my previous trophy. On enquiry I was told by Mohammed that my boar would be stored, with the others I had shot, in the larder. I followed my boar as it was unloaded and dragged away. The man dragging it staggered towards a large building set back behind the hotel. Even before they opened the door I detected a strong smell of dead boar but when I looked into the 'larder' I was taken aback. An enormous pile of boar was heaped in the room. Indeed, all the boar shot in the area over the last week were stacked in a great heap.

The animals I had shot had been carefully laid to one side, since I had warned Nadim that I would wish to photograph them all at the end of the trip, though, after my photographs were taken and my tusks removed, the animals I had shot could be added to the great heap of carcasses for export to the gourmet hotels and restaurants of France. It certainly makes a mockery of the legislation appertaining to carcass care that the EC impose on British game-dealers when you see meat being treated in such a way.

Over the next few days we finished off filming our background shots and sequences of local interest, then, leaving An Drahan, we set off for Tunis where I wished to film a few shots of Carthage. As we were driving along in the crew bus, we passed through the tiny community of Bullaregia. I noticed at the side of the road some ruins and enquired of Nadim what they were. 'Just a few Roman ruins,' he said with a shrug. I decided to stop the bus and take a look. What we found was beyond anything I had ever seen before: a large Roman fort, complete with walls, mainly intact. We walked inside along the cobbled road and started to explore. Not only is the Roman library building still intact, but the open-air theatre, complete with perfect mosaic floor in front of the stage, with a great decoration of a bear is splendid. Walking the narrow, cobbled streets of this once-thriving, Roman community I was filled with a great sense of wonder at this past civilisation, but an even greater surprise was in store. When I descended a stairway leading underground, I discovered a villa built beneath the earth, complete in every way, each room of perfect proportions and all of them with the most intricate mosaic flooring of tiny, coloured tiles. There were several other villas in a similar state of preservation. The Romans obviously found the heat too much, so did the logical thing — built their villas down into the cool earth, with open shafts to allow light in and air to circulate.

Tunisia was, for me, an interesting, exciting and rewarding location to work in and I regard myself as most fortunate to have been paid for enjoying myself!

Poland

HAVING ENJOYED my boar-shooting experiences while filming in Tunisia, I wanted to experience a proper European wild-boar hunt. Boar have, after all, been synonymous with European hunting since earliest times and represent for most Europeans a highlight of the shooting calendar. Sadly no longer found in the British Isles, boar range from France across the European continent.

A friend of mine, a Scotsman, who works as greenkeeper on a large, private golfcourse in central France has a novel disruption on his beautifully kept greens: boar coming out of the surrounding forests overnight are a constant nuisance as they root about. Areas of Italy have large boar populations; indeed, I visited a dog trial in Tuscany once when one of the principle and constant interruptions was the numerous boar that kept appearing from the thickets.

A few years ago, whilst working on a series entitled *Defence of the Realm* with the British Armed Forces, I was in northern Germany on exercise with the Devonshire and Dorset Regiment, taking part in a war game simulating European battle. We were therefore tactical as we played out our battle games in the forest areas. It was hilarious to witness tough, young, British squaddies on sentry duty suddenly being badly frightened as they were confronted in the early morning by large boar appearing out of the undergrowth.

Boar are particularly numerous in eastern European countries and I decided to join a shooting party on a three-day boar shoot, flying out from the UK to Poland, with two friends: Charles, a hotelier from Sussex, and Paul, a businessman from the Midlands. Neither had shot boar before but were excited at the idea of taking part in what we hoped would prove to be a memorable shooting adventure. The plane flew direct from London to Warsaw where, after clearing Customs, we were met by the representative of the Polish sporting-agency. His name was Peter and he was to act as our interpreter and guide. We loaded our luggage into a rather tired Ford mini-bus and set off on the drive northwest towards the Baltic. After some four hours driving through the Polish countryside, we arrived at our base — a small hotel near Koszalin — where we unloaded our luggage and were shown to our rooms. Accommodation in Poland is, by Western standards, fairly basic but the people are very friendly and make every effort to make you welcome. That evening Peter introduced us to the others who would make up the party: three Germans and a Dutchman. We spent a pleasant evening over a dinner of Polish sausage, vegetables, bread and, of course, copious quantities of good, local wine.

Next morning, after a good, cooked breakfast, we loaded ourselves into the Ford mini-bus and set off for the Bielik Forest, a short drive of three-quarters of an hour to an ancient hunting lodge where we met with the keeper and beaters. The lodge had obviously been quite spectacular in its day though it was badly run down, parts of it being barely habitable. One area had been cleared and furnished as a makeshift dining area with a long, plain table in front of a large, open fire which burned brightly. The beaters had with them about six little dogs: some terriers and others of indeterminate breeding. After a round of Polish vodka, we set off along a track, led by the keeper and Peter, whilst the beaters headed off in the opposite direction. They were to take a long, circular sweep through the forests, driving the boar in front of them towards where we would be positioned. As I walked along, I admired the wonderful mixed forest of oak, beech and pines. The colours were magnificent; being October the whole countryside was a rich series of autumnal browns and dark greens. It was in country like this where the Europeans developed their HPR breeds (hunting, pointing, retrievers) that are now so popular worldwide. The vizsla, Weimaraner, Munsterlander and, of course, the German smooth- and wire-haired pointers all come into their own in countryside where the quarry species can range from birds to enormous stags.

Eventually, after a short walk, the keeper lined us out quietly along a ride about 70 yards wide. Peter had explained to us the previous evening the manner in which the shoots would be conducted and the distance between the guns and areas of fire. We were to stand 50 to 80 yards apart. Most of us were using rifles, two of the Germans had drillings, Paul had elected to use his shotgun with Brenica slug, I was using a 0.308 with open sights. I stood there in the bitter cold and listened to the forest sounds. After a while I suddenly saw a movement at the side of the clearing and a fox crossed the line at a cautious trot in front of me. Not long after its appearance, a roe doe appeared and quietly crossed the ride some 50 yards to my left. I had still heard no sounds of the line of beaters but, as I stood there, three enormous red-deer hinds appeared and trotted across the ride to my right. It was permissible to shoot does and hinds, and, of course, foxes, but I had no interest in shooting driven deer. I was much more interested in the boar I hoped would appear.

Then I heard the distant noise of the approaching beaters, heralded by the excited yipping of the dogs. I heard a few shots further down the line but could see nothing. Suddenly, a few, small boar broke cover in front of me. They appeared so quickly that, though I was poised ready for action, I hardly had time to mount the rifle before they ran out of sight. I determined to be quicker next time. Then I heard several shots up and down the line. Obviously everyone else was having more luck than I was. I stood there, hoping that some large boar would present itself in front of me but, apart from another two, smallish boar which ran to my left and were promptly shot by one of the Germans who was next in line, nothing happened. The sound of a horn heralded the end of the drive.

I walked up the ride toward the other guns. Paul had shot nothing, Charles had taken a good boar, the rest of the party had shot one boar each. We walked back to the vehicle while the beaters set off to another block of forest.

Loaded in the vehicle, we drove down a series of tracks before parking and walking to the next position where we were to stand. Again the ride varied in width from 60 to 80 yards. I didn't have so long to wait as on the first drive before I heard the distant sound of beaters. I was standing musing on how lucky I was to be able to enjoy this sort of trip when suddenly a group of boar burst from the cover in front of me. I lifted the rifle, found the biggest of the boar and swung through on his shoulder, squeezing the trigger. The boar jumped on impact, ran a few yards and fell dead. As I worked the bolt, feeding another round into the chamber, I was taken completely by surprise as a very large boar burst from the cover to my right. As he raced across the ride, I frantically finished working the bolt and started lifting my rifle. On the sound and movement, he accelerated with a startling speed and, before I could swing on to him, he had crossed the ride and was into the trees. I heard a few more shots up and down the line, then the horn sounded to herald the end of the drive.

I crossed to examine my boar, I judged him to weigh about 260 pounds with nice tusks. The shot had hit him just behind the shoulder and obviously passed through his lungs, the big slow-moving bullet having exited at a lower point than the higher entrance wound. On comparing notes, I discovered that Paul had still had no luck; though he had fired a few shots his inexperience with the speed of the animals was obviously showing. Charles had shot a fox, one of the Germans had shot one boar, the Dutchman had shot two. The next drive was blank. Though boar did cross the line, none was shot.

We returned to the vehicle and drove back to the old lodge where we huddled round the huge fire and toasted each other with vodka before sitting down to platefuls of delicious, thick soup, served with local bread. The soup was splendid and each of us had several helpings, followed by several glasses of wine. The combined effects of the vodka, soup, wine and heat from the log fire soon had us all relaxed, chatting and enjoying each other's company, and it was with some considerable reluctance that we roused ourselves at Peter's prompting and set off in the vehicle to another part of the forest. We soon arrived and, as I walked toward my stand, I mused on that special part of any driven shoot, particularly for pheasants in

the UK, where lunch, wine and heat serve to take up so much time.

The first drive after lunch produced no shootable boar. Some did appear but for a variety of reasons, including no doubt our soporific lunch, we were very slow. We hurried on to another drive and this time we were all more switched on. Though I only managed one small sow, Charles shot two, Paul missed several and the others took four between them plus two does.

The last drive of the day was in a slightly different type of country. There were more pine trees, though they were still well interspersed with oaks. I stood at my stand aware that the temperature had dropped and the cold was quite biting, though, with the absence of any real wind, I was spared any chill factor. Two roe does came out further down the ride. Then, with a rush, several boar appeared. I had started to mount my rifle on a medium-sized boar when, out of the corner of my eye, I saw a larger boar. I swung back, saw an even larger one, swung through and shot it. Due to my haste the bullet hit it too far back and, working the bolt, I quickly swung on to the accelerating animal and shot a second time. My second bullet hit it in the base of the neck and felled it instantly. There was silence broken only by the sound of the dogs. Then I heard a few shots further down the line. Nothing else appeared, the horn sounded and I walked over to the boar. I had shot a very large sow with small tusks. The rest of the party had had mixed luck. Charles had shot a sow, the Germans had shot one boar between them, Paul had taken nothing and the

Dutchman, with another good-sized boar, was obviously feeling very pleased with himself.

That night, after dinner and quite a few drinks, Peter suggested visiting a bar in a little town an hour's drive away. We all accepted and set off. The bar was crowded and, after we had spent a short time there, a loud disco started. Charles, Paul and I decided that we did not wish to stay for what was obviously going to be a long night. Our Dutch and German companions made it obvious that they intended to have, as they described it, some 'fun'. The three of us asked Peter to get us a taxi and we set off back to the hotel, where after another few vodkas we retired for the night. As the three of us went upstairs, Charles turned with a grin and said, 'I suppose they'll think we Brits are just boring.' I had been asleep for some hours when I was wakened by the noise of loud voices. Obviously our shooting companions had returned and, judging by the giggling female voices, they were going to be successful in their determination to have 'fun'.

Next morning we three, boring Brits were bright-eyed and ready for the day ahead. Our companions, when they finally appeared, looked decidedly rough coming down the stairs accompanied by their lady companions, who, after a quick cup of coffee, were sent off in a taxi. Then, to a chorus of ribald comments from the three of us, we watched them, bleary-eyed, loading themselves into the vehicle. Day two was basically a copy of the previous day. We fitted in eight drives. By the end of the day Charles had shot one boar and one doe, I had shot one boar and Paul had shot nothing, whilst the rest of the party had four boar and two does between them. That night the three of us elected to stay in the hotel after dinner, whilst our companions determinedly returned to the bar of the previous evening.

Day three and our last. The weather had changed and it was much colder. As we drove to the hunting area we were regaled with tales of the previous evenings deering-do. We were shooting in a different area and, when we arrived in the van, were transferred to an ancient, bus-like contraption drawn by a tractor. The beaters were loaded so thick on an open, 4×4 vehicle that they looked like some sort of humanoid hedgehog. We set off and, after a bumpy journey into the forest, dismounted and, following Peter and the local gamekeeper, walked along a series of forest tracks until we came to a ride some 80 yards wide.

I was flanked by two of the Germans and, as we stood there, I watched one of them constantly sipping from a little flask. Both very experienced, they seemed to have a sixth sense as to what to expect and, as I stood watching the trees in front of me, there was a sudden rush of some small boar on either side of me. Before I could make up my mind to react, my two companions had shot one each. Several other shots went off up and down the ride, then a whistle sounded. The drive over, the gamekeeper hurried us on. The next two drives, though several animals were seen, produced only two boar, both shot by the Germans.

After a quick lunch of soup and bread served from the back of a tractor-trailer, we went for the first drive after lunch. Again only one boar was shot by one of the Germans and, after a fairly lengthy walk through the trees, we lined out once again. We seemed to have ages to wait but the gamekeeper had explained that this was a very large block and the beaters had some distance to walk. I was flanked on my left by the Dutchman; on the right stood Charles, then Paul. Three does broke from the cover between Charles and Paul. Charles shot one and Paul cleanly missed. Then, after another wait, we heard the dogs yapping excitedly. Several boar started to cross the ride up and down the line; everyone was shooting.

One huge boar burst from the cover in front of me, running straight towards me. As I mounted my rifle he seemed to swerve and I swung through and fired. He kept going but as I quickly reloaded, he fell and started to get up. I shot him again, this time through the neck. There seemed to be a flurry of activity and then, almost like tail-end Charlie, a little boar ran out in front of Paul. He swung through and fired. The boar collapsed.

The drive finished, we all congratulated Paul, then moved on for the last drive. As I stood there, this time second last in the line, flanked on the outside by Paul, we watched and waited. Then three small boar rushed out of the trees between Paul and me. I held my fire, hoping that he would take them, but by the time he had lifted his gun they had crossed between us and he correctly didn't swing through. Then I heard some excited yapping, which seemed to be right in front of us. A large boar appeared out of the trees, stopped and ran back, then reappeared running straight down the line in front of Paul. I watched as he lifted his gun, swung and fired. When the slug hit the boar it somersaulted and didn't move. The whistle sounded, the drive was over.

I crossed to Paul and congratulated him. Only when we examined his boar did we realise quite how large it was. He had had the good fortune to shoot the biggest animal of the week.

We had spent a most productive week with superb sport. We had made new friends, visited another culture and, as Paul pointed out on the way home, driven boar shooting is always a combination of luck and experience.

Playing cowboys

FORT OGALLALA, sitting on the River Platte, and the Little Bighorn were two places I wanted to visit when film work took me to the mid-west of the USA. Whilst travelling to Laramie, I drove through Cheyenne, the small, historic Wyoming town so often featured in cowboy history and 'western' films, where I intended to look up a friend of mine, the son of a rancher that I had met when he was on business in the UK. I booked into a motel and, after unpacking, walked down the main street window-shopping. I noticed with considerable amusement that many of the vehicles parked in the street were pick-ups, each with its windows open and gun racks behind the driver, adorned with shotguns and the occasional rifle. Imagine parking a car like that in the UK! I pushed open the batwing doors and went into a saloon called The Cowboy (about as imaginative as an English pub called The Plough), where I spent a couple of hours chatting to and watching the locals who were all dressed in 'western' gear, boots and stetsons, perfectly normal attire for any cowboy. They found my accent and dress curious and were obviously impressed by my knowledge of local history. When I told them that I came from the country where their local cattle, the Aberdeen Angus (known there as Black Angus) originated, they were fascinated, especially when I described fields where you could see two dozen of the cattle grazing together. The land there is so big, the grazing so poor, that that sort of density is unheard of. Next morning I telephoned my friend Larry and told him I had arrived. He gave me directions and I drove out of town some 30 miles before turning into the five-mile ranch road. On this real, working 'western' ranch, though they have all the modern implements, tractors, etc., they still find that the horse is very much part of their working day.

Next day Larry asked me if I would like to join him hunting for pronghorn antelope. I readily agreed. He leant me a .270 rifle and, after I had gone out to the back of the ranch and checked the zeroing, we set off in a pick-up across the prairie. The countryside was mainly flat with small, rolling, grassy hills. After we had driven for about half an hour, we stopped and walked cautiously to the top of one of the little hills, where we crawled the last few yards and started to examine the countryside in front of us through our binoculars. Way out on the prairie, at least three-quarters of a mile away, we could see a few animals. Larry went back to the

pick-up and returned with a spotting 'scope with a small tripod. After he had focused it, he lay and carefully examined the distant animals. Finally satisfied with one animal that he said conformed to the size that was shootable, we lay together and planned the stalk, then set off using every contour in the ground, dry stream beds, natural fissures, etc. until we reached a point at least 250 yards from the antelope. Larry invited me to shoot the animal which he indicated, but I felt reluctant to shoot an animal at that distance. I was not particularly confident in the rifle and didn't really feel that it was sporting. I told him of my uncertainty of performing a clean shot whereupon he lay down, asked me to watch the animal and carefully lined up. I was watching the antelope through my binoculars when I heard the boom of the rifle beside me. The pronghorn staggered and started to run. After some 60 yards it stopped, staggered and fell over. We walked toward it. On examination, Larry found he had shot it through both lungs. The animal was dead. It was one of the best long-distance shots I had ever seen. I was not confident that I could perform so well and suggested that, if we could find another group of pronghorn, I might try another stalk but would not be happy unless I could get closer. We returned to the vehicle, collected the carcass and drove over the prairie to another area, where after spotting some animals we set off on another stalk.

Leaving Larry to watch from a vantage point, I set off, keeping to every fold in the ground, occasionally risking a quick spy at the antelope. Eventually, slithering and crawling towards a little rise, with great caution I crept through the sparse grass and raised my head to take a look. There were no antelope where I expected them to be. They had simply gone. I looked back towards where I knew Larry to be lying when he suddenly stood up and started walking towards me. When he arrived he explained that, whilst I was crawling along, the antelope had suddenly lifted their heads and, apparently unalarmed, had all walked off. We could only assume that the light breeze had in some way swirled, taking my scent out to them. However, I had enjoyed the stalk and time did not allow another try. Walking back towards the pick-up, we were following one of the dry gullies I had crawled down when Larry suddenly called my attention and indicated ahead. He pointed out a large rattlesnake lying in the sun about 30 yards away. He lifted his rifle and shot it. I thought afterwards of how close I must have passed to the rattler as I crept down the gully. I had witnessed here in Wyoming two examples, one with the antelope, the other with the snake, of how experience in an environment is so important.

Over the next few days I enjoyed being a 'dude'; I rode out over the prairie, getting great pleasure in being a cowboy. I was, after all, doing an adult version of what I as a child, like so many small boys, had played at. At night, stiff from the saddle, we would sit around broiling huge steaks and Larry, an accomplished musician, would entertain. During the days, though I saw many pronghorn, the interest in shooting one had left me. Too soon I had to leave. As I drove along the ranch road towards the main highway to Laramie, I passed close to numerous pronghorn but they will still be there when I return.

Canadian adventure

AS THE JUMBO JET APPROACHED the city of Calgary, I looked out at the flat prairie. There were few signs of civilisation, apart from the occasional ranch-house and the dead-straight roads running north to south every few miles, intersected by others running east to west, giving the whole countryside the appearance of a giant chessboard.

As the plane banked I looked out at the city in the early morning light. It appears almost artificial, rising suddenly and quite dramatically from the flatness of the prairie into a cluster of tall buildings. To the west are the Rockies and, though some 60 miles away, they look much nearer because of the clarity of the air. The Rockies themselves seem at first to be part of the same artificial landscape. They are so dramatically jagged that they look more like a child's drawing of mountains. I thought of the last time I had been in Calgary. I had flown to Alberta to buy some quarter horses since I am an enthusiast of that delightful 'western' breed. I had made some good friends and was now returning to go hunting, at their invitation.

After landing and clearing Customs — a formality since I was intending to borrow a rifle from my host, Don Garrett, who was waiting for me at the airport — we collected his car from the car park and left the city, driving north with the Rockies on our left. I soon found myself in the town of Red Deer, where on a previous trip my chum Paul Gibson and I had had a memorable Canadian steak dinner. There is a 'western' store in Red Deer run, rather incongruously, by a Chinese family and I stopped off to buy some inexpensive 'western' shirts, boots and, of course, a new stetson. Then we continued west towards the Rockies.

For the first couple of nights, I was staying with Don at his ranch before we headed off together into the wilderness. Next day Don suggested we drive up to Edmonton and visit the Edmonton Shopping Mall. To hear anyone say that a shopping mall is fascinating and well worth a visit is perhaps unusual. For me to say so is unheard of! Yet the Edmonton Shopping Mall must be one of the wonders of the world! No amount of advance warning or sales blurb can possibly prepare you for the vast scale and excitement of this enormous development. Of the many halls, I will describe only one: an enormous, two-tier, oval shopping mall, overlooking a central lagoon. The lagoon is so big that small submarines can take you for an underwater tour, whilst on the surface floats a galleon. Indeed, such is its size, that at one end is a dolphinarium where regular performances are given.

After a couple of days Don and I packed his pick-up and set off for the long drive to the hunting-camp. When we arrived at the camp, a cluster of several log cabins set aside from the main log building, we were met by a tall, lean man who introduced himself as Eldon. He showed us to our cabin and we unpacked before going over to the main house to meet the other two guests who were there to hunt. They were both from New York State and worked in electronics; this was their annual trip.

Our first two days were blank. We rode well-schooled quarter horses each morning to the areas in which our guide, Michael, a local Indian, wanted to hunt. We enjoyed the spectacular scenery, my unfamiliar muscles being stretched and pounded from spending such a long period in the saddle. Though we saw signs of elk, we never saw any animals. I was so tired coming in at night that, after dinner, I was only too happy just to fall into bed.

On our third morning, I was given a breakfast of such proportions that I felt more inclined to spend a few extra hours in my bed than mount the horse which I would be riding for the next several hours.

Don and I headed out along the lakeside. Soon we were climbing up through the trees. Michael had explained that he wanted to get to the high meadows since he knew of several good bull elk in the area. In the main, the trail we were following was no more than a series of game paths and made easy riding, though occasionally we would come to some more precarious, narrow paths along the steep slope. Here it was better to drop the reins and let your mount find its own way rather than try to guide it. Horses that are used to this sort of terrain know how to pick their way through obstacles with safety.

We stopped high above the lake to rest the horses and glass the countryside around us. The ground on the other side of the lake rose steeply at first, then became more rolling. We knew our two American friends were hunting somewhere in that area. Michael spotted and pointed out to us several good animals in the high meadows on the other side of the valley. It certainly looked as though our American friends had every chance of success.

We had brought a packed lunch in our saddlebags and, as we sat by a mountain stream enjoying our alfresco lunch I looked at the surrounding beauty and reflected on how fortunate I was to be able to visit these wild places. After our meal we moved on and rode higher, out on to some rolling, hilly ground with plenty of low brush and long grass. We came to the edge of a small, high valley. We ground-tied the horses, moved forward and sat down to glass ahead of us. There below us, out on some undulating ground near a little stream, about three-quarters of a mile away, were three bulls. Carefully, we studied them. One was certainly of the age and size that neatly put him into the category of a shootable, trophy animal and I sat back to watch Don try to stalk him. We had drawn straws on who should take the first stalk. Don had won.

The wind was drifting from the left and Don set off on a long, circular route out to the right which would bring him along the hill below us, slightly above the elk and perfectly downwind. I made myself comfortable amongst the heather and blueberries and alternated between watching the bulls and keeping a keen eye open for Don's appearance. When I did finally spot him, I was impressed. He was an excellent stalker and, whilst from above he was in my sight most of the time, he would occasionally disappear, either in a fold of the ground or behind some thicket.

There was a little ridge between Don and the elk, which were still some 500 yards from him, when just ahead of him and above a thicket I saw movement amongst the bushes. From its colour, at first I thought it was another elk. Michael had already seen the animal — it was a grizzly bear. It was difficult to know what to do. Don was too close to the bear for us to be able to warn him. To fire a shot or to shout would be more likely to frighten the bear and move it closer to Don. I watched as Michael got his rifle and, asking me to stay where I was, started moving cautiously downhill. By this time Don had disappeared behind the thicket, above which the bear appeared to be sniffing the ground. He was either looking for mice or eating the berries. For one of the very few times in my life, I was afraid of what might happen.

Suddenly, as I watched, the bear lifted its head. Don must have passed below it and the bear had caught his scent. It stood for a moment then turned and started to make its way uphill on a course parallel to where I thought Michael would be. I couldn't see him. The bear disappeared. I sat with my rifle across my knee looking for the bear, Don and Michael. When the bear next appeared he was high up the hill, almost in line with me. It was remarkable how such a large animal seemed able to disappear between folds in the ground and undergrowth and move so quickly. Michael reappeared. He had seen the bear move away and he continued up the hill to the horses. He was concerned that they might catch the distant scent of the bear and bolt, leaving us with a long walk.

This little drama had been played out completely unbeknown to Don or the distant elk. I could no longer see Don. With my glasses I watched the big bull I knew to be the one Don was stalking. I saw the bull seem to give a little lift and collapse, immediately followed by the boom of Don's rifle.

I made my way up to Michael and together we led the horses downhill. They were obviously concerned as we passed the thicket where we had first seen the bear, its lingering scent causing them to flare their nostrils and snort. They were agitated and we had to hold firmly on to their bridles. When we arrived where Don sat, close to the big bull, we told him about the bear. He didn't say anything at first, but I could tell he wasn't sure whether to believe us or whether we were kidding. I insisted that he had probably passed within 50 yards of the grizzly. Then, with his typical

dry humour, he turned to us and said, 'Hell, I knew the bear was there all the time, but I don't have a licence for a bear!'

We assisted Michael in the gralloch and caping out of the elk before setting off for the long ride back to the camp, where the other hunting party reported a lack of success. They had had two unsuccessful stalks and were obviously impressed that Don had got a good elk.

Next day we set off to hunt in a different area. it involved some fairly steep climbing and it was more sensible for us to dismount and lead the horses. We had travelled some distance on foot before the weather closed in, making further stalking impossible. We decided to abort the day and return to camp. All the following day it rained heavily and a low cloud hung over the tops. The Americans and I welcomed a day off from such a lot of unaccustomed riding. We stayed around the camp eating venison, drinking Canadian whiskey, swapping stories and relaxing.

The following morning was bright, crisp and clear. We set off along the lakeside before starting to pick our way up the tree-covered slopes, heading for an area where Michael hoped to find elk. I was getting as much pleasure from riding these agile and tough quarter horses in these mountains as I have ever had with a horse. I must confess that sitting in a 'western' saddle, dressed as I was and wearing my new stetson, I was enjoying an adult fantasy of playing cowboys. To complete the outfit my rifle was in a saddle scabbard.

163

Though we searched and glassed all day we saw only a few elk, either cows or calves or young bulls, and we never saw a stalkable beast. I was aware, as we returned to the camp, that it was the end of my sixth day. Since I had also arranged to spend a couple of days at Banff in the National Park, I only had two more days left before I had to leave.

Day seven. We rode along the lake for several miles, then unsaddled the horses and turned them into a small, log corral next to a little lakeside cabin that was occasionally used by the guides. It was basic but extremely useful when the weather was really bad, or when the guide wanted to hunt further afield. The cabin was equipped with a food stock and battery-operated radio; a small, aluminium boat lay up-turned on the beach.

We stalked on foot, the terrain lending itself better to this sort of stalking which I am more used to in Scotland. By mid-afternoon we had made our way to several likely vantage points and seen nothing. Then, as the light was beginning to fade, Michael spotted a good bull in a meadow across the valley on the other side of the lake, some two miles distant. In the diminishing daylight it was too far away for us to attempt a stalk. By the time we could have made our way across to the area, the light would be gone. Michael suggested that, as we had only one day left, we could get an early start next day by staying in the cabin overnight. When we got down to the cabin, whilst Don and I busied ourselves lighting a fire and opening tins from the cupboard, Michael got on the radio and informed the base of our decision.

After an uncomfortable night in a bunk it was no hardship to jump up in the morning and make a breakfast of tinned beef, tomatoes and beans with strong, black coffee. Leaving the horses, we set off by boat — the aluminium, flat-bottomed affair. We only had to travel across the narrow neck of the lake, so we left the little outboard in the cabin and paddled.

We climbed up through the trees and started glassing the various meadows and clearings but, apart from a few cows and young bulls, we saw no trophy animals. We searched all day, but it was as though my luck had evaporated. By mid-afternoon I had resigned myself to not getting an elk. Because of the distance we had to travel back and because it had started to rain, we decided to return downhill, eventually reaching the boat and crossing to the cabin. We saddled the horses and set off on the ride back to the base.

I had mixed feelings. I had had a wonderful time and seen lots of wildlife, but I had not managed to stalk a bull. Then, about a mile from the base camp, I had one of these strange premonitions you sometimes get when stalking. I stopped and dismounted. Taking my rifle from the scabbard, I suggested to Michael and Don that, as there was still plenty of light left, I would make my own way back to the cabin.

Michael, obviously alarmed that I would either get lost or run into a bear, hopped off his mount and, drawing his rifle, said he would come with me. Don took the horses and set off along the trail on his own, leading our two mounts.

I started up through the trees and came to a long, open meadow. The rain had stopped and a breeze was blowing gently into our faces as we walked along. I was leading and it felt more as though I was in Scotland. I glassed ahead and spotted, at the edge of the meadow, four bulls. One of them was exactly what we had been looking for. Michael examined him with his glasses and agreed he would make a good trophy. I set off on the stalk, leaving Michael behind. I had spotted a little ridge to one side of the meadow and felt that, if I could make my way to it, it would give me the perfect place from which to take a shot. Off I went, keeping low, taking every advantage of clumps of brush. I hadn't gone far when the idea occurred to me, what would I do if I came face to face with a bear? Fortunately, I never found out.

I eventually made the cover of the little ridge. On my hands and knees I crawled forward; lying flat in the wet grass, I inched my way the last few feet and cautiously lifted my head. They weren't where I had seen them. I lay there in frustration looking at the undulating ground. Just as I was about to stand up I realised that there was an animal no more than 100 yards from me lying down amongst some short brush. I could see his head and neck right down to the shoulder. I was surprised that such a large animal could be so difficult to spot, but once I had my eye on him I slid the rifle forward and examined him through the 'scope on the rifle. It was the same bull I had set out to stalk. Since he was lying down I decided to shoot him in the base of the neck. I was sure of the accuracy of the rifle, having checked it on the target at the base camp. I settled down and started to take careful aim when suddenly he stood up. Perfect. I moved the reticules behind his shoulder and brought the cross down on to his heart. I gently squeezed the trigger. On impact he staggered, jumped forward a few yards and collapsed. I had already worked the bolt, feeding a new cartridge into the chamber. My heart was pounding as I lay watching him; he was obviously dead. I stood up and walked over to the elk. For the few moments I spent on my own with him before Michael arrived, I experienced that familiar mixed feeling of many experienced stalkers, one of elation tinged with regret. He was a huge, old beast, his brow tines referred to as 'wolf-guards', long and curved.

We gralloched the beast and returned to the cabin. Michael would return with a couple of assistants to bring him in. Back at the cabin, our American friends reported that one of them had had success. So it was that, on our last night, we each had reason to celebrate before setting off on the return journey that would take us back to the realities of our individual lives, leaving the wilderness that would certainly live in our memories and inevitably draw us back some day.

Kenyan advice

AS A YOUNG LAD I read avidly the books of Jim Corbett and was greatly inspired by the wonderful writings of his Indian adventures. I suppose that, since he was a Scotsman, I identified with him. I also read various books on Africa. I was determined that some day I would visit those countries which sounded so exciting. Though I had read a great deal, nothing prepared me for the thrill of seeing Africa, with its huge variety of wildlife, delightful people and spectacular scenery. It was so different from anything I had ever seen and so distinctly 'Africa'.

My first African trip was to Kenya and, after visiting the obvious landmarks, such as the New Stanley and Norfolk Hotels in Nairobi, the Muthaiga and Karen Country Clubs (the Karen is named after Karen Blixen who wrote *Out of Africa*), and Treetops (a great disappointment), and having outfitted myself in a bright, new bush suit from one of the many Indian tailors, I journeyed down to the Masai Mara with a Kikuyu friend.

We flew in a tiny, eight-seater plane. Since there were only the two of us, plus the pilot, I sat in the co-pilot's seat, chatting to the pilot — a young, blond, typical white African. He said he was Zimbabwean and, indeed, had a passport from that country; he was, however, really South African, something he could not possibly admit to. Once we were airborne and out over the plains I sat chatting with him. He turned to me and asked if I had ever flown a plane.

'No,' I said.

'Would you like to?'

The next thing I knew was that I was flying the plane whilst he told me what to do. I held the small, half steering-wheel and, after a while, found it almost as easy as driving a car. The pilot sat back in his seat opened his little side-window and casually lit a cigarette. He assured me that, if anything should go wrong, he could immediately take control. I gazed out of the window in wonder at the myriad plains game below. When we spotted some elephants in the distance the pilot asked if I wanted to take the plane down lower and fly over them and, under his instruction, we came lower, passed over the small elephant herd, and flew on.

In the distance he pointed out to me a large, black, cloud mass. This was a storm so he directed me to give it a wide berth and fly round it. In the back, Kari, my cool Kikuyu friend had fallen asleep. Eventually the pilot took back control and we came in to land on a tiny, level piece of ground with a little flag. We had to make several passes over the runway to clear a pride of lions lying in the middle of it. Then we landed and, after a wait of some 20 minutes, an ancient Toyota Landcruiser appeared with a cheerful Kikuyu driver who introduced himself as Jakob.

For the next few days we based ourselves at Governor's Camp, travelling out each day to watch and photograph lion, elephant, plains game and cheetah. It is difficult to find words to describe Africa. Not only are the beasts and the people so different and wonderful but even the African sky, huge and with a distinctive light beloved by artists, is 'different'.

One afternoon, Jakob came to me and asked my permission to take the vehicle to visit the distant community of Nyeri, telling me he wished to visit a lady. Warning him to be back in time for our early-morning game-watching, I wished him a pleasant evening. Next morning, Jakob, who was

167

a small, wiry fellow, and who I knew did not drink alcohol, was looking decidedly rough. Bleary-eyed, he had obviously spent a night of vigorous activity!

We stopped around mid-morning and, while I was drinking a cold beer from the ice-box on the vehicle, Jakob sat yawning. I said to him, 'You had better watch out, Jakob, chasing ladies. If you're not careful you'll get AIDS.'

Jakob looked at me knowingly, then in his typically African high-pitched voice said, 'No, boss. I'll not get AIDS. You see, when lady get AIDS she get ve' thin.'

He gestured with his hands describing thin arms and legs.

'If you no wanna get AIDS, when looking for *kuma*, you mus' look for lady like big buffalo!' With his hands he described a lady of gargantuan size.

My mind immediately conjured up the picture of wiry little Jakob perched on some great big mama, looking like a pea on a drum!

African safari

IT WAS WITH ENORMOUS ANTICIPATION that I had planned and booked a return visit to Africa.

This time I wanted to sample a safari. There are several countries in Africa that license hunters. Under the strict control of their Wildlife Departments, licences are issued only for species which are in great abundance and should be culled for good management. The revenue from these licensed hunters is directly responsible for the very survival of many species and, of course, aids the local economy. I chose South Africa because I had friends there who had told me of the superb hunting opportunities and had invited me to join them.

My South African friend, David and I left Johannesburg with our hunter–guide, Willem, and headed north in his customised, long-wheel-based pick-up. The cab was large enough to seat five adults, whilst the cargo tray could carry a huge payload.

With his extensive experience and knowledge of the country, Willem had decided it would be best to hunt in the Transvaal and had arranged the appropriate licences. After some four hours' driving, we arrived at the campsite, one of several Willem has dotted around. These gave the facility of semi-permanent tenting with the advantages of proper flooring, toilets and showers, and other such luxuries. There are, of course, quite fabulous hunting-lodges and ranches all over South Africa where guests can stay in splendid luxury whilst still enjoying their safari. However, I preferred to experience a more basic hunt which, anyway, suited my pocket.

The camp was staffed with Willem's two tracker–hunter assistants — Moketi and Impho — and four camp-boys, all of the local Sotho tribe. They were a terrific team and had worked with Willem for some years. The camp was equipped with two vehicles: Willem's pick-up and a small, flat-bed truck with canvas sides.

Taking my .270, I went off with Willem and Moketi in the pick-up, driving for a mile or so. After a quick stalk, I shot an impala for camp meat. Returning to the camp I had enough time to shower before dinner was served. Willem, David and I sat there having a pre-dinner drink, the light faded with great speed and the lamps were lit. We ate at a table spread with a tablecloth and laid with cutlery and ate a splendid meal. As we sat drinking excellent South African wine, it was easy to be transported back to the time of Hemingway and Roosevelt.

When I went to my tent and climbed into my camp bed, behind the mosquito nets, I lay there listening to the sounds of night. I thought I was too excited to sleep, but I was wrong. The next thing I knew it was morning and a camp-boy was waking me with a mug of tea.

Breakfast was thin slices of haunch of impala served with eggs, pancakes and coffee. I found out later that, apart from the meat reserved for breakfast for David, Willem and myself, the boys had eaten the lot the night before.

We set off in the pick-up, the three of us, with Impho and Moketi. We three got out of the vehicle and set off walking single file across the open, undulating countryside, mainly grasses with lots of bush. We hadn't walked far when Willem, who was leading, signalled me to stop. He had spotted some wart-hogs a few hundred yards ahead. We immediately turned and walked a circular route to a little hillock from where we could glass them. The nearest large male with good-sized tusks was about 140 yards away. Willem suggested I shoot him, probably wanting to see how I would perform at distances over 100 yards. With my .300 Holland & Holland, with 180-grain rounds, one bullet through the shoulder felled the hog.

At the sound of our shot the pick-up, which was well back, perhaps a mile, came forward and, whilst Moketi dressed him, we moved on. There was game everywhere on the rolling grassland and we walked for about an hour before Willem spotted some fine blesbok and we sat down whilst he worked out a line of approach. I stayed back and, after a good stalk, heard the report of David's rifle. When I made my way over to them he had shot a nice male. The vehicle caught up with us and again we moved on, leaving Moketi to deal with the animal.

Later that afternoon, as we drove back towards camp, we stopped to watch some Cape buffalo. We kept our distance so as not to spook them. Suddenly, they all seemed to start at some sound we didn't hear. Several of them stood looking down into a hollow about a quarter of a mile away.

Impho, who was driving, headed down towards the hollow where we thought there might have been a lion. Then we saw the source of the sound. Two large hyena had caught and were eating a young gazelle. I stood there in the back of the vehicle, watching with revulsion these animals crunching up the little creature. They ate every bit — skin, bones, guts — before eating the bloodstained grass.

That night Willem entertained us after dinner with some wonderful safari stories. My few stories of stalking experiences seemed tame indeed after listening to him.

Next day, David and Impho were to hunt to the east of the camp for zebra. Willem, Moketi and I set out west, driving across country to an area where Willem felt I would have a chance to shoot a good buffalo. Since we hoped to shoot a large animal, the other vehicle with some of the boys followed behind.

Known as the Cape, or southern buffalo, these animals weigh from 1,500 to 1,800 pounds and, when roused, are among the most dangerous in the world. For me they have always represented the ultimate in stalking-trophies. I have no interest whatever in shooting lion or leopard; I prefer to look at them. But Cape buffalo had been my ambition since I first started to read about hunting. I really wanted to shoot a big bull with my bow but, after discussion with Willem, he advised that, unless I was absolutely determined, I would be better to stalk the beast then shoot it with my rifle. While he was confident of getting me within 100 yards, he wasn't so sure of getting within 30 yards. He also told me that he thought shooting a buffalo with a bow and arrows to be taking unnecessary risks.

I had taken his advice and had brought with me David's .465 Holland & Holland double-barrelled rifle, loaded with 480-grain rounds which I insisted on carrying myself rather than take advantage of the willing Moketi. We left the vehicle and Willem, Moketi and I started walking into the wind. The countryside was grassland with a lot of short trees and bush. Every now and again we stopped and Moketi would go on ahead, then reappear and signal us forward. After several hours, when a combination of heat and exercise had me feeling quite tired, Moketi came back and had a whispered conversation with Willem and me. He told us that three good bulls were grazing some 400 yards ahead. We unslung our rifles and I silently checked the chamber to assure myself that it was loaded. Moketi leading, we set off, walking with great care. I was aware that my pulse was racing and I felt full of nervous exhilaration. All tiredness had gone; my every sense was honed sharp. I didn't even feel the occasional thorns on my arms or the sharp stones when I knelt to watch and listen.

Moketi made a tiny flutter with his fingers behind his back and Willem signalled me to move alongside. He indicated some bush, approximately 150 yards away, and there they were — three huge bulls. One was greater in size and weight than the others and had massive, curved horns, which had a dull gleam at their ends. We started forward on the final part of the stalk, Willem and myself, followed by Moketi. We kept our eyes fixed on the buffalo, moving only when their heads were down or looking away. Silence is imperative. Buffalo have equal excellence in all three senses. We finally made it to a spot where I had a clear shot of about 80 yards.

I lifted the rifle but felt that I couldn't shoot. A few small branches obscured the target. I didn't have a clear view of the massive, black shoulder. Then the bull moved a few paces forward and stopped. I lifted the heavy rifle and held steady behind the huge shoulder and pulled the trigger. I didn't feel the recoil of the big rifle as it jumped against my shoulder. On the sound of the shot, and at an astonishing speed, the three bulls shot forwards towards a thicket. My bull seemed to be unharmed. I swung through and fired again. Frantically, I reloaded two of the fat cartridges into the rifle. The bull had run another 20 yards and sunk to his knees, then dropped his head. I stood holding the rifle, aiming at him, praying he wouldn't move, not quite knowing what to do, when Willem touched my elbow and whispered in my ear, 'Good shot.'

We approached the bull carefully, ready to put another shot in him, but he was dead. Both my bullets were mortal shots, my first being a heart shot, the second a bit higher, striking him in the lungs. Once I realised that he was down I became aware of a feeling of enormous relief. I was shaking like a leaf, bathed in sweat, and not just from the heat and exercise. I sat down as Moketi and Willem congratulated me on stalk, shot and trophy. I felt drained, yet as I looked at the huge bull lying there, I must confess to mixed emotions. I was elated, yet at the same time the feeling was tinged

with regret — a feeling peculiar to true hunters, particularly when they have shot an animal that they greatly admire. I examined the bull, from his scarred hide to his great neck and massive, rough boss over his forehead and to his huge, curved, gleaming black horns, his long tattered ears, dark eyes and large, moist nose. I wondered what dramas he had experienced in his lifetime. Certainly he was old and well past his prime. His death was instantaneous, infinitely preferable to being eaten by lion or hyena.

It was late afternoon by the time the other vehicle had been called up and Moketi had supervised the removal of the skull and the dressing and loading of the meat. We set off back to camp and by the time we arrived it was pitch dark. David had already returned and was enjoying a large whisky. He reported that he had shot two nice zebra. I had a quick shower and a pre-dinner drink before we sat down to eat, then went early to bed. I slept like a log.

Next day I wanted to concentrate on bow hunting, leaving David and Willem to continue to look for and stalk the animals which David had on his licence. I felt sated with my big buffalo. Moketi and Impho and the boys showed a great deal of interest in my bow and arrows as they watched me practise. I gave them all a shot at trying to draw the bow but, with the exception of Moketi, none of them was successful.

I had brought with me a Hoyt Compound, cranked up to a shade under 75 pounds, with fast flight strings and energy wheels. It provides both remarkable speed and flat trajectory. My shafts were 2317 XX75 tipped with either Bear razorheads or Hoyt bow bullets. For birds I used blunts or judo points. I carry a belt quiver to hold the blunts and a converted bow quiver screwed to the outside of my belt quiver to hold the broadheads. The whole lot has been thoroughly oiled and makes a silent, efficient, working unit which I have developed through experience in the field over the years.

Willem decided that Moketi should guide me and the two of us set off on foot, Moketi carrying the .465 Holland & Holland double-barrelled rifle in case we ran into dangerous game. Moketi was a superb hunter. He had an athletic, muscular build and looked entirely at ease in this environment. We enjoyed each other's company, having mutual respect for each other's abilities. He certainly is one of the finest hunting companions anyone could wish for and, as I was to find out, in a tight spot he had nerves of steel.

During the morning I shot some guinea fowl and franklin and, by midday, we had sufficient to provide roast fowl for the whole camp. In the afternoon I stalked and shot a duiker. This tiny antelope was a challenging stalk and delicious on the table. Moketi was anxious for me to try for a larger animal and, since I had waterbuck on my licence, we agreed to have a go the following day.

Taking the pick-up, we drove for a few miles to an area of grassland with bush, surrounding extensive reedbeds and marshland. Moketi parked the vehicle, checked the wind and we set off in a large circular walk. We spotted and stalked several waterbuck unsuccessfully and, by late afternoon, we returned to the vehicle having shot nothing, which is not uncommon for a bow hunter.

Next day was my last and I thought I would like to try for one of the antelope with my bow. After discussion, it was felt my best chances of success would be for Moketi and me to return to the grassland area running down towards where we had hunted unsuccessfully the previous day. The countryside where we parked the vehicle was particularly attractive: typical grassland with small bushes scattered around. A feature here is the rolling, undulating topography which allows you to stalk quite close.

After walking some distance we sat down on a little ridge to glass the area in front and spotted several hartebeest. We planned the stalk and set off. We were both dressed in desert boots, shorts and light, short-sleeved shirts. I carried my bow whilst Moketi lugged the double-barrelled rifle. After a good stalk we reached a grass area with lots of shrubbery. I stalked to within about 30 yards of one average animal and shot it, the arrow disappearing up to the fletches in his lungs. He took off at a gallop. Moketi and I sat down and let him go. After some 15 minutes Moketi started following the trail of blood. The hartebeest had run a good 200 yards before going down. When we found him he was dead. We started back towards the vehicle, intending to return and collect him.

As we went on through the grass I unslung my camera and took a few scenic shots. We walked over the undulating ground and came round the side of a small hill. Moketi, who was in front, suddenly stopped and pointed at the grass some 150 yards away. I saw it at once: a single, large, young, male lion. He was watching us and looking at some unseen object in the grass close to him. Then a lioness stood up. Both animals were now watching us. The lioness started walking across our front, moving closer. Moketi quietly removed the rifle from his shoulder and signalled me to stand still. The big male was coming towards us, looking alternately at us and at the female. By this time he was less than 100 yards away. He suddenly snarled. It was the most frightening sound I had ever heard.

The female had apparently disappeared. Then, simultaneously, Moketi and I noticed some 30 yards in front of us a slight movement in the grass. I looked carefully, then realised the lioness was crawling towards us. I lifted my camera, quickly focused and pressed the shutter. Moketi signalled me to start to walk backwards while he stood his ground, the rifle held across

his chest ready to mount. I could see his whole body was poised for action. Slowly, he started walking backwards towards me and we moved away. When we had got some distance back, Moketi explained that it was a young male, feeling possessive about his first lioness, who was obviously in season. We took a cautious, circular route watching carefully for the lions, which we never saw again. Back at the safety of the truck we sat in the cab. I picked up a can of warm, soft drink and realised that, with the release of tension, I could hardly grip the ring-pull. I looked at Moketi. He sat drinking from his can, then looking at me with a grin said, 'That was close!' He seemed to be as cool as ice. We then set off to collect the hartebeest.

Back at the camp I related the tale of the incident with the lion. David and Willem were obviously impressed. Next day, before we left, I thanked the boys for all their help then, calling Moketi aside, I gave him my hunting-knife, which I knew he admired. Shyly he took it and, removing his bracelet, he handed it to me. I thanked him and put it on my wrist. As we drove back to Johannesburg, Willem noticed the bracelet. When I told him Moketi had given it to me he told me that it was a considerable honour and confirmed what I already felt, that I had obviously made a friend. David had successfully collected the various species for which he had licences. The two of us had enjoyed a memorable trip, thanks to a professional team and an abundance of game.

Leaving Africa and on my way home, I reflected on the wonderful country, the people and my new friends, vowing I would certainly return.

Some months after I returned from Africa, looking for something to do in the evenings, I sat down and modelled a head of my buffalo which I had cast in bronze. The bronze was eventually exhibited at the IWA in Germany to considerable acclaim. Probably, the finest compliment I got was from an eminent wildlife authority who, after studying the bronze for some time, turned to his colleagues and said, 'The man who sculpted this buffalo has captured the essence of a most magnificent beast.'

Caught out by my own greed

I WAS DRIVING ALONG ROUTE 66 on my way to visit some friends and enjoying my tour of the Great Plains of the USA. It was in the Texas Panhandle that I saw the first huge sign at the side of the road. This sign was in form of a tall, thin cowboy holding a noticeboard on which was written the message 'The Tall Texan Challenges You'. I noticed the sign but couldn't work out what the challenge was until, a few miles down the road, I came to another sign of the cowboy. This time the notice board read 'The Tall Texan Challenges You To Eat A 36-ounce Steak Dinner, Finish It, You Can Have It Free'. I was bored with the driving, feeling hungry and, if I'm honest, I must confess that I liked the prospect of getting a free meal. I looked at the map; the town with the Tall Texan was still 100 miles further on. Surely, I reasoned, if I took my time, I could eat a 36-ounce steak. Yes, I convinced myself. I could manage it without too much difficulty.

I stopped off at several roadside diners, ostensibly for coffee, but my real reason was to visit the washroom. My plan was that, by the time I reached the Tall Texan, if I went to the toilet often enough, I could arrive with an empty stomach.

Eventually the signs at the side of the road announced the small town where the Tall Texan was to be found and I drove into the car park in great anticipation at showing these 'good old boys' what a Scotsman was capable of.

I left my car in the car park and walked towards the building, a long, low, ranch-style design with lots of glass. The interior was cool, with a tiled floor and gingham tablecloths. A scattering of customers sat at the tables, including several families who were obviously on vacation. I chose a seat and sat there looking around as the waiter approached with a welcoming smile.

'I'd like the 36-ounch steak dinner,' I said.

His smile broadened. 'Are you a challenger, Sir?'

'I sure am!' I replied.

He turned over his shoulder and called toward the chef standing at a charcoal brazier. 'We gotta challenger here!'

I felt the first tinges of embarrassment as every eye in the place turned toward me. I was now even more determined to beat them!

The steak, when it arrived, was of prodigious size. As the waiter carried it across the restaurant, the other patrons looked at it making a variety of 'Oohhs' and 'Aaahhs'. Then he laid it in front of me. A great slab of cow's bum, resting on a large, oval, earthenware plate. I looked down at it, determined not to show any sign of misgivings. I was going to eat it!

My hand was reaching across the table towards the mustard pot when the waiter returned, setting down two huge bowls: one with coleslaw, the other full of French fries. As I sat looking at the ridiculous amount of food with the first feeling of misgiving, the waiter returned. In one hand he carried a large bowl of salad, in the other a wooden platter with fresh-sliced bread. He set them in front of me and stood back to survey the table. I remembered the sign, 'a 36-ounce steak dinner'. I indicated the various brimming bowls and looked at the waiter.

'I've got to eat it all?'

He smiled. 'Sir, if you eat that lot we bring the ice cream in a bucket and we do a real nice pecan pie.'

In my desire to get the dinner for nothing I had simply not taken in the significance of the word 'dinner'.

The other patrons watched me, grinning, waiting for my reaction. I felt such a fool but I couldn't stop myself laughing. I ate most of the steak and some of the salad, and didn't mind at all paying for it. It wasn't expensive and I had walked into the most elementary sales gimmick. I had simply been caught out by my own greed.

The Glasgow clippie

DURING THE MID-1960s I acquired some rough shooting and roe stalking in the area to the southwest of Glasgow known as Howwood. I would travel by Glasgow Corporation bus from my home in the north of the city into the centre, where I would change to one of the Scottish Motor Transport buses which ran services out of the city. This would take me through Paisley and out to Howwood.

One evening I returned to the city with a rather nice roebuck. I carried it, four legs tied together, over my shoulder up to Hope Street and waited for the No. 54 bus to get home. When it arrived I put the roebuck in the luggage compartment under the stairs and sat in the nearest downstairs seat to the roe. The conductress came up and I handed her my fare and, nodding at the roe, I asked her, 'How much for the dog?'

She looked at the roe, lying there complete with antlers, and was obviously slightly bewildered. Then she looked back at me and said, 'It's aw right, son. You don't have to pay for it if it's deed.'

Bob Scott

THE LATE BOB SCOTT, the old retired stalker from Marr Lodge, enjoyed sitting in the bar behind the Lodge on a winter's night. A charismatic character, he would chat away as he quietly sipped the whiskies that guests were only too willing to provide.

One night, three elderly German guests came into the bar. Typical successful industrialists, they were large, overweight and slightly bombastic, with a definite air of superiority, particularly when surrounded by what they assumed to be Scottish peasants. They were talking to Bob and the other stalkers about deer, both past and present, when one of them turned to Bob and asked:

'Do you ever go away from here?'

'No, no. I'm fine and happy here,' Bob replied.

'But surely you go for a holiday now and again, ja?' the German persisted.

'No, no. I'm not one for holidays.'

The German ordered more whiskies and turned again to Bob. 'I find zis incredible. Surely you have not lived all your life in zuch a lonely place, and not zeen how ozzer people are living?'

Bob looked at him for a moment then replied, 'Well, I was on holiday once. It was a bit of a working holiday.'

'Ja, good. Vat vere you doing?'

'Oh, I was stalking.'

'Stalking? Vat vere you stalking?'

Bob replied, deadpan. 'Germans.'

Ronnie

RONNIE is a small, wiry man. His physique and broken nose give a hint of his boxing hobby as a young man. Popular with all his friends, a brilliant shot and a fund of great stories, his keenest pleasure today, now that he has retired, is teaching young people about the world of wildlife in which he is so expert. Those who know Ronnie Steele soon come to realise that he has a highly mischievous sense of humour.

Ronnie was head keeper on a large Perthshire estate which members of the Royal Family frequently visited. The estate owner and his hangers-on were a snobbish bunch, different from the Royals themselves, who were popular with the estate workers.

On one occasion a Most Important Young Man was shooting with the party when he shot his first snipe. The snipe fell into the long grass and the line was held up as this most important snipe was found. Patiently the guns stood as the dogs searched without finding the snipe.

Then, as Ronnie's big dog, Dirk, picked the snipe, Ronnie gave a cry, 'I have the bird, sir.' All eyes turned on Dirk in time to see him swallowing the snipe.

The Most Important Young Man looked at Ronnie and said, 'Your dog has rather a hard mouth, Steele.'

Drawing himself to attention Ronnie replied, 'Yes, sir, as hard as a crocodile!'

On another occasion a number of the aristocracy were up for the grouse-shooting season. There was some talk of the possibility of one of the Royal Family joining the shoot. Great preparations were made, the butler and staff transporting up on to the moor a great feast for the alfresco lunch. As Ronnie and his staff of under keepers were waiting for the guests to arrive, one of the under keepers drew Ronnie's attention to Dirk, hopping on three legs around a tray of pies, urinating on them.

Ronnie, not wanting to draw attention to the incident because of the obvious repercussions, quietly allowed the dog to finish and called it over. Then the guests arrived, obviously disappointed at the non-appearance of the hoped-for Royal visitor and the shoot commenced.

At lunchtime the guests sat down to their magnificent meal, served on linen tablecloths on tables and chairs in the midst of the grouse moor. At a respectful 50 yards the keepers sat in the heather, drinking their flasks of tea and eating the sandwiches prepared by their wives. It had never been known on this estate for the keepers to be offered any of the goodies; anything that was uneaten was taken back to the big house. Suddenly a young man called across, 'Steele', he cried.

'Yes, sir!' Ronnie leapt to his feet.

'There are a few pies left over that you and your chaps can have.'

'Thank you very much sir,' said Ronnie, tipping his cap, 'but just you boys wire into them yourselves.'

Every year at the end of the last day of the grouse-shooting season it was customary for the individual members of the syndicate to give Ronnie their tips for the season. Normally it worked like this: whilst the guns were having an end-of-the-day drink outside the lunch hut, each in turn would come over and discreetly hand Ronnie a few folded notes. This could range from £10 upwards but the amount was left to the discretion of the individuals. So no one ever knew what the others gave.

Colonel Forsyth was a crusty bombastic individual, known behind his back as 'Friendless Forsyth'. He had been a member of the syndicate for only two seasons. At the end of the first, with his customary meanness, he had badly tipped Ronnie — and Ronnie is not someone to forget.

Ronnie determined to get his own back on the Colonel and bring the matter to the attention of the other syndicate members. At the end of the Colonel's second season, as each guest discreetly made his way over to Ronnie with his gratuity, eventually the Colonel did so too. Ronnie, taking the gratuity, slipped it quietly in his pocket then started searching the ground in a very obvious fashion. Eventually several members of the syndicate noticed Ronnie's search. 'What are you looking for Steele?' they enquired.

'Oh,' said Ronnie. 'The Colonel gave me a £1 tip and I've dropped it!'

When the syndicate members were announced for the following year, the Colonel's name wasn't on it.

Ronnie lived in a house overlooking the estate road leading to Loch Turret. One night, about 10 o'clock, he heard the sound of a car going up the private road, and knowing that no one should be on the road at that time without his knowledge, realised that the most likely people to be travelling towards the loch were fishermen. Not wishing to go pursuing the car at that time, he nipped out and shut the heavy iron gate, securing it with a padlock. This meant that whoever was in the car could not escape while Ronnie was in his bed.

Next morning early, Ronnie got in his Land Rover and drove up the road towards the loch, where he found three men fishing from the bank. Approaching them, he asked them whether they had permits. They told

him that they had just arrived and no, they did not have permits. Ronnie produced the permit book from his pocket, 'No problem,' he said. 'I'll issue them now.' The men became very abusive. They had no intention of buying them and threateningly told him to leave them alone. Ronnie explained to them that he would simply drive down the road and get the police and, since he had their car number, there was nothing they could do. At this the three men fell silent but then, realising the futility of their position, they grudgingly and with much threatening of reprisals, and further abuse, agreed to buy three tickets. Ronnie wrote out the permits, took their money and, getting back into his Land Rover, drove some yards away. Stopping, he leant out of the window and told them to pack up immediately and leave.

'What do you mean? We have just bought permits,' one of them replied.

'Aye,' said Ronnie, 'you've got permits right enough, but the permits are daily and finish at midnight and you've not just arrived. You arrived last night. So pack up or I'll go for the police.'

'And what about the permits?'

Ronnie laughed. 'Look at the date I wrote on them. Yon's yesterday's permits.'

A miscellany

AFTER A LONG DAY stalking hinds in a deer forest near Pitlochry, and having spent the evening chatting over a meal with a friend, I set off at about midnight to drive home, my rifle lying on the back seat, I had four hinds in the trailer behind my vehicle. As I drove along I was enjoying that feeling of tired self-satisfaction. I had spent a delightful day out in the hills, had had some excellent stalking and was looking forward to a good night's sleep.

I travelled down the A9 and turned into the road leading to the Sma' Glen, a narrow mountain pass. As I drove on in the bright moonlight, approaching the small hamlet of Amulree I came round a bend in the road to discover the way blocked with red deer. They were not only on the road; the herd was spread out on either side. Always interested in deer, I stopped the Range Rover, produced a spotlight and sat playing the lamp over the beasts, enjoying looking at the different animals.

I had probably been sitting there for 15 minutes when I realised the stupidity of what I was doing. In clear sight of the village surely someone must have spotted the lamp. I imagined all manner of telephone calls to keepers and police. I started down the glen. There are no turn-offs and I was certain that I would find the police waiting for me. Whilst I could explain the existence of the beasts in the trailer and my rifle, it could certainly be embarrassing and take a little time to prove my bona fides. I never saw any other vehicles and drove home without incident.

A friend of mine, a detective in the Metropolitan Police, had joined me for a few days' roe stalking in central Perthshire during the summer. Late one evening returning home from where we were stalking, I noticed at the side of the road, not more than 50 yards away, a couple of roe. We stopped for a few moments whilst my friend and I watched the animals, then continued home. Next morning, around half past four, we were heading back, intending to stalk the area we had been in the previous day. As we approached where we had seen the roe, we slowed down and, seeing a rather nice buck in the early light, stopped whilst my friend tried to take a photograph. As we sat there, a white Land Rover suddenly appeared fast behind us, overtook us and swerved sideways across the road. Two burly keepers jumped out and rushed towards us. One of them, an aggressive

Englishman, new to the area, jerked open my door and tried to take the keys. Obviously, I prevented him. He stood there shouting that we were poaching. I pointed out that we were on the public highway and were merely watching the deer; besides we were going stalking. I could not convince the man and he simply couldn't understand how anyone with stalking of their own could possibly be interested enough to stop and watch someone else's deer. Eventually the other man, the head keeper, who knew me slightly and had a less aggressive attitude, waved us on, though I know they will always be convinced that we were poachers.

The head keeper, a huge man with a gargantuan appetite for whisky and cigarettes, was in the habit of meeting a local woman who was of easy virtue and a little simple. It was their habit to disappear into the woodland, find an appropriate area out of sight and there enjoy some vigorous and hasty activity. The keeper, naturally, removed his trousers and probably resembled nothing other than a great, vibrating hill of lard as he dealt with the lady. There he was, writhing about in bovine ecstasy, when he suffered a fatal heart attack. The woman, when she finally managed to extricate herself from beneath the enormous burden, ran off for help. Being not too bright, she went to the nearest cottage, which was the keeper's, and asked his wife to phone for the ambulance. When I heard of the incident, my only comment was that the whole wildlife of the area must have breathed a sigh of relief; the chap was little short of a one-man, ecological disaster unit. After his funeral a large freezer was found in a locked shed behind his cottage. It was full of birds of prey. The keeper had been doing a roaring trade, supplying a well-heeled collector with birds for his private collection and, though the authorities knew the identity of the collector, there was insufficient evidence to charge him.

There was a head keeper of a large Scottish estate who had a strange and highly dishonest habit. If he took a liking to some item belonging to a foreign guest he would watch for an opportunity to steal it when the circumstances would suggest that the unhappy individual had lost it on the hill. In this fashion, he built up a substantial collection of expensive binoculars, sunglasses, knives, gloves, scarves and other items. He always restricted himself to small items that could have been easily lost.

One day, whilst the guests were in the big house having lunch, the head keeper decided to have a good rummage through the 'goodies' in the back

of a guest's Range Rover. He was accompanied by an acquaintance of mine with a wicked sense of humour. As the keeper was delving through the guests' equipment, opening bags and one small suitcase, he suddenly realised my acquaintance was very quiet. Looking up from his search for something to steal, he discovered my friend had found a video-camera in the front of the vehicle and was merrily filming the whole event. Not knowing how to erase or open the camera, the head keeper was in a quandary. He couldn't possibly steal the camera; that would be too 'serious'. Too late they realised the guests were returning and had time only to replace the camera and shut the vehicle. One wonders what the foreign guest thought when he finally viewed the tape. Perhaps he thought it was a Scottish custom.

Walking along a small country road in the West Highlands late one summer's evening with my little terrier at my heel, I was surprised to hear a police car approach me from behind. Passing me, the car pulled in and the constable walked back toward me. Politely he enquired where I had been, where I was going, etc. As I stood speaking to him I glanced down at his feet. The terrier was neatly balanced on three legs, pissing on his trousers. Controlling the urge to laugh, I kept the officer's attention until the dog had finished. Then we went our separate ways.

☆   ☆   ☆

A number of years ago I was asked to take part in a television programme which was to be filmed in a large theatre in Glasgow in front of a live audience. I had little to do. The principal scene I was in required me to enter stage left with a large black labrador at my heel, walk across to centre stage and sit on a seat under an old Victorian streetlamp. I was supposed to sit there, dog at my feet, as the action took place around me. During rehearsals everything went perfectly well and the dog, a very experienced working dog, quickly got the idea of what was required. We walked on stage, I sat down, he sat at my feet. Simple! We had rehearsed on an empty stage with the seat as a prop — very different from what the set would look like during the filming of the actual programme, when it would be built to represent a village square. Then came the evening of the filming, the theatre full to capacity with an expectant audience, the set beautifully laid out, complete with streetlamp. The whole set had been lightly dusted with artificial snow. When the time came for my entrance I walked across the set, sat on the seat and, to my horror, the dog kept going. Walking over to the lamp, he lifted his leg and proceeded with a long pee. I sat there as the water created a little stream down the gently sloping stage, creating a dark line through the snow. The audience, no doubt convinced that this was all part of the action, was delighted. Howling with laughter, they obviously greatly approved. At the end of the show, when everyone took the curtain call, the labrador received the greatest applause.

One night I sat up late to watch an old Hammer Horror film on television. This featured some demented beast that was kept in a cellar in chains, until it eventually escaped and spent the rest of the film murdering people. Their only warning of their impending, horrific death was some deep-throated growling and the rattling of chains before the creature appeared. It was quite a scary film in a silly way and, the programme over, I switched off the television and stepped out of the front door for a breath of air before bed. As I stood there in the dark, listening to the sounds of night, I distinctly heard the rattling of a chain and rasping breathing. I almost jumped out of my skin. I stood listening for the sound, my hair no doubt on end. Then it came again, a chain rattling and a growling sound. Armed with a torch, I approached the shrubbery at the edge of the garden. As I came closer to the bushes, the chain rattled more frantically and the breathing became even deeper. I shone the torch under the shrubs. At first I could see nothing but then I spotted the source of the sound. An enormous mink was caught in a Fenn trap, one bar of the jaws across the back of its neck, the other pressing against its throat. The nearest Fenn trap I had set was a good hundred yards away down a stream. The animal had managed to break the anchor and had dragged the trap all the way behind it. So powerful were the muscles in its neck that it was still able to breath but, eventually, the chain had become snagged around a thick root. Finding itself fixed, the mink was furiously shaking the trap, rattling the chain and growling with frustration.

I once had a very fine Scottish boxlock, 12-bore shotgun. A fellow I knew vaguely was keen to have it and constantly tried to buy it. I finally agreed to sell him the gun and told him to look after it, that it would retain its value, probably appreciate and could prove a good investment. I saw him a short time later. He was obviously delighted with his new purchase and told me that he had been fortunate to find an antique, blocked-leather case for a single gun and that together they were most attractive. I didn't see the fellow for a number of years and then one night he telephoned me in a fit of rage. The gun I had sold him, that I had assured him would be a good investment and retain its value, was, he said, worthless. He went on to explain that he intended to sue me. I couldn't understand what he was talking about. Who had said it was worthless? He told me he had taken it to Dixon's in Glasgow to try and sell it. The manager, after examining the gun, told him he wasn't interested in it at any price. Eventually I managed to get the fellow off the telephone after he had repeated his assurance that 'he would see me in court'. Curious, the following day I phoned the gunshop manager who I knew quite well.

'What,' I said, 'was the problem with the Harkem?'

He laughed, then replied, 'The fellow who owns it must be a nut. He came in here trying to sell it. The only problem was he had cut several inches off the barrel to make it fit a leather case. He even went on to show me how he had neatly refitted the foresight bead with Araldite. The gun is ruined. It would require new barrels. Not wishing to get involved with him, I simply told him I wasn't interested in it since I couldn't sell it.'

I phoned the fellow with the gun and told him that he was responsible for ruining it since he had removed the chokes.

'Chokes?' he replied. 'What are they?'

When I was in my late teens I was introduced to pike fishing in Loch Lomond. Large fish were numerous, particularly around the Endrick

estuary, and most weekends I and two friends would catch several. We had discovered an upmarket fish shop in central Glasgow run by a Pole who would buy as many as we could catch. Though he paid us a pittance for the pike, he constantly tried to cheat us, insisting the fish were lighter than we knew they were. Then, on one occasion, I delivered a large catch of fish to him on a Monday morning. He took them, telling me he would pay me later but, when I called in for the money, he made various excuses, saying some of the fish had been spoilt, and paid me only half of what I expected. When I reported back to my two chums, one of them, David, decided to teach the Pole a lesson. The following weekend we fished frantically, trying to catch as many big pike as we could. Our luck was in. We caught several large fish and then returned to David's house. In the garden shed he had a large quantity of old lead shot. With the use of a long funnel we carefully poured the lead down each pike's throat, packing it with a wad of cottonwool. The following day David went into the fish shop, stood there as the fish were weighed and then insisted on payment. I would love to have seen the expression on the man's face when he cleaned the pike and realised the biter had been bit.

Out roebuck stalking one early morning, I spotted a doe which was obviously in distress. I saw and watched her for a while and could see she had a badly broken foreleg, probably caused by a car. There was no alternative; I shot her. When I examined her I realised she had very recently given birth. I searched the long grass and eventually found a tiny, new-born, little roe. I put him inside my jacket and took him home. I phoned the zoo and asked if they had any advice on baby roe. The fellow I spoke to said that they had a bad success rate with young roe handed in to them and he wasn't particularly encouraging. I decided, however, to try and keep the little creature alive. It was undoubtedly one of the most beautiful animals I had ever seen. I found myself completely captivated and never tired of watching him. It really was a privilege to be so close to him. He fed greedily from a baby's bottle and seemed to have no fear of my two dogs, who inspected him minutely. I made a bed for him in the kitchen. The little roe grew quickly and was soon running around with the dogs. Once he started eating solids I fed him high-protein supplements to assist his bone and muscle development. I had moved him out of the house into an enclosure and handled him every day, getting him totally familiar with being touched. He started to develop a habit of greeting me, particularly if he hadn't seen me for some time; running towards me, head down, he would make a snuffling sound. Eventually he grew into a large buck. When he first came into rut, he became very aggressive and, for the period that it affected him, I didn't go in beside him since I did not wish to risk being stabbed by his antlers. The rut over, he once again was easily handled, though I could see it was time to find somewhere to release him. Obviously I could not turn him into the wild. With little fear of man he would surely have quickly been shot. I took him to a private deer park run by a friend and released him into a large, fenced area. Several months later I was visiting the park and went into the enclosure where I walked around looking for him. He appeared, obviously having picked up my scent, and came towards me. Then, to my surprise, he dropped his head and started making the familiar snuffling sound. He obviously recognised my smell. He lived in the park for several years in the company of a doe, sired several sets of twins and then, one morning, he was found dead of natural causes.

Twa stalkers

Of all the stories in this book, the only one I cannot vouch for is this story of twa stalkers, which was told to me late one night by an old stalker.

DONALD WAS STANDING at the bar of the wee pub, at the far end of the little, Highland village, quietly drinking his whisky. Outside, the large snowflakes gently drifted down, turning the remote Highland glen into an arctic wilderness. The door opened and in hurried Murdo, brushing snow from himself. He hurried over to the peat fire and stood rubbing his hands in front of the heat. Then, turning and lifting the tail of his jacket to warm his behind, he greeted the one or two regulars, the inhabitants of the glen — Duncan the shepherd, McLeod the farmer and his daft daughter, Black Maggie.

Finally warmed, he crossed to the bar beside Donald and ordered a large dram from Fat-arsed Jackie, the unsmiling barmaid. He picked up the dram and poured it down his throat in one swallow, with a deep appreciative 'Aye', and signalled for another.

Turning away to avoid having to talk to McLeod, who was forever extolling the virtues of John the Bull's big balls, he addressed Donald. 'Are you still working for His Lordship, the Duke?'

Donald looked up. 'No, I'm afraid I told His Lordship to stick his job right up his arse.'

Murdo was amazed. Donald had been head stalker to the Duke for the last 20 years and ruled the estate with a fist of iron, held inside a steel glove.

'Och away, why would you do a thing like that?'

Donald regarded his empty glass. Realising the prospect of some wonderful gossip, Murdo quickly signalled Fat-arsed Jackie to fill Donald's glass with the comment 'And make it a large one.' The whisky served, Donald lifted the glass to his lips and took an appreciative sip, then turned to the expectant Murdo.

'Well,' he said. 'It was Christmas Eve. I was sitting at home with my feet up in front of the fire and a dram in my hand when there was a knock at the door and yon big ponce, the Duke's butler, put his head round, telling me that his Lordship wanted to see me up at the castle immediately. Well, I quickly put on my boots and hurried up the hill, wondering what the hell could be so urgent on Christmas Eve.

'When I got there, the Duke introduced me to his house guest, a great, big, fat, English manny, dressed in a beautiful shiny gown, all blue and gold, right down to the floor, and on his head he had a great, pointed hat. In his hand he had a muckle, great, fancy, golden crook.

'"This," said the Duke, "is the Archbishop of Canterbury."

'The Duke went on to explain that the archbishop had been looking at all the stags' heads hanging on the walls and had asked the Duke if there was any chance of him having one, since he thought it would look grand hanging above the altar in Canterbury Cathedral. Well the Duke, wanting to please his guest, had immediately sent for me.

'"Donald," he says when I walk in the door, "I would like you to go and get a good beast for the Archbishop to hang in his church."'

Donald emptied his whisky and looked expectantly at Murdo who immediately signalled for a refill.

'Well,' said Donald, lifting his glass, 'as you know there is no time like the present. So off I went, back to my house where I got my rifle and telescope, packed a couple of cheese sandwiches and hurried out on the hill. By dawn I was far up the glen, glassing the hill for a good beast, but I couldn't see a thing. All day I wandered the hill and still I found nothing. That night I snatched a few hours sleep in an old hollow tree and ate one of my sandwiches.

'The next day was the same; nothing. Indeed I was there for three days. I never saw a thing. All the stags seemed to have disappeared. Well, well, the time was wearing on, my cheese sandwiches had long been eaten and I was beginning to feel thoroughly pissed off. Then I had an idea. There is this big, tall tree that grows at the top of the mountain. I made my way to it and, putting my rifle down, I climbed right to the top of the tree. I thought I could use the added height for a better view. Just like yon men in a crow's nest on a boat.

'Well, there I was, clinging on to the thinnest branches when it happened.'

Donald drained his glass, putting the empty vessel on the bar in front of Murdo who quickly signalled for another refill.

'What happened?'

'Well,' said Donald, savouring the replenished glass, 'the tree started to shake. I looked down at the ground and I couldn't believe my eyes. There was the biggest stag I had ever seen in my life, scratching his arse against the tree. Well now, I thought. How the hell am I going to catch that stag? Then I had an idea.

'Nimble as a cat, I dropped out of the tree and landed on his back.

Grabbing his antlers, I wrapped my legs around his body and away we went. The stag running like hell, with me hanging on, guiding him, just like one of them motorbike fellows you see on the roads in summer. Downhill I guided him, my arse getting sorer by the minute until I managed to steer him into the loch. Out he swam, my legs trailing in the water, when I noticed the steamer coming down the loch, full of English tourists. The captain, seeing me, slowed down the steamer letting me pass in front.

'There was so many English tourists with their cameras all trying to take pictures that I swam the stag around the steamer a couple of times, and all yon people running from side to side on the boat, waving and shouting what a fine fellow I was, and me giving them a bit of a wave back and shouting that it was nothing at all.

'By now my feet hanging in the water were beginning to get a bit cold, so I guided the beast in towards the shore. I got my knife out of my pocket and got ready. Just as his hooves were touching the rocks I reached down and slit his throat. I didn't want to catch pneumonia so I quickly gralloched him and, throwing him over my shoulder, I ran the twenty miles back to the castle. When I got there I marched in and threw the beast on the floor in front of the Duke and the Archbishop.'

'"Well now," said the Archbishop, "Yon's a grand stag. Have you any more like that?" he asked the Duke.

'"Och aye," says the Duke. "I've got hundreds and hundreds all over the hill."

'Well, I didn't have to think about it. I just told the Duke to stick his job.'

Murdo looked puzzled. 'But why Donald? Yon was a good job?'

Donald looked him in the eye. 'I've got my pride and I won't work for a liar.'

THE TANGLE

Justin Robertson

WHITE
RABBIT

First published in Great Britain in 2021 by White Rabbit,
an imprint of The Orion Publishing Group Ltd
Carmelite House, 50 Victoria Embankment
London EC4Y 0DZ

An Hachette UK Company

1 3 5 7 9 10 8 6 4 2

A CIP catalogue record for this book is
available from the British Library.

ISBN (Hardback) 978 1 4746 2282 0
ISBN (eBook) 978 1 4746 2284 4
ISBN (Audio) 978 1 4746 2285 1

Typeset by seagulls.net
Printed and bound in Great Britain by Clays Ltd, Elcograf S.p.A.

www.whiterabbitbooks.co.uk
www.orionbooks.co.uk

For Andrew

Foreword

What happens in The Tangle stays in The Tangle. It is a
self-generating organism, a Word Horde.

    The poet Jack Spicer claimed that the moment of
inspiration in writing is akin to a visitation from a Martian
– an entity – that must attempt to communicate using twenty-
six building blocks. The Tangle is alphabet as entity.

    Caxton Wood holds time. Each Tangle functions as a
point of ingress, and as exit, too. Time too, in The Tangle,
is palimpsest. What has happened keeps on happening.

    In the time of apocalypse, which is all-time, animals speak.
Trees speak, insects word. The grotesque is atavistic, the
return of animal souls, as language, from the underworld.
Our first language, our first art, our first attempts at
communal speech, took place underground, on the walls of
the caves – the hybrid animals, rising up, in speech. In the
sepulchres too, the early Christian burial sites, we see art, and
language, begin their ascent from the underworld, and evoke
The Tangle.

    William S. Burroughs made the terrifying assertion that
language is something that we have been infected with and
that we can never be cured of, this constant low-level babbling
of words in thought – but Burroughs got it wrong. Push
further, to the very precipice of language, out into the air,
and there stands the thing itself, revealed and un-worded.
Through The Tangle to the clearing, Justin Robertson points

to the end of language with words, to the silence at the heart
of the wood with sounds, to The Tangle with twenty-six
building blocks.

The stories are like tarot cards, The Tangle itself a
constantly morphing spread. There is uncanny life in these
pages. Every time I reread it, I feel like the scenes have
shifted slightly, that there is something newly out of place,
that behind the scenes the book has been creepy-crawled,
an item misplaced, a character you hadn't really noticed
before, a movement, there in the trees, the snap of a branch,
in the dark.

The Tangle is a classic of New Weird fiction, a rewilding
of the terrain of M.R. James, Denton Welch, Ballard and
Burroughs, Catling and Grant, and a spell – via those twenty-
six blocks – set on assassinating modernism with modernism.

David Keenan

When I am in that darkness, I do not remember anything
about anything human, or the God-man, or anything which
has form. Nevertheless, I see all and I see nothing.

Angela of Foligno, *The Memorial*

Everything is blooming most recklessly; if it were voices
instead of colours, there would be an unbelievable shrieking
into the heart of the night.

Rainer Maria Rilke, *Letters*

Come walk with me to lilac glade, through woodland,
    stream and knot.
Come stand beneath the gallows' shade till all weeping
    is forgot.
Leave the tears and terrors to the mischief of the town.
Come walk with me to lilac glade, to the oak tree's
    shady crown.

In darkness now from darkness born, circumference,
    length and span.
In lilac glade the wreath and thorn, wove mockeries of man.
In lilac glade beneath the earth, in death's ecstatic bond.
Come walk with me in lilac shade, to the emptiness beyond.

Unknown, *The Ballad of the Tangle*

The Maker's Mark

The fleece dangled from the branch like so much morbid laundry left out in the rain. As the water fell in persistent rods, blood and gore dripped down severed sinews onto the mud. On every branch hung animal skins. Freshly cut from village herds. Weeping fluid into the bark. Erwan, head shaved. Woad running down his cheeks. Waved a ceremonial sickle. The holy man called on the gods to bless the trees of the wood. For their gift of shelter. For their branches to be bent into bows. For the timber of their trunks to be cut into planks and honed into oars. Erwan called on the gods. Here under the holy ash, ruler of the third lunar month. Come spring, its berries would be plucked from its twigs and placed into the cribs of children to keep the spirits of the Tangle at bay. Through the winter rains Erwan brought the sacrifice. Blood and skin to buy the favour of the woods. He rubbed his bloody hands into the trunk until it was slick. Red darkening the grey into black. But the ash tree had no need for blood. No need for skin or sinew. Its roots sucked deep from the soil. Its leaves bathed in the sunlight. It had no need for the charnel gifts of men.

Every year, for centuries, in the last days of winter before the sun grew strong enough to break the grip of frost and snow, they traipsed through the Tangle. Every year they brought their sacrifice. Death paying for life. Yet the ash remained unmoved. Their children died and their crops failed.

1

Their oars still broke in the swell and their boats foundered on the rocks. Still they came in joyful procession. Then, as times changed in the world of men, the sacrifice was made by God instead. No longer did they call on the spirits of the wood. Though their presence lingered. They renamed the day for a saint and brought trinkets and toys, carved to represent the animals. They hung them in the trees and sang hymns. Still the ash remained unmoved.

The village began to grow. Spreading out like an unctuous wave. It became a town. The Tangle shrank back from the settlement as it was hacked and cleared. Trunks were cut and hewn, bent and carved to make pews for the faithful and roofs for the righteous. The ash became curious. These troublesome creatures had once lived in the Tangle. But they had changed. They would pass away in time and the forest would reclaim the land. That was how it always went. Memories were measured in millennia in the woods; these inconvenient animals had occupied only a micro-moment of it, an insignificant blur, like a fly buzzing by. The ash stirred. Some intangible part of the forest had once been human. Young wraiths that had only recently joined the web. They were struggling to shed their former concerns. But they were instructive on a number of points. Humans yearned for transcendence. But lacked the skills to achieve it. Humans liked to make things. But lacked the finesse to make them truly beautiful. They killed, cut, broke and smashed living things and made them into dead parodies of their former forms. Furniture. There were buildings too, like nests but more rigid and prone to decay. They made vehicles, like wings or feet, but too numerous to function as efficiently as either. All these things made them unhappy, yet they kept on making them. The ash consulted the other entities of the forest. Scouts were sent to the world of men.

*

Detective Inspector Sarah Ward of Caxton CID slipped under the police cordon that had been set up around a crime scene tent. The tent flapped in the winter wind. Under the canvas was a body. She pulled back the hood of her cagoule as she trudged across the muddy grass to where the victim had been discovered by a late-night dog walker. She felt older than her years. The force was sucking the life out of her. The rain hissed in her face, insolent and rude. Her superiors were public school misogynists or talentless hacks. The wind drove the drops into her eyes, blurring her vision. The younger officers were a mixture of bored hotheads and those who just never got around to leaving. Just like her, they had joined the force because there was fuck all else to do. The rain rasped and punched. In Caxton there was the meat processing plant, the sawmill or the call centre. You moved on, did acid or joined the force. The crime rate was lively though. Public drunkenness, urinating and affray every weekend. Domestic violence was popular, as was cannabis cultivation. There was a scattering of amphetamine laboratories, a thriving heroin trade and a range of sexual crimes to deal with. But murder was rare. Especially murders like this one. She nodded, attempting a smile for the young PC who was emerging from the forensic tent. One of the better ones. Anthony Barrowman was his name. Her smile stalled as PC Barrowman pushed past a colleague and threw up through his fingers.

'Fuck me. Are you alright, Barrow boy?'

Barrowman's concerned co-worker saluted awkwardly when he caught sight of DI Ward approaching through the rain.

'Sorry, ma'am, didn't see you there.'

She shot him a resigned look.

'Language on duty, what have I told you, Franklin? Barrowman, are you alright? Take the contents of your stomach away from the crime scene, if you please.'

She placed a reassuring hand on the young PC's shoulder as she passed. But he didn't look up or acknowledge her. His eyes stared fixedly into black drizzle.

She pushed the flaps of the tent open and stepped inside. The only sound was the buzzing of the spotlights and the occasional supressed wretch. She looked around at the gathered group. Caxton's finest, and even a couple of forensic scientists from the city. Hardened professionals. They were all staring in silence at the grizzly pile that stained the floor like offal in an abattoir. At first, she thought it was a carcass that had dropped from the back of Sullivan's butcher's van. It was gleaming and glossy. Freshly slaughtered. Maybe it was the poachers? They'd been at the deer again. Caught lugging it across the park, no doubt. They must have decided to dump it here rather than risk getting nicked. She looked at her colleagues. Why the silence? Why those wide-eyed stares? She looked again at the mound of flesh. Gradually her eyes began to decode the muddle of blood and tissue. A form began to take shape. It was a man. She knew it was a man because she could just about make out his testicles. They looked like two plum tomatoes dangling from white fibrous stalks. The penis had been removed. The scrotal skin too. In fact, all the skin had been removed from the entire body. As had the legs below the knee, the arms below the elbow, the eyes, the hair and the nose. All that remained was a bloody stump. She wanted to run out of the tent, but she was too fascinated to move. There was no reason why anyone should have to witness this kind of carnage. It just wasn't reasonable. One of the forensic team finally broke the grim stillness.

'Time of death was somewhere between eight and ten post meridiem, though I'd have to run some more tests back at the lab to be certain. Cause of death was . . .'

Her voice was shaking, and you could hear her gag reflex triggering as she tried to hold her professional tone.

'Judging by the pattern of the arterial spray and the pooling of blood, also the angle of the cut here on the legs, it suggests the victim was still alive while the amputations took place. Again, I'll need to run some more . . .'

The forensics expert jumped up and ran out of the tent. Vomit had begun to escape from the sides of her face mask. Sarah Ward followed her out as the reluctant clicking of cameras began inside. She tried to arrange the picture. The murderer was stealthy, quick and skilled. A doctor? A butcher? A vet? Or perhaps a keen amateur. She paced around the perimeter of the crime scene, projecting theories that might account for the atrocity inside the tent. The rain blackened her shoes and began to work its way inside. Mud sucked at her soles. She cursed and started to make her way back to the certainties of concrete. But something on the grass between the path and the edge of the woods caught her eye. She turned and lifted the tape. She squelched through the gloom, her curiosity momentarily eclipsing her discomfort. Pulling her torch from her pocket, she scanned the ground. The beam settled on an object. It looked like a makeshift mausoleum. She shone the torch over the surface. It was a pyramid of leaves; actually, it was more like a cone. The leaves had been neatly twisted to form the structure. About 7 inches tall, it gleamed through the downpour. It was glistening with fresh blood.

*

Mike Stains turned off the lights and tutted as the cold winter rain spat at his window. It would be a miserable walk home from Mike's Militaria. He decided to wait a while until the rain had died down. He'd have a couple of cans, maybe flick through a few of the specialist magazines he kept out the back for his more discreet customers. He shuffled behind the counter and slid through the curtain to his back office. There was a door on the right, sealed with a padlock. He fumbled for his keychain and unlocked the door. This was Mike's inner sanctum. A space where he could commune with the past. It contained a desk, a small kitchen, a fridge and the memorabilia from several unsavoury regimes, their insignia, uniforms and propaganda. Mike casually donned the cap of a dead field marshal. He imagined himself as a powerful man. He coughed and cleared his nose into the sink, before opening the fridge and helping himself to a can of lager. He sat down, pulled a magazine from the pile on the table and absentmindedly flicked through the pages. He belched and turned the magazine around for an alternative view. A knock on the door disturbed his recreation. Not the police again? Nah, they wouldn't be bothering him since the sergeant's last parcel arrived. Maybe it was one of his special customers? They sometimes came late. Fucking degenerates, no respect for opening hours. He retraced his steps back into the shop, leaving his shrine open. He turned on the lights and peered out. There was no one there. A branch from the tree that was planted on the pavement outside clattered against the window. Rattling the pain. It made him jump. That must have

6

been it. The wind was fierce tonight. It was the tree, nothing else. He turned off the light and returned to the back of the shop. The weather was getting worse; it looked like he might be here for a while. Mike Stains paused at the entrance to his secret room. Something was wrong. There wasn't a tree outside the shop this morning.

*

Rik Storm clinked the ice against the edges of his cut glass tumbler, admiring the reflection of the open fire in its multifaceted surface. He clicked the stop button on the remote control. His VCR clonked to a halt. He'd seen this one before. It failed to raise even the faintest stirring in him. He let out a sigh. Things had been so much better when he'd been on tour. He'd had the finest then, no questions asked. But things had changed. That fourth album. The reviews were bad; the record was bad. People stopped coming to the shows and the favours dried up. Then people started asking awkward questions. Worried parents wrote to radio stations. That's why he was holed up here in Caxton. He knew most of the cops out here couldn't give a shit about a washed-up pomp rocker. He could just about manage on his royalties. He had enough to pay a few people off. He would ignore the rest. He could call up Mike Stains for the necessaries. The guy was a prick, but he delivered. He even liked the fourth album. Fuck me, he must be a prick. Rik Storm put down his tumbler and reached for his cordless phone. He dialled Mike's Militaria. No reply. Prick must have gone home. He opened a draw and pulled out a spliff. Lighting it, he got up and went to his record shelf. He reached up and pulled out the first Rik Storm album, admiring the svelte figure of his former self as he placed it on the deck. Rik began to nod his head in time to

the beat, eyes closed, smoke sucking in and out. He was on
a stage gyrating and pointing at the crowd. A smile began to
break out on his face. Outside, the sound of the storm was like
the roar of the Storm's faithful fans. Rik Storm, Rik Storm,
Rik Storm! The rain pelted against his French windows.
Rik Storm, Rik Storm! He air guitared as the solo came in.
All of those hands reaching to touch him. The trees in the
garden swayed violently in the gathering gale. Rik Storm,
Rik Storm, Rik Storm! He cranked the stereo to maximum.
No neighbours, no bother. His fingers ran over the invisible
fretboard. Rik Storm! Rik Storm! Rik Storm! The French
windows buckled. At first the glass bulged like a membrane.
Leaves and stems spinning in the cavity, drilling through the
soft boarder between life and afterlife. The Tangle was here.
The Tangle was here to harvest. The window could not resist
any longer and came crashing in. Branches, like the arms of
roadies, pushed the frame aside and streamed into the room.
Creepers and vines crawled across the walls, dislodging silver
discs and the arrogant gallery of a lifetime. Arms around
politicians. Arms around actors. Arms around royalty. Arms
around the blossoming waist of an uncomprehending rock
star. Rik Storm! Rik Storm! Rik Storm! With a scream that
was once loud enough to fill the Odeon, he was dragged into
the darkness.

*

Brigitte Molin was a sadist. A reluctant teacher with no time
for children. Always wanting, grasping, needing. She hated
their optimism most. She adopted punitive measures to drive
such thoughts from their young minds. These indolent dolts
in her care, fat through indulgence and slack parenting, chips
and fizzy drinks. These punk rock and rollers with their

ripped trousers and blasphemous haircuts. No discipline, no future. She sought to belittle and harry them at every opportunity, to crush their confidence with her relentless, barbed commentary. At least then a new generation might yet rise, one that would be nearly as miserable as her. The Reverend Molin wore his resentment for all to see. In the creases of his anachronistic suits. In the pomade that held firm his dictator's wedge hair. He gave sermons of monstrous length with dispiriting content. Long, rambling diatribes about sinners and hell that, in an earlier age, would have been characterised as 'fire and brimstone' had they not been so tortuously dull. He was pissed off. Promises of a respectable position in a respectable town had vanished as his prejudices emerged in the seminary. But his father still had enough clout with the bishops to allow his son to find a quiet parish in which to ferment his bitterness. Caxton was deadly dull, but monochrome enough for his tastes. Besides, hardly anyone attended these days, so he had plenty of time to indulge in his other pursuits.

'Pass me the knife, would you?'

Brigitte passed the reverend the special curled blade used to cut the precious pods. He skilfully sliced into the flesh, biting down on his tongue in concentration.

'There she goes.'

Dark, thick sap oozed from the cut, brown and gummy. The reverend scooped it up and let it drip into the brick moulds his wife was holding out for him. It was warm in the greenhouse; he wiped a bead of sweat from his brow before attending to another pod. Such hard work, much harder than marijuana, but he did so prefer the outcome.

'Just one more row, then dinner. I have a lot of marking to do.'

'You'll need a little bit of relaxation to help you through that pile of bollocks!'

The reverend waved his knife and mock injected himself, making a comical show of 'nodding out'. Stupid, talentless bastard, she thought. His smile died on his lips. Dried up hag, he thought.

'Right you are.'

He turned his attention back to the poppies. He stuck his knife into the flesh of the next plant in the row. But the knife refused to cut. He tried again, applying more pressure this time. Still the knife seemed to skim off the surface.

'Bloody thing's gone blunt.'

He drew the blade across his finger to test it. A bright red line burst from his skin as the knife sliced a gully through it.

'Fuck it.'

He sucked the cut and returned to the pod as the metallic tang dribbled down his throat. The bulb was like thick leather, impervious to his cuts. Brigitte sighed and leaned in.

Unseen backs bent to the purpose carried the parts for the art of the woods.
Unseen hands silently weaving the flax and the thread for the throne of the gods.

'Here, let me try.'

She snatched the blade testily from her husband's bleeding hand. Blood dripped into the soil. Its lively signal generating a pulse. These were the subjects of interest. The material, the matter.

Unseen eyes measured the cuts.

Take only what you need. The filament probed beneath the surface. The harvest was here. Brigitte harrumphed and curled her spine. She moved closer, raising her arm to cut the bulb. The filament passed the command and the poppy shot from the soil. Its stem lengthening like an electrical flex. Green fibres wove across the space between teacher and plant, grasping her hand, directing it in an alternative arc.

Unseen arms directed the cuts.

The blade in Brigitte's hand swept down. It sliced the reverend across the eyes, splitting his corneas like ripe tomatoes. At first he was too stunned to scream. By the time he had found his voice, the poppy-primed hand of his wife had slashed his throat, reducing the scream to a gurgle. All she could do was stare.

Unseen shoulders would carry the load.

To the maker in the woods. On quiet stems. On quiet stems. The other poppies in the greenhouse rose. Their fronds spread across the bed at speed, shooting towards the reluctant teacher. The stems whirled around her like a tornado, binding her tight. The filaments began to crawl up her cheeks, until they reached her mouth. An incoherent moan was emanating from her like the sound of a failing foghorn. The filaments entered her mouth, pulling her lips apart. She stared, wide eyed, the tuneless tone continuing to rattle around the greenhouse. Her hand groped towards her own gaping mouth. The knife, like a bloody harpoon lashed to her fist, plunged into her. Her knuckles, moist with sap and gore, were pulled across her teeth as the knife took her tongue.

The moan was drowned as bright arcs of blood-spray hit the panes of the greenhouse.

> *Unseen backs bent to the purpose carried the parts for the*
> *art of the woods.*
> *Unseen hands silently weaving the flax and the thread for*
> *the throne of the gods.*

Then there was silence. Caxton was a quiet parish.

*

DI Ward stared at the hastily assembled incident board. Photos had been pinned to the cork. Barely believable images of broken bodies and severed limbs. She was late in this morning. Her phone unanswered all night. She thought of the whiskey bottle on her kitchen table. Empty. She'd woken up face down on the Formica surface, still dressed in the clothes she'd come home in. There was blood on her shoes and trousers from the grass in the park. The glistening stalks. The phone had been bleeping out an irritating Morse code. She remembered replacing the receiver, bleary eyed and hungover. Fuck.

'Get me a car, I want to visit all three sites immediately! And get hold of whoever's in charge at each crime scene and tell them to secure them properly. I don't want any press snooping about or kids looking for souvenirs. And tell the duty sergeant . . . tell him to . . . just tell him to check my number in future and send a fucking squad car if he can't get me on the phone!'

Fuck. She remembered the tone pulsing through the receiver. The boss had talked about getting those new mobile phones for the DIs, but they looked like house bricks and weighed nearly as much. She didn't fancy lugging that about. It's what all the dealers were using though, that's how you could spot them. Leisure wear and fucking massive phones. She mustn't screw this one up. They were watching her, all those nicotine-stained lads, five pints at lunch, cosy with the gangsters at the golf club. Blind eyes turned, backhanders paid. They didn't much like women cops. 'You call that progress?' She'd put up with it for years, the leering and sniggering. But she was better than them and they knew it. Because she cared just enough not to be a monster like them. Not that she liked people. Most of the ones she came across were awful, it went with the territory. The body in the park, now that was something else, no one could process that. Only the monsters could, only the monsters. An eager-faced policeman poked his head around the door of the incident room.

'Your car's ready, ma'am. Oh, and we had a call from that dog walker from last night, reckons he remembers seeing Tam knocking about near the woods about twenty minutes before he found the body. I've sent a couple of officers to see if they can pick him up. They're checking the usual haunts, but nothing yet. You don't reckon it's Tam do you, ma'am? The body, I mean.'

Not Tam Stamp? The happy hippy? She liked him. He was a local character, more eccentric than insane. The kids taunted him, but he always took it well. She had no idea where he lived, if indeed he had a place to call his own. Some said he lived in the woods; some said they had found his shelters hidden in the dark nooks of the forest. Others thought he lived with his mother. He kept her body in her bedroom like Norman Bates, they said. The nonsense these gossips came out with. He was adrift, in another world.

A smiling traveller. No trouble, no killer, but perhaps a victim? He used to make little figures from sticks. He would hang them in the trees for children to find. She thought of the glistening cone of bloody leaves and shuddered. She knocked back her coffee and pushed through the swing doors.

She sat in silence on the way to the crime scene. The driver was a junior detective, cocky, thick as mince, with the beginnings of a beer belly troubling the buttons of his Burton shirt. It was doubtful he could offer any insight. It was true that all the victims had skeletons in their closets, barely concealed sins that could well warrant a degree of retribution from outraged family members or criminal gangs. But that wasn't unusual round here. There were so many secrets behind Caxton's twitching curtains that she wouldn't be surprised if a thunderbolt didn't smite the whole fucking place one day. The victims were known to each other to a greater or lesser extent. Rik Storm bought gear and dodgy videos off Mike Stains. Stains got the gear from the Reverend Molin, or at least that was the working hypothesis. Once they had discovered the reverend's laboratory, it looked likely that he was serving up in some capacity. The officers that were called to the rectory had found his head and feet in the blood-spattered greenhouse. They'd been crudely squashed into the torso of his wife, who's own head was missing, along with her legs and arms. They also found rows and rows of empty flower beds, with neat holes where the plants had once been. From the residue found in containers, the presumption was they were opium poppies. But all the poppies were gone. There was a strange neatness to the carnage. No upturned pots or loose soil littering the floor. It was as if the plants had upped and left of their own accord. So, there was a connection between them. All except Tam. Tam was a strictly magic mushrooms

14

type of guy. Acid maybe. But morphine and smut? It wasn't his style. If the body in the park turned out to be him. Who'd want to kill a hippy?

They started at the rectory. It was the closest to the station. When she arrived, everything was in order, cordons up and protective clothing issued. The outrage was obvious, but the clues were less apparent.

'No prints? With all this blood? Not a shoe print? No fibres?'

'Not a thing, ma'am. It looks like they did it to themselves?'

'What? Why? When? Cut their own fucking heads off and scurried away?'

Sarah Ward left the question hanging in the horror. She walked out of the blood-spattered greenhouse and into the large rectory garden. She greedily gulped in the fresh air. Only the monsters. Only the monsters. She started to walk towards the back of the garden, where it dipped down to a tall privet hedge. Beyond the hedge was the Tangle. A vague sense of foreboding rose in her veins; her nerves began to tingle. Only the monsters. Only the monsters. She reached the hedge and paused. She looked back at the crime scene. She could smell death in the air. Turning back to the solid wall of green, she began to push through the hedge. The spindly density of branches scratched and stabbed at her face, causing small lesions to swell on her cheeks. The hedge was too thick to pass through. But then, quite gradually at first, the hedge seemed to give way, as if it was begrudgingly letting her pass. She felt like Lucy in the wardrobe, pushing coats out of her way en route to some inverted Narnia. Sarah stepped through the other side. There was silence. No birdsong or the expected distant thrum of traffic from the new bypass. Only the static buzz of emptiness. Across a thin strip of scrub lay the edge of the wood. She stepped into the spiteful stalks, their roughness scratching her calves as she walked. She knew it was there before she saw it. The knotty stalks lay flat, arranged in a circle as if they had been scythed down. In the centre of the circle was a green, glistening cone of blood and leaves.

*

The backyard of Mike's Militaria was a jumble of rust. Old bikes, exhaust pipes and discarded panels from a host of stolen vehicles were decaying in untidy piles. Loosely secured plastic sheets hovered over the mountains of debris like ghosts. Driven by the wind, they fluttered violently, making a cracking sound like the volley of a firing squad. DI Ward pushed past them, looking for bloodied leaves amongst the rotting carcasses of machines. Her colleagues looked on, detached and uninterested. She knew it was here somewhere, that grim trademark. The assailant considered themselves an artist, or at least a keen apprentice. A collector of parts and materials for some great work, a sculptor or craftsman. That's what she thought now. Not a medic, the parts had been chosen for aesthetic reasons. The killer was making something. But here, so far, she had drawn a blank. She rooted about in the rubbish that was piled up against the back fence. That strange tingle again. She shouted up the yard to where two young PCs were loafing about.

'Get this lot shifted away from the fence, will you?'

'Yes, ma'am.'

The two constables raised their eyebrows and looked at each other in a quiet conspiracy of misplaced superiority. Sarah pretended not to notice. The young coppers clumsily shifted the rubbish, cursing as pools of water that had gathered on the plastic sheets overflowed onto their shoes.

She was reminded of her father putting up furniture without
reading the instructions. Armed with bluster and a toolbox
he would fire into every task in the same way: as if the world
would bend to his will if he swore at it enough. Eventually the
fence was clear of debris. She began to explore along
its perimeter. The tingle was growing into a pulse. A loose
slat tipped and opened. She squeezed through. Mike Stains's
yard backed onto the railway, where freight trains rattled
down from the town to the docks. The embankment plunged
and rose, forming a drab valley of ragged grass and weeds.
On the far side, the trees of Caxton Wood stood on the edge
of the embankment like a squadron of cavalry tensed to
charge. She inhaled sharply. She held onto her breath. She
slowly exhaled as the vague outline of a theory took shape.
The woods, always the woods. Was he hiding out in there?
In the trees. Watching, planning, waiting for his materials to
ripen. Checking on the sturdiness of his victims. Waiting to
carve them open. Was he there now watching her? The sides
of the cutting were dotted with cans and plastic bags, looking
like ugly flowers blooming out of season. She began to tack
her way down, scanning as she went. She reached
the track without finding anything. On the other side, the
cutting rose up in the same untidy fashion. The pulse was
now throbbing like a kick drum. She began to climb, less
diligent in her search this time; she knew she wouldn't find
it here. Breathless, she reached the top. The fence at the
summit provided only the vaguest suggestion of a barrier.
She climbed over the fence. She was drawn to a shape where
the thick, ugly scrub had been scythed down. Circles. Circles.
The pulsing stopped. The static hissed. On the edge of the
Tangle the green cone glistened red.

*

The siren's strangled whine was jarring. Out of time with the rhythmical metronome of the squad car's windscreen wipers, it sounded like a nursery school music lesson. Inside the car, the atonal anti-rhythm was not helping DI Ward's concentration.

'Do you need to have that thing on?'

PC Barrowman had collected her from Mike's Militaria in his squad car. He had volunteered for the job. Sarah offered him a weak smile. He's got potential this one, so let's hope the lads at the station don't get to him any time soon. She tapped impatiently on the dashboard, trying to get a clear picture of what happened that night. The more information she got, the less sense it all made.

'I don't understand the preliminary pathology reports, Barrowman.'

She was talking at him, not to him.

'They put the time of death between eight and ten for all the murders. How can that be right? It would mean the assailant had to kill and dismember all the victims within half an hour of each other. They'd have to get across town, kill the next victim, butcher them immediately, and then move on to the next one. All the while leaving no trace, either at the crime scene or between locations. Something isn't right, even the most skilled surgeon couldn't do that. So, there's got to be a team of them, highly organised, well co-ordinated. But why is there no trace of them, no witnesses, no prints, nothing? You would have thought someone would have noticed groups of people dismembering bodies in four locations at exactly the same time.'

But she knew there was a single intelligence behind all of this. Those blood-drenched cones were identical in every respect, dimensions the same down to the last millimetre.

They could have been made before the murders. Taken by each team and left as some kind of warning? No, that wasn't it, they were too obscurely placed to be warnings. They were the trademarks of a craftsman.

'Did the lab have any luck with those cones?'

'Ash, Barrowman. They were leaves from an ash tree, freshly cut and twisted, by fuck knows who.'

They were approaching the country pile of Rik Storm. Tasteless columns and faux grandeur. The squad car scrunched to a halt on the gravel. DI Ward nodded to PC Barrowman to follow her round the back of the house. He looked confused, but she was insistent. They pushed through the side gate and entered the back garden. She wasn't interested in picking through pop memorabilia, old LPs and gold discs. She wasn't into Rik Storm's bombastic nonsense. Nor did she want to spend her time pulling up floorboards looking for elicit magazines and dirty photos. She knew they were there, they all did. She was there for the tiny tower of blood and leaves that she knew was nestling in the scrub. That was death, alive in all its terrible ingenuity. She wanted to know its secrets.

She drifted across the garden, pulled by imperceptible ropes. She was only dimly aware of Barrowman and the other officers. They were milling about, analysing the crime scene, doing police work, wasting their time. Again, the tingling sensation began to rise. An impossible itch making her twitch as she walked across the lawn. The same glances were exchanged, the same old tuts and shaking heads. Sarah was floating above it all, drifting through trailing stems, covered in soft weeping leaves. She smelled the strong aroma of honeysuckle and witch hazel. Her head began to swim. She was caught in a tangle of flowers, each bloom's perfume more pungent than the next. Her nostrils flared. There was a sour note lurking in the perfume. It tried to hide, but she could smell it. The note of decay. The metallic hum of blood. What are you hiding in that beautiful coil? She started to run. Rik Storm's garden was long, blending from well-kept lawn to rough brush before colliding with a wall at the forest's edge. The reek of death asserted itself above the sweetness of the garden. Sarah pushed the stems aside. Still floating above the ground. In another world. In another dimension. The tingle of the Tangle. The raw buzzing screech of silence. She could see it now. There on the edge. A blood-black cone. Barrowman's breathless voice dragged her back through the stems until she found herself staring at Rik Storm's garden wall.

'Sorry, ma'am, we just had a call from control . . .'

Barrowman was panting hard, steaming in the drizzle. He was struggling to get the words out. She looked at him through strobing eyes. She was still hovering between the dimensions, unable to settle. Everything seemed to be out of focus and flat like a medieval painting. The constable's words extended into protracted tones, as if his voice was playing on a broken tape recorder.

'There's been another. Up at the playground on Wentford Hill, a couple out for a stroll . . .'

'There's a witness too. Says he saw them being dragged into the woods. They were still alive.'

'Wentford Hill? That's not far from here.'

Her words had a dreamlike quality to them, almost as if pronouncing them was alien to her. Barrowman looked concerned and confused.

'Is everything OK, ma'am?'

She didn't answer. Her movements were entirely without urgency. Slow and languid. She pressed her palms against the wet bricks of the wall. Beyond it, the Tangle rippled. A shock passed up her arm, causing her to spasm suddenly. She spun around.

'We must go. Radio control. Tell them to set up a perimeter. No one in. No one out. Tell the others to bring weapons.'

'Yes, ma'am.'

The squad car tore down the country lanes, its blue light flashing across the fields like a hyperactive lighthouse. Windscreen wipers beat out a doleful rhythm as the fine rain fell. DI Ward was glued to the radio, gathering every bit of information she could. They had a witness. To find a witness was a stroke of luck. But the testimony being relayed to the detective was nonsensical and garbled. Barrowman kept glancing over at her as she spoke to control. His face was blending from a perplexed frown into the wide-eyed incredulity of an officer who was used to hearing bullshit stories every day.

'They thought it might be kids?' The detective rolled her eyes and banged the dashboard. 'Because? What? Why? Where? Yeah, yep, yes.'

She clicked off the radio and stared out of the window in silence. Barrowman started to say something but thought better of it. The road looked like a river of mist on which they floated, the car a faint outline like a fading pencil drawing. Thin arms bent at knobbly joints. Deformed limbs with tiny hands at their end. Dragging bodies through the undergrowth. Barely visible above the grass. She saw razors cutting, and cruel blades skinning. Two humans lost in the woods. Two humans offered as a sacrifice to the artisan of the forest.

*Unseen backs bent to the purpose carried the parts for the
   art of the woods.*
*Unseen hands silently weaving the flax and the thread for
   the throne of the gods.*

'Hurry, Barrowman, we haven't much time . . . Time, time,
time, time to run, time to run.'

The car had reached Wentford Hill car park, a popular spot
for doggers and lovers alike. This morning it was empty except
for the single patrol car that had responded to the 999 call.
A bored-looking, plump PC was leaning on the bonnet with his
arms folded as his wiry colleague paced around the car kicking
the loose stones and scratching his scalp under his peaked
cap. They looked up with only mild interest as the squad car
screeched into the car park with sirens blaring. Barrowman
remembered this place from his school days. A path bisected
a picnic area on one side, dotted with rickety wooden tables
covered in tediously obscene graffiti, whittled by bored
youths. On the other side, a playground of rusty swings and a
roundabout so dangerous it should have been condemned long
ago. No children came up here anymore. The youths would
progress from the tables to the swings as the Thunderbird
wine took hold. It was great for sex and drugs; the cops never
bothered them. Barrowman wondered if the couple who had
been snatched had really been 'out for a stroll'. The detective
just kept staring out of the window, her eyes flickering this
way and that, as if she was experiencing an entirely different
view from him. Her gaze settled on a spot beyond the
playground. Somewhere beyond the dark fringe of the Tangle.

'We're here, ma'am. Shall we wait for backup?'

She looked at him as if he had asked the most ridiculous
question in the world.

'Oh, no, there's no time for that.'

In this world, she jumped out of the squad car, ignoring the two officers already at the scene. She offered them no direction. PC Barrowman, though it was above his pay grade, tried to give them some instructions of his own.

'Get a perimeter set up, will you, lads? No one's to go up to the woods. The DI will be back to direct the team when they get here. Alright?'

But he couldn't help looking somewhat unsure about that statement. DI Ward was already quite some way up the path. The two policemen glared at him. They looked like a washed-up comedy duo on receiving a less than favourable review in the Caxton Gazette. The plump one unfurled his crossed arms and gave Barrowman a mock salute.

'Right you are, guv'nor.'

'Wanker.'

The wiry one muttered under his breath. Barrowman smiled to himself and followed his boss up the path. He'd get a couple more stripes, maybe a pip or two on his collar. He quite enjoyed the feeling of command.

'Ma'am, shouldn't we wait for the firearms team at least? Won't we be just adding to the casualty list if we charge in there?'

He was confident now. Powerful. In charge. He was striding towards the detective. Here to save the day with his instinct for detection. Sarah Ward had stopped at the end of the path, where the cinder track changed to worn earth as it entered the woods. She didn't react to the constable's voice. His confidence began to dissipate in the fine drizzle. His voice softened to a shy schoolboy murmur.

'I was thinking it might be better if we wait for backup, ma'am. The perimeter will be set up soon, so they won't be able to get out without being spotted. We can push in from all sides that way.'

Sarah turned around slowly. Her eyes were expressionless. Her pupils, like black pools, reflected back his dripping, uncertain face. She reached out her hand and grasped him firmly by the arm. Her mouth began to arch up haltingly as if her lips were being winched into place. A smile was suspended on her face.

'Bless you, Barrowman, bless you. Don't you see? There's no time. We have to go now. They are waiting.'

She took his hand and led him into the Tangle.

*

Inside the wood the air was dense. The hiss of white noise underpinned a faint throb, like the pulse of a heartbeat. It was warm. She had played in these woods as a little girl, and so had he, but things were different now. The path had been swallowed by the undergrowth, so they picked their own passage through the stems. Directions and distance became impossible to judge as the world outside the wood vanished from view. There was no sound of traffic. No car horn chatter, no sirens or shouts of command. All the usual points of reference were absent. This was a new, alien landscape. Here they were strangers, interlopers, invaders.

Sarah Ward let go of his hand. The two officers wandered steadily through the boughs, brushing against the soft leaves with their faulty skin. The womb-like cadence of the woods reduced any feeling of urgency. Time had no meaning here. Had they been searching for days, hours or years? It was impossible to tell. Neither seemed to care. The abducted couple. The murderous artist. The severed limbs and broken corpses, all parts of the pitiless necropolis they lived in.

The constant flow of construction and destruction, death, birth and the stagnant torpor in between. The snap of a twig broke the reverie like a needle skidding off a record. Sarah froze and signalled for Barrowman to follow her example.

'Over there,'

She whispered as the dimensions of the forest settled into recognisable shapes. Up, down, left, right. Barrowman nodded silently. They crept through the undergrowth. Another crack. This time a faint cry too. Human wailing. They picked their way with increased urgency. The sounds became clearer. A woman and a man. They were close enough to separate the tones of their cries. But the wood was still too thick to see them clearly. Snap. A desiccated branch broke as something was dragged over the ground. More cries. This time the sound seemed to come from behind them. They wheeled around and stopped, momentarily disorientated. Thumps and scrapes and a hideous scuttling sound. They froze. A sound rose through the hiss. The crackle of thin limbs scampering over dead leaves. Pincer-tipped tarsus tapping. Barrowman instinctively reached for a stick to use as a weapon. DI Ward scanned the trees. Another scream, this time long and continuous. Both sexes harmonizing in a terrible anguished howl. The scuttling sound grew more intense.

DI Ward signalled a manoeuvre with her eyes. They split up and approached the source of the cries from different directions. The undergrowth began to thin. Sarah was drifting through the mist again. She was a little girl in a procession of village girls and boys, skipping towards the great ash. Erwan with the scythe, the vicar with his hymn book. Come to sing for the spirits of the winter and all the saints. All the saints. All the saints are here. The branches melted away as she

glided through the woods. The chanting rose. The animals
lowed in mournful tones anticipating their demise. The scythe
swept, and the blood flowed. The hymns rang out as the
villagers danced around the ash. God is here. God is here.
DI Ward stood on the edge of the clearing, her eyes as black
as Dante's well.

Barrowman tried his radio, more out of habit than hope.
The wood had done things to him since the DI had dragged
him in. His perspective had shifted onto a new, unfamiliar
axis. His duty was still his duty, he guessed. But in some
strange way it felt like someone else's concern. He crept closer
to the sound. He could make out a glade up ahead where the
trees had formed into a natural amphitheatre. The soft hum
of the forest began to blend with the unsettling cries that
were growing in intensity as he got closer. He was a boy again.
A boy scout within a troop of boy scouts. They had whittled
figures to hang in the branches of the great ash. He was proud
of his. A man with no arms or legs, grinning through a mouth
with no lips. They hung them on the boughs and sang songs.
PC Barrowman stood on the edge of the clearing, his eyes as
black as Dante's well.

Two bodies hung from the branches of the great ash.
Ruler of the third lunar month. Queen of the glade. The
bodies kicked and swung. Cut and bruised but alive. Around
them busy artists were at work. DI Ward stepped into the
clearing. Her mouth wanted to form a scream of her own,
but she drove it back down. She was face to face with the
craftsman of the forest. Behold her work. The ash seemed
to spread its branches, like arms, proudly displaying the
fruits of its labour. Down its trunk, spider entities scuttled
on spindly twig legs that jutted from a brain-like core. The
brain looked like a furry walnut oozing with sap. They were

perfect facsimiles of arachnids, born from the bark of the ash tree. Outriders of itself, sent into the world of men to hunt and gather. They reminded her of huge huntsman spiders. Sightless and fast, they filled the glade with their hideous industry. A fresh scream pierced the momentary silence. A spider creature was using its pincers to pull a strip of skin from the leg of the flailing man. It gathered up the skin and ran down the branch to join the flow of its comrades who were scuttling down the trunk. Sarah followed its progress, unable to turn her gaze from the fascinating tableau. The spider thing crossed the forest floor where it joined a further group of creatures hard at work. The skin was passed carefully between mute mandibles before being skilfully stitched onto an evolving patchwork using fine strands of silk woven from their abdomen. They were upholstering furniture.

Barrowman staggered into the glade waving his stick impotently in front of him. The wood spiders ignored him. They were too busy to kill. Besides they had all the materials they needed for now. Take only what you need. That was the first law of the Tangle. He glanced across the clearing to DI Ward, looking for guidance. But they had not been trained for anything like this. The two dangling captives. Hostages, victims, prisoners. He recognized those designations. It was in the handbook. What to do in a hostage situation. But this . . .

'Help us, please, for pity's sake.'

'I don't want to die. Oh, God.'

The spider things cut another strip. Barrowman looked desperately over to the DI. Sarah Ward shook her head. Don't do it. It's no good. Barrowman struggled. Duty, training, instinct, all rendered irrelevant by the artistry of the Tangle. The black blood and stitch, the weaver's bobbin of sinew and skin. Barrowman broke from his mooring and ran towards the hanging couple. A line of ash spiders formed a palisade with their stick legs. Sharp points menaced the constable as he tried to get closer.

Sarah Ward turned to admire their work. Her eyes as black as Dante's well. She was a little girl in her best Sunday robes, holding a doll made from the stalks, sat on a cushion, patiently embroidered. She stepped to the altar and placed the cushion on the simple wooden table. In the centre of the cushion, she placed the doll. She sat it upright. Like a monarch.

'Oh, that is wonderful Sarah. You are so talented at weaving the stems, and such delicate needle work. Would you like to make beautiful things when you grow up?'

The ash continued its craft. She smiled.

'Thank you, reverend. I wanted to make something special for the festival. She's the queen, the queen of the woods.'

Across the bloody workshop, Barrowman watched his commanding officer's face in horror. She was smiling. At this? Yet even he had to admit it was beautiful. Bones, bent and carved to form a delicate frame, were being carefully engraved by the sharp tips of the spiders' legs. Over the frame they then carefully fitted the upholstery of skin and sinew. Faces cut from skulls poked out from the folds of the fabric, like curious children behind their mothers' skirts as the parade passed by. The beautiful furniture of humanity. A throne of blood. The legs were legs, the arms were arms. Eyes inlaid, tongues tied and stitched in an exquisite tapestry. The ash had mastered its craft. Just a few more details and the work would be complete.

'Take me.'

Sarah's voice was barely discernible over the busy clicking of the creatures. The ash swayed as it caught her words.

She wanted to make beautiful things. She wanted to make a difference.

'Let them go. Take me instead.'

Louder this time, more insistent. The ash swayed. The voice. The voice of God. The spider creatures paused, lowering the palisade of pincers. Barrowman seized his chance and ran towards the dangling couple. Jumping over the ranks of spiders, he managed to clear their menacing spikes as they attempted to impale him. He hurriedly untied the twine of stems that held the dangling couple. They dropped screaming to the floor. As they rose, they found themselves surrounded by agitated creatures. They began to swarm around the captives, waving their pincers menacingly. The humans were trapped. Barrowman looked anxiously at his DI. Too impetuous, that's what his scout master said.

'Don't do anything, Anthony, just stay there.'

Sarah Ward held out her arm, palm facing the constable and the shivering couple. She was ready to go now. She saw it all. The master maker. The final detail. She edged towards the tree. The spider creatures clicked and prickled. Barrowman looked uncertain. Paralyzed. Initial spontaneity marred by a lack of caution. That was his fateful flaw. It had always been that way. Too quick to make bold choices without considering the consequences. He'd joined the force on a whim, just to piss his Dad off. He shouldn't be here. He should have left Caxton years ago. Got a trade like his old man, travelled a bit, gone to the city, made a life for himself with the talents he squandered.

'Your father won't be happy.'

He could hear his dead mother's voice.

'You'd better not mess this up.'

Barrowman swept his stick like a sword, trying to cut a path out of the glade. The ranks of spikey stick legs broke momentarily as he smashed at them with his desiccated weapon. But they soon surged again.

The spider creatures cut his legs at the ankles and he toppled to the forest floor. His cries were soon drowned in the frantic click-clack of creaking pincers as they swarmed all over him. Stabbing and cutting with precision. Blood began to pour over the woodland floor. Dark reeking rags from his torn uniform were chucked out of the seething pile to be collected by yet more scurrying things. Sarah saw Barrowman's severed head being carried along through the mesh of tangled legs. It was passed along the swarm until it reached the macabre monument they were constructing. His face joined the gallery in the upholstery of the furniture. Tears welled and overflowed, staining her cheeks. They never listen, these foolish boys, they never listen. She looked over at the helpless couple, bleeding and useless on the blood-soaked ground. Pincers click-clacked. Sarah ran to the tree. Pressing her filthy hands against the trunk she spoke into the bark.

'Take me, for God's sake, take me.'

The ash swayed. The spider creatures stopped. God? Yes, God. The ash had heard of God. The offerings. The dangling effigies of dead men and women. The hymns and chants. The blood. This was not God. The ash knew God. The ash swayed. The spider creatures began to reverse away from the cowering couple. A path formed from the tree to the edge of the clearing. In the far distance DI Ward could hear the sound of sirens. She pressed her palms against the bark with increased intensity.

'Take me. Take me. I am ready. *I wanted to make something special for the festival.*'

She wasn't sure if she had spoken. Her words were a whisper, uttered in a language that was not her own.

Erwan's scythe. The bloody skins hanging in the branches, the hymns and the corn dolls.

'Oh, that is wonderful Sarah. You are so talented at weaving the stems.'

The offerings piled high on the altar. Tins and toys, dolls and games. Skulls and blood. Erwan's scythe and the woad on his face running in the rain. The spider things scuttled backwards up the trunk until they were re-absorbed into the bark.

'Run!'

Her last words, imperious, like a decree. The woman nodded mutely. Standing on shaking legs she dragged her bleeding partner up and ran out of the clearing. Sarah watched them until they had been swallowed up by the Tangle. The sirens. Run to the sirens. Silence returned to the glade. Slowly a branch curled down from the canopy and gently slipped around her waist, like a partner at the start of a waltz. She felt herself float through the air. She was a windblown leaf. The glistening cone was forming silently below her. The branch deposited her tenderly on a cushion of human furniture. She noted absentmindedly that it had been fashioned from the bloated stomach of Mike Stains, she remembered his distinctive birthmark from the photographs in his special room. Her hands spread over the soft skin. Such exemplary work. Faultless. She was a monarch on a throne. A queen of the forest. But there were no monarchs here. No subjects either. She felt a stillness that she had never felt before. The tears ran in steady streams. But she was not sad, nor even frightened. She could no longer hear the sirens or the sounds of her world. Perspectives began to shift. New vectors opened and revealed themselves. The warmth of the womb enveloped her as she sat on the throne of skin and blood. Through a crack in the membrane that separated the dimensions, she saw herself dancing around the throne, the blossoms of spring in her hair. The delicate scent of the Tangle flooded her senses like the perfume of a cathedral. A prelate stood in the chancel waving a ball of incense on a silver chain as DI Ward was adorned with the baubles of her office. Orb, sceptre and Crown. Another branch unfurled from the knot. It straightened its length and pierced her stomach. Its twigs spread out across her, pulling her apart. She was sucked into the structure of the throne until her spine splintered and her features fused with the fabric. The prelate waved the ball of incense as the officers of state came up to the throne one by one to pay homage to their new queen. A faint gurgle escaped the remains of her mouth. The ash welcomed her into the roots, and with the last tiny spark of her former human self, she complimented it on its fine craftsmanship. So very comfortable. She smiled.

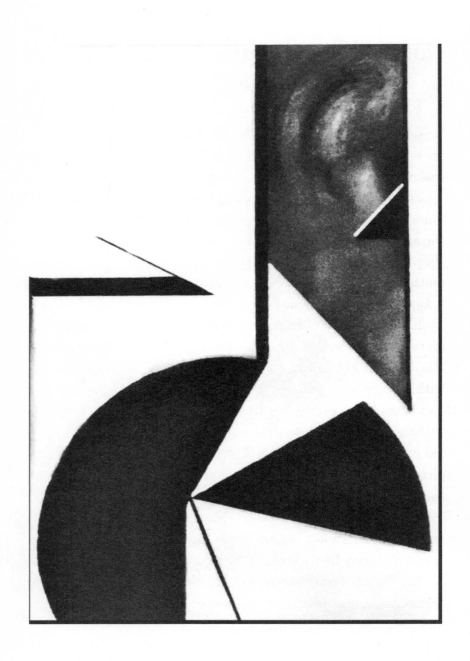

Notification from the A.B.A.C.U.S.

No one went out any more. The outside world was difficult, uncertain and probably best avoided. But Kavendish Jeremiah was one of those rare Citizens whose desires could not be satisfied by fresh air generators or daylight synthesisers. He knew some would mock his strange customs, but he did enjoy the simple communion of foot on concrete from time to time. People may call him a 'Walker' with a faint sneer, but it didn't matter. He was content with his carefully constructed oddity; it kept his quotient healthy.

Kavendish had been delivered from the annexed womb of an unknown Service Citizen in the Inner London Hatcheries. His designated 'How Are You?' device had declared him fit within acceptable parameters. His appearance, 'strikingly handsome', was only a few points short of 'gorgeous'. Although he enjoyed surgery as much as the next person, he did at least bear some resemblance to his hatchery graduation picture. Kavendish was a member of the most privileged cadre, selected and designated according to an ancient line of inheritance that stretched back into the distant past. Tall and lean for an Aristoian, he was something of an athlete. At least sexually. Today he was wearing his hair long.

Kavendish Jeremiah adjusted the position of his Sensory Nexus Mask and selected the odour of a freshly mown meadow. The sweet scent flowed through the plexi-holes of his nose piece, exciting the neatly trimmed hairs of his nostrils. He shook his velvet fedora and placed it on his head at a rakish angle, enjoying the feel of its stout brim on his fingertips. He smoothed the mask over his features, relishing its sleek, shiny texture. The mask covered his face with a translucent film that offered excellent clarity of view whilst maintaining his connection to the Nexus. The mask was his second skin. Every Aristoian wore one. It was the only tolerable way to deal with the outside world, after all.

Kavendish harmonised the tint of his mask to compensate for the bright blue tones of the sky. The huge, open sky. Untroubled by aircraft or pylons. Free of pollutants and urban gas. A perfect azure dome. A sudden breath of wind raised the brim of his hat. Kavendish secured it and pulled his jacket closer to him as phantom gusts swept between the buildings, playing a haunting melody like an orchestra tuning up before the conductor's arrival. He let his eyes play across the panorama of his home. This was London. A former capital of nowhere. A bewildering conurbation on a small island. A city where all your desires were met with a blink of an eye. A place of carefully controlled disorder. A temple to indulgence, whim and fancy. Outside the dome lay the Tangle.

He turned his attention to his screen. He blinked rapidly, registering his reaction to the posts and images that were flowing steadily across it. Faces stared out at him. Faces in rooms. Rooms revealed by cameras and open access feeds. The pornography of everyday life. The constant exhibition. Kavendish was on near-permanent display. His outer life was completely transparent most of the time. Only his inner life remained hidden, even from himself. It was rare for him to log off. Others would become suspicious if you were absent for too long, and anyway, the A.B.A.C.U.S.

didn't like it. There was a risk of melancholy creeping in with the silence.

Kavendish began to walk along the riverbank, heading towards the park. He consulted his Personal Advisory Terminal, looking for inspiration. When it came to suggestions for pleasurable diversion, it had never let him down. Kavendish winked open an icon. The Terminal scrolled into life.

- The Oil Pit
- The Mystery Coupling Cubicle
- Jelly Man
- The Willing Torturer
- Dream Capsule
- The Gentle Pastures of Pleasure

Kavendish digested the list. Most of the suggestions seemed a little stale to him. He had fucked, dined and swallowed in most of these establishments. That was the problem with going outside. The architects never really kept pace with desire. Kavendish was impatient for satisfaction. He had left the pleasure café early. He found that particular establishment boring and had especially deplored the décor. But narcotics and nature were something that never failed to please him. The chance to dream amongst the blooms. It was always changing in unpredictable ways. That was its attraction. The chaos. The park was a reliable solution. It would be the perfect start to another perfect day.

In a glade of lilac shadows, a ripple turned to a wave.
The child race was at a crossroads. Or at an end, who
could tell?

Erwan cut the bough for me, let the sap drip down. Send a
sign to the child of the magus. For the reckoning is now.

The outside world was conspiring against him. Disruption
of the normal was its mode. Dark clouds contaminated the
sky. It began to rain. Unscheduled, uninvited rain. This
was strange in itself, as one was used to the accuracy of the
A.B.A.C.U.S. weather reports; every day was dissected and
predicted in a generally efficient manner. The unexpected was
rarely unexpected. Dark clouds were not welcome here. Only
the perfection of perpetual daylight. Twenty-four hours of
sunshine, every day, every year, for as long as anyone could
remember. Though 'day' was not an idea anyone entertained.
There was something like the passing of time, marked in
hours and minutes and so forth, but it bore no relation to any
changes in the apparent movement of the sun. It was simply
an ancient affectation inherited from some previous mode of
being that had long since been abandoned. If the light faded,
then the powerful daylight bulbs of the city would spring into
life. Pushing back the darkness, banishing the night. Night-
time was a waste of time. Once a week he would sleep. If he
needed it or not. But otherwise, he would fill his time with
amusing diversions. Stimulants kept him awake and alert.
Pleasure could not rest, there was no time for it.

As the unexpected rain began to splatter on the pavement,
Kavendish looked around for shelter. He was keen not to
ruin the new suit his auto-tailor had recently created and
was, in any case, too far from a terminal to get a new one.
The riverside was exposed. There was little need for havens
or hiding places, as so few people ever went out. But now
Kavendish needed shelter as splatter turned to torrent.
Gazing down the riverside path, his attention was drawn to a

wild oak that looked like it had burst through the pavement. That was not the way of things. It was an ugly looking object. Twisted and gnarled. Not at all like the beautiful oaks found in the city's parks. Was this something new? The latest fashion in arboreal decoration? He had not seen it mentioned on the Nexus. He stared at the bizarre carbuncle. It was without structure or symmetry. Its very presence violated his sensibilities. He watched its ugliness pulse. In out. In out. Like a lung. Like a heart. Like a valve. As he stared, its canopy began to swell and expand. Kavendish was fascinated and repulsed. As he watched the tree suck and blow, the dizzying confusion of London dissolved around him. The roots split the pavement. Concrete buckled, then shattered. Branches streamed into the cracks, occupying every crevice. Soon he was under the spreading leaves, his palms pressed on the contorted trunk. Time and location momentarily forgotten. Under the dense structure of branches, a strange atmosphere began to smother him. Kavendish was alone, and for the first time in as long as he could remember, he was separated and detached from the city. His mind began to wander. A rare and unwelcome feeling. A strange darkness grew. Shapes emerged, then splintered. The branches began to twist, creating the walls of an endless tunnel. The unruly stems began to knot into a thick weave. The roots began to writhe. The whole strange clump then began to spin, as if dancing a frenetic reel. Faster and faster it spun, until a vortex formed that threatened to suck him into its core. He was sweating uncontrollably. This was not the way of things. Waves of nausea travelled around his body. The dislocation was horrifying. This was not the way of things.

Who will carry the weight of the golden seed to the door?
Who will turn the key to the vault under the floor?

Who will find the prize hidden deep within the tomb?
Who will see the lights glinting in the gloom?

The vortex slowed and stopped. The wave changed back to pulse. The Tangle retreated. Reversing into the trunk. Back down through the cracks in the pavement. The message had been delivered. Kavendish sat on an empty walkway in an empty city. His mask regained its connection to the Nexus and chimed back into life with a melodious tone. Most blessed notifications!

- The A.B.A.C.U.S. benevolent resource.
- The A.B.A.C.U.S. locus of all desire.
- The A.B.A.C.U.S. omni-competent living device.

The icons had returned one by one, but now they seemed distant and strangely shrunken. A new suggestion occupied the centre of the screen: a map. But not the map he was used to. A single dot that looked like an acorn blinked on a crude street plan. Above it the words:

The Museum of Ignorance.

The script had an almost hieroglyphic quality. Letters elongated. Words twisting about the page like vipers. Crude words. Primitive words. Words that were unfamiliar, their meaning obscure.

The Museum of Ignorance.

Kavendish blinked to raise an enquiry with his Sensory Nexus Mask. But there was no response. Was this a mystery?

He wasn't sure he had ever experienced a mystery before. He was certainly not a seeker of wisdom. No one went in for that kind of thing. Many years ago, before the time of the Complete Theorem, before the Great Equilibrium, people had had awkward 'opinions': they argued about everything, from economics to physics, philosophy to politics. No one knew the best way to do anything. There was discord, disagreement and unhappiness. But now, thank the A.B.A.C.U.S., that dark time was hundreds of years in the past. Now all was known. All was in balance. It was the way of things. Scientists had become historians, before themselves becoming history, and, as we all know, history finished years ago.

The dot winked on the map. The acorn fading in and out.

The Museum of Ignorance.

These obsolete hieroglyphics. This primitive map. What were these awkward anomalies? Why hadn't they been dissolved like all the other useless things? The dot pulsed on the map. The dot like a seed. The dot like a kernel ready to sprout.

Who will carry the weight of the golden seed to the door?
Who will turn the key to the vault under the floor?
Who will find the prize hidden deep within the tomb?
Who will see the lights glinting in the gloom?

His Environment Wall was near, reliable, fun, easy. He had devices to try, positions to adopt, cocktails to taste. The dot winked. Kavendish followed the path.

He stepped onto the pneumatic pavement and made for one of the riverside's many elegant crossings. As he glided along, he felt as if he was flowing through the city like the ancient river. When he reached the crossing, he engaged the interchange and stepped onto the bridge's moving pathway. The glass bridge sang as the wind caught its delicate fronds. The river magnificent in perpetual sunshine. Now the unexpected squall had passed, London was all shiny, a sumptuous paradise of architectural excess: glass-fronted apartments, baroque towers and mock Tudor maisonettes nestled next to brutalist concrete cubes and quasi-medieval artisan huts. The A.B.A.C.U.S. indulged and the cyborg tradesmen built. The dull cramp of overindulgence settled on the city. The surfeit of desire. Dulling the appetites of the perpetually bored occupants. Pleasure cafés, arousal points, the love theatre; a schizophrenic vista of decadent brilliance. All flamboyantly constructed. All mainly empty.

As he sped along, a flock of green sea parrots darted over the water. They had been bred to compliment the azure tones of the purified river. As they swooped over the surface they appeared as polished emeralds cast by some unseen hand. Perhaps one last throw in an intangible game of chance. Making their elegant progress up the river's marble embankment they joined a host of other colourful birds that were darting to and fro amongst the exotic plants that covered the riverbanks. Here and there one could spot curious creatures who had been designed to frolic amongst the boughs for the amusement of the dissolute citizenry. Monkeys with brightly coloured backsides, sloths of unfathomable charm, fangless snakes, Antipodean marsupials stoned on eucalyptus, lobotomised bears, toothless big cats bred to be small cats, here a warm-weather penguin, there a polar camel. The parrots added their call to the chaos. The plants shared the same unfettered exoticism as the animals. They had been selected in accordance to the contradictory whims of the city's inhabitants. A ghastly explosion of conflicting colours and overpowering odours emanated from the foliage as it erupted along the embankment. This riotous garden was tended to by Service Citizens dressed in the plain green smocks of their class. Their dreary costumes rendered them virtually invisible amongst the exuberant shrubs. These were the hidden drones of the city, resigned to a life of comfortable drabness. Pruning the arbours of the detached populace.

> *Under the thin city soil the filaments creep and crawl.*
> *Through stone and filth 'neath battlements, palisade*
>   *and wall.*
> *The acorn and the dandelion, the bird's foot and the dock.*
> *They come to break the fetters and the master's bitter lock.*
>
> *They come to free the captives, the tortured and the lost.*
> *They come to slay the gaolers, mad with tyranny and lust.*
> *Through cracks and jagged injuries, in stems, in roots,*
>   *in flowers.*
> *They come to bear grim witness in the gaoler's final hours.*

Kavendish left the bridge and headed along the edge of the park. Silently gliding. Following the path of the blinking seed. The map flattened the landscape, deadening the psychic geography of the city. It exulted only the destination. The single relevant terminus. Diversions popped up along the way. The 'Bulging Man' ecstasy café; a superb venue. Kavendish had a very enjoyable encounter there recently. The Service Citizen had received a great boost to their Utility Quotient. He glanced in as he passed. No time to stop. Buildings of every shape and size drifted by. They cast bizarre dark shapes on the spotless pavements, like figures in a shadow play.

As his journey continued, so his Kudos Quotient grew. Like the spreading roots under the pavement. Kudos. The only thing of value in a world where everything was free. It was the contentment index, an equation for a successful world. It was the language of performance, the language of efficiency. It stood for the maintenance of the Great Equilibrium, a public affirmation of a perfect society. Anything that resisted quantification simply ceased to be. For in the time of the A.B.A.C.U.S. there was but one crime: the crime of unhappiness, the only possible act of sedition.

Happiness is everything.

The park was behind him now. Great stone monoliths from a less-amusing time dominated the riverside. There was none of the random jumble of architecture that was to be found elsewhere. Kavendish had now entered the ancient heart of the city; it had been frozen in time. A mummified nostalgia platz. Kavendish passed an old statue, green with age, its head permanently caked with the shit of the city's birds. No amount of scrubbing by droid or man could keep it clean. There were many similar statues dotted around this part of the metropolis. Some were carved from stone, others forged from bronze. All frozen in time in the midst of some dramatic action: pointing towards an imagined future or waving swords on the backs of horses. Their deeds were long forgotten. Kavendish glided by the Gothic frontage of a particularly ancient pile. Something to do with politics or some such decrepit notion. His friend Quintella had a dildo that was shaped to resemble the imposing clock tower; its tiny bell would ring as she climaxed. So important to preserve the past.

Kavendish continued to glide through the city, turning away from the river now and into yet another lattice of mismatched buildings. He followed the blinking seed. Though in truth, he simply let it pull him through the streets. Like a leaf looking for light in a crowded bed, he wriggled through the byways of the city of Ra. The quiet buildings towered above him, reflecting the permanent daylight off their pristine shells. Behind the glass the Citizens fucked. They drank and ate. They puked and shat.

Happiness is everything.

Kavendish raised his eyes to the summit of a great stone monolith carved in the perfect likeness of a great cock and balls. Veins full and ripe. He laughed as the seed pulled him on. His Kudos Quotient surged. The Nexus was happy.

Happiness is everything.

He paused at the Brompton Road to allow a noisy pack of hunters to pass. He was pleased to see that the rain had not put them off either. He knew them all, of course. He knew most of the people in the city. But those who stepped outside tended to be drawn to one another, like peculiar magnets. Kavendish admired their attire: they were clad in the traditional scarlet. Hard hats, knee-length boots, rubber shorts. They hallooed as they galloped by. Kavendish touched the brim of his fedora in reply, beaming and shouting his greetings. As the tooting of the huntsmen's horns faded into the distance, he found his eyes losing focus. The acorn sigil now swelled and began to sprout. The screen of his mask faded into the distance. For a few brief seconds, the confusing skyline of the city was replaced. The pneumatic pavement was the track of an ancient railway. Kavendish was a passenger clunking along its rusty girders. He pulled into a station. It was familiar to him. It was home. Caxton Wood. He was inside the calm interior of a library. The ground on which he stood was no longer the pavement of London, but instead, the herringboned lattice of a parquet floor. He had the impression of being inside a country cottage. He could see a pleasant meadow from out of its lead-lined window. An old clock tick-tocked in the corner. His eyes were drawn to some well-appointed shelves. They were full of leather-bound volumes. These must be books. He reached out and took one from the shelf. The clock struck. The whiplash of a switch stung his cheek. Kavendish spun around to confront his assailant. He was under the tree. Palms pressed against its gnarled trunk. The black vortex of roots spun. Whispering, broken network chatter, moans and pillow talk from a variety of sex parties. A Discipline Drone hovering. His barber's pre-programmed synthetic gossip module. A gathering of hooded figures chanting incantations in the night. A gallows. A girl. A courtroom. A mob. Drug talk, fuck talk. A.B.A.C.U.S. talk. Kavendish's head clattered and rang like an old telephone. The clock struck again. He was back on the pavement, looking through the prism of his Sensory Nexus Mask. The whole episode lasted no more than a few seconds, so fast in fact that he doubted it had even occurred. The map flickered back into focus. The acorn flashed.

On his screen the seedling was now a sapling. The roots began to travel along the streets of the map. Kavendish followed. Train track. Clunking over points. Click. Clack. Stations flashing past. The hanging baskets of Caxton Wood. Alight here. The sapling swelled. Its juvenile branches swayed like foals on untested hooves. They clattered at the surface of his screen, trying to break through the translucent skin. To pierce his eyes with their woody fingers, or perhaps to point the way? Soon the branches were so thick he couldn't see beyond them. He became lost in a forest that was wrapped around his face. The London that he knew seemed to dissolve to nothing. Images from a forgotten past. Images from an uncertain future.

Under the thin city soil the filaments creep and crawl.
Through stone and filth 'neath battlements, palisade
*   and wall.*
The acorn and the dandelion, the bird's foot and the dock.
They come to break the fetters and the master's bitter lock.

They come to free the captives, the tortured and the lost.
They come to slay the gaolers mad with tyranny and lust.
Through cracks and jagged injuries, in stems, in roots,
*   in flowers.*
They come to bear grim witness in the gaoler's final hours.

Hallucinations occupied his mind and spun him up into the air. He was far above the forest. He could see the city, but it was not his city. It was a grimy, busy place, full of conflict and fumes. Kavendish was repulsed, but he couldn't break free. These bleak visions offended him. He was floating above a vile version of his beloved London. Millions of Citizens teeming on its litter-strewn pavements. There was no space, no grace; it was an unhappy place. The sight made Kavendish sick. He fought to keep his stomach in its place. Now he was diving down out of the sky towards the tangled web of a forest. Kavendish tried to slow his fall. He flapped his useless arms, trying to stay aloft. The ground was coming up fast. Kavendish shut his eyes tight. Braced for impact. The impact never came. Instead, he found himself in front of a single structure, standing all alone at the end of a broad tree-lined boulevard. He recognised it immediately.

The Museum of Ignorance.

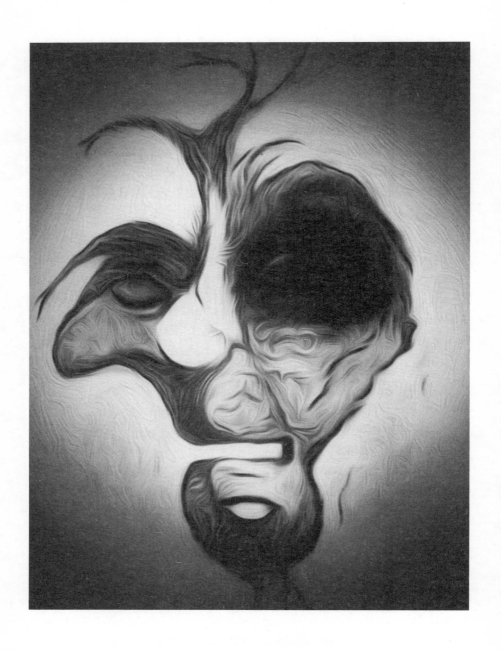

The Queen Anne Chair

In the folds where all worlds touch. At the intersection of
tessellating planes. The jagged edge of a wound is exposed.
In this wound a dark magic broods. Born from the discharge
and the dislocation of joints. It seeks for reasons for its
painful cuts. The bleeding weal where the cruel rope eats
into its back, reminds it of its doom. It asks why it alone
carries the burden. That terrible knowledge. Ripped from the
heart of the Tangle. As a weapon. As a gift. As a right. As a
curse. Once the dark magic was without form. It seduced and
occupied the child creatures of the forest. It lent them armour
for their war on creation. Confidence. Ignorance. Blindness.
Will. The children flourished and died. Alone. Their souls fed
the wound, and its dark magic grew. But it needed names.
It longed for shape and purpose. It needed blood and skin.
It needed sacrifice. Erwan's scythe swept in those first
moments. When the first number was counted. When the first
second ticked. Carry the weight of the curse. Until there are
no seconds left to count.

The Bull was busy for a Wednesday. Tobias Lean had put
a few quid behind the bar for his sister-in-law's wake. Cut
sandwiches. Modest spread. There had been a reasonable
turnout for the funeral; she was a popular woman. Her
brother-in-law was less popular. But he was paying, so why
not. It's what she would have wanted. The lounge bar was
buzzing with gossip, shaking heads and impromptu eulogies.

They were two deep at the bar already. The landlady had
called in help. Caxton youth. Hilda Wilton. Last days of
school. Don't touch the taps, I'll lose my licence. Hilda picked
up plates. Hilda picked up pots. Hilda sidestepped drunken
hands. She deposited a tray of empty tankards at the end
of the bar. Foam scum and lip spit. The landlady pushed a
frothing pint towards her, pointing at the old high-backed
Queen Anne chair that lived in permanent residence in front
of the fire. Hilda raised an eyebrow and exhaled. Erwan's
pint. Never leave him with an empty glass. It was unlucky.
That was the lore around these parts. Like the ravens at the
Tower. Hilda found his presence unnerving, and she always
deposited his drink and left as quickly and politely as she
could. 'Here you go.' Never catch his eye. He'll have your soul.
That's what they said.

Erwan was a fixture, like a beam or a door. The landlady
had inherited him, just as the owner before her had done.
Before the Bull there was the Packhorse. Before the
Packhorse, the Cup. Before the Cup, Ad Cucu. Then the
hut, the fire, the cave. Erwan stared into the flames, sipping
his ale. Waiting. Waiting. No one ever saw him come in,
no one ever saw him leave. Occasionally he would speak.
He told stories. Long, rambling, barely comprehensible
tales. Sometimes in a recognisable dialect. More often not.
The Caxton youth liked to try and take the piss out of him
when they were drunk. It was a 'rite of passage' type of
arrangement. But few found it funny when he turned his
eye on you.

Eyes without sight, vision or focus. No lens or pupil,
motion or locus.

By the evening the sandwiches had curled and the quiche
was but a distant memory. Beer flowed and tears were shed.
Many returned to their homes. Dedicated drinkers stayed.
The wisdom of the saloon bar philosopher began to be heard
above the clack of billiard balls. Debates about politics. Rights
and wrongs. What does it all mean, eh? Young woman like
that, taken so young. That poor boy. How can there be a
God that allows such things to happen? A group of scholars
searching for enlightenment picked up their pints and bags of
scratchings and moved instinctively towards the fire. Erwan
stared at the flames as the hungry fire ate through the logs.
He sat at the junction of many interlocking planes. Waiting.
Waiting. The sound of a glass placed on a table drew him to
a particular place, a particular time. A young woman was
retreating having just placed a foaming mug of beer by his
hand. He knew her. Or would know her. Or had at one time
known her. For a split second she caught his eye. 'Here you
go, Erwan.' He saw the blood yet to come. The pincers and the
thread. She saw it too. Their paths intersected as the vision
was shared. She shuddered, unable to escape, held by his
gaze. But it was not yet time. There were trials still to pass.
He nodded his thanks, as was customary in this world. Hilda
hurried away carrying his empty glass.

'Erwan will know, won't he? I reckon he's cleverer than
he looks. Has us all at it with his mad tales. Gets free fucking
drinks all day so he's certainly not daft. Here, Erwan, Barry
wants to know . . .'

Beer fumes and shots. The miasma of public house
summits. Erwan was only dimly aware of their ridiculous
chatter. They often came seeking his council. For the harvest.
For the pox. For wealth, health and good fortune. He told
them stories they didn't understand, for they had long

ceased to speak the language of the Tangle. These dolts were not different. They served an entity they could not name. Who dwelt in their doubts? Who dwelt in their fears? A Mesmeriser. One of the clodhoppers stumbled. Beer was spilled. The amber stream flowed slowly across the floor until it reached Erwan's swaddled feet. The ale soaked into the cloth. For a moment there was silence in the Bull. Hilda put down her tray of empty glasses. The landlady froze at the optics. The drunken men stared at the tragic pool. Erwan turned his black eyes on them and spoke.

At the summit of a dais made of broken glass and razor blades sits a rough metal throne, on the throne a twisted figure shifts its skeletal frame. In its hands it holds a dark globe. The entity is known by many names, in many places and times, and yet you do not know him. It is the deceiver, the sower of confusion, the pitiless will, the father of desire, the mother of longing. In your world it is known by a name of human tongue. The Mesmeriser. The magic in the cut. The spell woven from blood. The Mesmeriser waves a taloned hand over the globe. An image emerges from the mist, revealing a lonely speck floating in the void. You call this speck the sun. It is the only sun in this universe. The solitary source of light in the blank emptiness of space. You are alone. Now the cut grows wider. The sebum and the sap. The sacrifice is called. The Mesmeriser will tap the surface of the globe with its metal claw. Can you see it? Another speck, smaller than before. Hugging the sun like a new-born chick huddled up to an incubator's lightbulb. Do you see it now? This was your home before the war in heaven.

The Bull public house is frozen. Its occupants still. Unblinking. Static. Only Hilda moves. Only Hilda hears. She will forget all that has been said. For now. The amber stream reverses into the glass. Erwan raises his wrinkled hand. His words cascade from his mouth.

Now the dark black pellet is near. See the ancient sarcophagus. This is the weapon you requested. You have paid well for it. The Mesmeriser utters an incantation that sounds like a thousand penitent souls crying at once. The sarcophagus opens and a bright rainbow of smoke drifts out. Can you see? Can you see the smoke?

The fire in the grate is held by his stare. It does not move. It does not burn.

Look at the smoke. Look as it fills the darkness of the globe. The speck comes alive, its dull surface transformed into a swirl of colour. Can you see? Can you see? Faces bulge from the surface, melting and morphing before being sucked back inside. Flames flicker in its obsidian heart. It begins to spin at a terrifying speed, colours shooting around the interior before blending together

to form an intense anti-colour of infinite darkness. The
Mesmeriser waves its talon over the globe again. The
spinning stops in an instant. A smile forms in the blank
cavity of its mouth. The Mesmeriser is pleased. The tiny
speck has changed. Millions of years of slow, unfolding
evolution condensed into a single moment. Can you see?
Can you see? This is you. This is your home. You are
alone. This is what you asked for, is it not? This palace
of infinite happiness. Where the sun never sets, and the
darkness never comes. Look into the fire. Now can you see
the name of your lord?

Hilda threw down a paper towel on the bitter lake of beer.
It darkened the weave like the blood from a gunshot wound.
She placed a fresh mug of ale on the table by Erwan's wizened
hand. Never leave him with an empty glass. It was unlucky.
That's what they said. His black eyes stared into the fire as
the flames began to lick over the logs again.

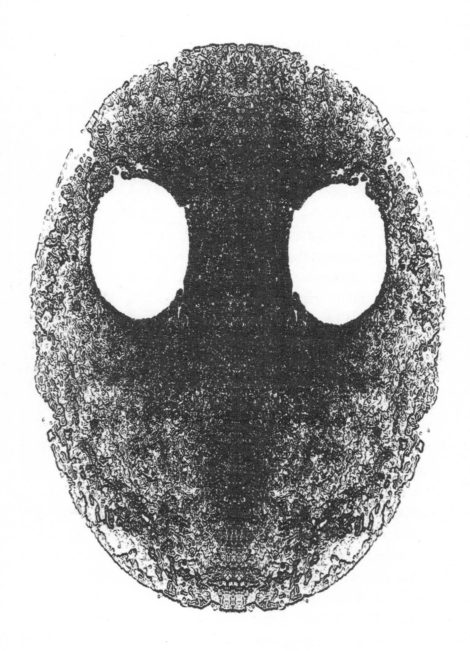

The Museum of Ignorance

Grey slabs of stone buttressed dirty grey windows. Grime
seemed to cling to it all like a dust cloth. Huge pillars led up
to a roof made from some undefinable amalgam, tarnished
and pitted by age and the elements. Under the roof was
a carved frieze. Effigies had been hacked into the stone.
Signifiers of a grubby era. A time when an ignorant populace
had attempted to grasp its place in a lifeless universe.
Kavendish approached with caution. As he drew nearer, he
made out the figures of human beings. Not Aristoians, but
human nonetheless. Around the entrance to the museum
a small team of low-grade Service Citizens were sweeping
the paths, clearing the way for the crowds that would never
come. They were nestling somewhere near the bottom of the
alphabet, maybe R or S. Bowed and silent they continued
their routine. He thought their Utility Quotient must be
quite low. Surely these Service Citizens would soon be re-
designated, or simply dissolved? This kind of difficult problem
was for the A.B.A.C.U.S. to decide. He passed by the Service
Citizens. He ignored them, they ignored him. A Discipline
Drone hovered above, quietly policing the balance.

Inside, no one laughed, no one fucked. The dank foyer
of the museum was illuminated by an unenthusiastic, dull
orange glow that was struggling out of some ancient light
fittings. A few faded portraits of long-forgotten pioneers hung
on the walls. An engine of uncertain purpose occupied a plinth

at its centre. Kavendish shrugged. It all looked cumbersome and useless. The air was musty and unused. More like a tomb than an attraction. His feet disturbed deposits of dust that sprang up from the floor as he walked. The sound of his heels clicking echoed around the room. Everything was grey. The vaulted ceiling was high, with elaborate cornices and panels, the images painted on them now faded beyond recognition. Gothic pillars held the ceiling in place. It felt like the interior of a cathedral. There was an air of sturdy permanence in the carved stonework, confidence in its sweeping arches. Just like the edifices of the A.B.A.C.U.S., it spoke of certainty. The foyer swept under an impressive arch into a large hall that was accessed via some worn-out stone steps. The hall was filled with a variety of dusty exhibits.

Kavendish made his way down the steps and entered the exhibition hall. His eyes were drawn to a tall, tubular, metal vehicle. It had a living unit crudely bolted to the top. It seemed to be a significant exhibit judging by its prominent position in the hall. Kavendish approached with only the faintest hint of interest. A series of ladders provided access to the summit. Kavendish climbed. At the summit he found a dull, grey gantry. He stepped around the living unit until he found a grimy porthole. He wiped the glass and peered into the dark interior of the capsule. Inside there were bodies. Inert and static. Cracked plastic dummies. They were sat mutely at the controls, with great bulbous helmets on their heads like filthy fishbowls. Kavendish was puzzled, but bored. These dead things.

In the seams of the cut as the sutures dissolve
The filament weaves as the tempest revolves
Under the thin city soil the filaments creep

Through concrete and stone while the prisoner sleeps
The acorn and oak, the dandelion seed
The trunk and the bark, the stem of the weed
They come to free captives lousy with lust
They come to find secrets hidden in dust.

He descended the steps. He located the relevant sign. He wiped away a thick layer of grime to reveal the information underneath.

Space Capsule

His face creased into perplexed folds. Space was a dead useless place, a vast ocean of nothing. The Museum of Ignorance appeared to house hundreds of similarly pointless artefacts, the relics of a more unfortunate time. There were trinkets pillaged at the point of a bayonet. Ugly, brutal, barbaric things that made Kavendish wince. A primitive motorised vehicle. Why would anyone want to go anywhere? A pre-A.B.A.C.U.S. computer. Inefficient. Incorrect. Why were they here, these dull instruments? Kavendish wondered why they hadn't been dissolved long ago. That was the way of things.

The Great Equilibrium

The sound of his footsteps ricocheted around the shrine of futile things. All around him, shadows hid spores that settled on the barren materials. Hoping to gain the slightest purchase in the gloom. Further down the hall he came across more cracked dummies. They were bent over an open wound filled with plastic gore. They held knives and saws. They wore masks and gowns. One of the cracked dummies had lost an eye to decay. She was consulting some type of medical appliance. A plastic patient was lying on the surgeon's table. The patient would always lie there. No hope of recovery. No chance to walk again or spend quiet hours in the arms of its loving plastic family. He thanked the A.B.A.C.U.S. for his 'How Are You?' device. All these cabinets full of archaic contraptions. The fetishes of ignorance.

The Great Equilibrium

The hall narrowed into a passageway that was lined with noticeboards full of informative nonsense. Kavendish wandered past, barely registering. He began to move down lanes, paths, byways, snickets. The fusty interior of the museum came apart as he stepped. He was in the park. He was heavily stoned. He was slumped against the trunk of a gnarled tree, the same unruly tree he had encountered earlier. The tree loomed over him. From out of the branches a figure muttered, a conclave of hooded acolytes chanted, a Discipline Drone hovered. Everything was out of focus. He caught sight of something from the corner of his eye. There was an unmistakable shadow of a figure sat at the end of the echoing corridor. Kavendish was drawn towards it like a hapless insect sucked into a whirlpool. The figure sat at the end of the vortex. Beckoning him. Kavendish spiralled out of the building and into the sky. The dark empty sky. He travelled towards a dimly flickering light that hovered on the edge of space. As he drew nearer the light, it became brighter. Too bright to look at. Like a thousand suns focused to a point of unbearable intensity. Kavendish raised his hands to shield his eyes, fearing he would go blind.

Eyes without sight, vision or focus. No lens or pupil,
motion or locus.

He was back in the corridor. The dust of the museum dancing
in the weak shafts thrown by the pendulous light fittings.
A wizened administrator sat dozing at a tired-looking
information kiosk. An old man. Kavendish had never seen an
old Service Citizen before. In fact, he wasn't sure he had ever
met anyone old. Service Citizens were young and vigorous.
Useful. Useless things must be dissolved. It was the way of
things. Demand must be managed if desires are to be satisfied.

The old man seemed completely unaware of Kavendish.
He remained motionless. Still. Static. For a few moments
Kavendish thought he might be an exhibit. Another cracked
dummy enacting another pointless task. Closer. Closer. He
was so close now he could smell his musty odour. The scent of
soil and decay. Closer. Closer. Inches from his back. His breath
ruffled the hairs on the old man's neck. The fine follicles
waved in the breeze of breath and then settled back gently
into the folds of his ancient skin. The old man turned around
slowly, rising like an uncoiling snake. As the old man settled
on his feet, he enacted a mocking bow. He adjusted his cap on
his balding pate. Two plumes of curly orange hair stuck out
from the sides of his head. He looked like an old-fashioned
clown. His uniform was tatty, held together with mismatched
patches. His shoes were not a pair; they didn't even seem to
be the same size. He fixed Kavendish with a look that was
both amused and dismissive.

'Are you lost?'

A smile seeped out of the old man's skin, settling into a
grotesque crescent. He drew closer to Kavendish. Walking
around him, sizing him up, as if he was examining a newly

found artefact. The old man produced a monocle from his pocket, placing it over his left eye, then his right. He looked Kavendish up and down. The monocle had no lens in it.

'Are you a scholar? You have the look of a scholar, if you don't mind me saying so. A wise face. Is it your own?'

The old man drew his face up to Kavendish's. His eyes were black. Bottomless pits. Kavendish could smell his breath. It smelled of honey. The old man tapped a gnarled finger on the translucent screen of Kavendish's Sensory Nexus Mask.

'Do I know you? I feel we have met before. Or will meet soon. I forget.'

The old man tapped his forehead with a bent finger. His head moved from side to side as if his face was being slapped by an invisible hand. His tongue dangling out like a strangled man. Eyes crossed. A resident of Bedlam. His face snapped back, suddenly serious. Riddled with reflection. He looked younger. Closer to Kavendish's age than the wizened, bent creature he had first met. His black eyes sparkled.

'Are the artefacts not to your taste? You look disappointed. Is this not what you were expecting?'

Kavendish tried to form words but his mouth was a jumble of roots. His tongue was a trunk, pitted and bent. The old man. Now a young man. Tilted his head in curiosity. The clown entity thrust out its arm. Like a tentacle covered in suckers. The arm wrapped around the roots. The arm tugged and pulled. The roots began to separate from the soil. Blood filled his mouth. Kavendish spat out gore and teeth. The clown entity's eyes bored into him. You shall not pass. You shall not pass. The clown spun him around. The clown spun too.

'I'm a scholar and a dancer, once a famous romancer! Quite the twinkletoes in days gone by. All the people said so.'

A medieval jester. A fool. A joker. You shall not pass. You shall not pass. The A.B.A.C.U.S., the gossip module, the Sensory Nexus mask. The Discipline Drone. You shall not pass. The roots resurged. The roots began to twine around the entity's tentacle. Suffocating and cutting. The roots wrapped the suckers tight. The arm was cut, falling to the dusty floor of the museum. The old man merely looked puzzled as his body evaporated into the murky air. As he dissolved, he tipped his hat theatrically, leaving a vague outline of a final bow hanging in the gloom.

The corridor was empty. The information kiosk was empty too. A Cleaning Drone hovered past.

In the seams of the cut as the sutures dissolve
The filament weaves as the tempest revolves
Under the thin city soil the filaments creep
Through concrete and stone while the prisoner sleeps
The acorn and oak, the dandelion seed
The trunk and the bark, the stem of the weed
They come to free captives lousy with lust
They come to find secrets hidden in dust.

Kavendish stood in a glum trance. He was facing a drab room filled with dusty shelves. They were stuffed with endless rows of files and folios. The acorn had led him here. Into this pleasureless palace of ignorance. It was no fun, no fun at all. Difficult situations call for reliable solutions. Kavendish felt inside his pockets. His fingers lighted on the smooth surface of a stimulant vial. Perfect. He needed something speedy to focus his mind. He pulled the vial free of his pocket. But it was slippery, and it slid through his fingers. The capsule rolled across the old wooden floor and disappeared under one of the shelves.

He sank to his knees in the manner of a supplicant, pressing his cheek to the floor. He could see it glinting in the gloom. Kavendish attempted to reach under the shelf to pull it free. It remained out of reach. He activated the torch on his mask. The light lit up the shadows. The vial was wedged in the crack of a door. A door. Hidden behind a shelf. There was a gap between the shelves and the wall that was just wide enough for Kavendish's modest frame to squeeze through. He shuffled through the crack until he reached the door. He manged to free his hands. He located the door handle. He pushed and grunted. The door creaked open. The vial, now free of the door, clinked down the stairs and disappeared into the dark. Kavendish instinctively recoiled. Darkness. As unfamiliar as the wastes of space. As rare as a rainstorm in summer. Darkness. It was ugly and repulsive. But the need for speed was too great. He stepped inside. The cold stone stairwell stank of ancient damp and was decorated with a complex latticework of cobwebs that the spiders had abandoned years ago.

His torch lit up the stairwell as he revolved like a lighthouse lamp. He took in the Stygian surroundings. He brushed away the cobwebs, blowing and spitting as they collided with his mouth. The torch played across the drab steps. He spotted the vial in the middle of an old, grey flagstone. Kavendish headed down the steps, keeping his torch fixed on the vial, trying to blot out the darkness that pressed all around him. He stooped to collect it. He examined the delicate white powder, it's clear crystalline shine standing testament to its potency. Kavendish smiled. His torch lit up the room beyond the vial. As above, so below. This room was also full of shelves packed with grimy boxes. Kavendish had no desire to investigate these dull containers. He turned around and began to climb the stairs, eager for daylight and drugs. But his feet were fixed to the flagstones. As he tried to lift his feet from their imperceptible bonds, the staircase flattened out into an endless tunnel. The floor changed from cold stone to a viscous bitumen that began to suck his feet under the surface. Branches, like the arms of barbaric wrestlers, burst out of the walls, entwining their sinewy limbs around his torso. Tiny tendrils sprouted from the bark and began to crawl across his face. They insinuated themselves into his eyes. He could feel them, inching through his nerves. Entering his brain. Altering the pathways. Kavendish saw himself as a child in the hatcheries. As an old man. He saw his friends from the Nexus. Fucking, sucking, pointing. They were surging around him like phantoms, swirling up into the black void. The eddies from their frantic reel spun Kavendish around. His feet made a sickening sound in the glutinous river as he turned. The nightmarish figures swirled. Pointing, pointing, pointing. Then they were gone. Kavendish was facing the vault once again.

He located a panel of old brass switches. Tarnished and filthy. He flicked them on. The bulbs sputtered into life, emitting the same dull glow as the museum above. Now he could see the entire room. It had an arched ceiling like a wine cellar constructed from brick. It was full of metal shelves identical to the ones in the room above. There were no tables, no chairs; this was clearly a forgotten storeroom.

Kavendish explored the shelves. Digging in dirt and dust. Small tornados of crumbling fragments mushroomed as he removed each box from its shelf. He produced an elaborately monogrammed handkerchief to wipe away the layer of grime that had gathered on his mask. Why he searched he could not say. Curiosity was not a feature of modern life. But something lurked in the archive. Something hidden.

SCIENCE MINISTRY CAT NO – 0006754

CONTENTS – photographs, graphite pencil sketches, field
notes, biographical ephemera
LOCATION – Caxton Wood. Sector 9
A.B.A.C.U.S. CONCLUSION – irrelevant/dangerous . . .
destruction recommended

Kavendish lifted the box off the shelf, leaving a dark rectangle
in the dust. It was tightly sealed with bright yellow and black
tape. DESTRUCTION RECOMMENDED. The faintest feeling
of recognition flickered. The knot. The root. He clasped the
box close to his chest, cradling it like a new-born child. He left
the vault and headed for the surface.

Kavendish walked around the table like a wary animal
circling a waterhole. He had placed his find at its centre. The
box was present. The box was now. A faint hum hovered in
the room. He moved closer to the box. Pulled in like a fish
caught on a line. Filthy nails on wizened fingers. Gnarled
digits jutting from decaying hands. The clown entity's face.
Lift the lid. Look inside. Voices whispered. Lift the lid. Look
inside. His hands felt for edges. His fingers bent round the
crease. The lid began to rise.

The box was deep. Deeper than a well. It was empty. Not
simply an absence of objects but a pure anti-object. A void.
Kavendish was disappointed. The pleasure café. The narc
parlour. These were the places where useful work could be
done, and where true discoveries could be made. He picked up
the battered lid and went to replace it.

Who will carry the weight of the golden seed to the door?
Who will turn the key to the vault under the floor?

Who will find the prize hidden deep within the tomb?
Who will see the lights glinting in the gloom?

The hum changed pitch, up and down the scale like a child let loose on a synthesiser. The light in the museum grew darker and darker. Night was approaching. Dread night. Dread darkness. Kavendish needed light to live. Like an orchid in a hothouse, he could only flourish when the sun shone. Night was a curse. Sleep was a curse. His eyes swizzled to catch a beam. The box was glowing. Holy sun. Holy light. He looked into the box. Patterns were forming, slowly becoming solid. Objects. Things. Artefacts. He looked down into the box. The light in the room reverted to the dull glow of ancient lamps. The hum settled into silence. The box was still a box. But now it was full.

Inside there was an assortment of papers and documents. Some printed with official stamps and letterheads, others handwritten in an almost childlike scrawl. There were graphs and tables, assorted lists and annotations. There were photographs too. A face stared out from the stack. A woman's face. His face. Aquiline and handsome. Dark hair cut into a rough bob. Clothing functional but worn with flare. Kavendish picked it up and studied it. Something in the curve of her mouth, the tone of her eyes, the shape of her limbs. It was an undefinable reflection. A feeling of connection across time. Her figure again, this time standing with a ragged-looking man. Long beard. Unkempt. A hint of wild eyes behind thick spectacles. They appeared to be on an expedition. They were stood around a makeshift bivouac. Canvas carelessly hung from trees, a pile of scientific gadgets at their feet. They were smiling. In the foreground was the handsome woman. She was holding the camera at arm's length, attempting to capture the moment for posterity. The picture disturbed him. It was the sky. The sky was dark. Dark. But not black. There was light. The blankness of the vault was alive with tiny luminous pinpricks, dotting the inky darkness like sequins on velvet. A thousand glimmering particles cast into the sky by the hand of some careless god. Kavendish had never seen the stars before. No one had. The dark was where useless things dwelt. Where time was wasted and pleasure forgotten. The dark must be dissolved like all the other useless things. Her face. His face. This woman. She occupied a very different dimension to him. A dimension of darkness. A dimension of contrast and change. Her face. His face.

Who will carry the weight of the golden seed to the door?
Who will turn the key to the vault under the floor?
Who will find the prize hidden deep within the tomb?
Who will see the lights glinting in the gloom?

He pulled out more documents from the box, spreading them out on the table. They were meaningless. Scribbles and charts. Another picture. Scrolls and accolades. Gowns. Awards. Professor Helen Cavendish, chair of Psychic Ecology, Caxton University. His face. Her face. She was a scholar. Someone with something to learn. Doubts rose like a spring tide. Inside the Great Equilibrium, a fault line grew. He looked into the box. Unfamiliar feelings of curiosity spread inside his nodes. He removed more documents. Scribbles and charts. Ignorant signs and markers. At the bottom of the stack was an obsidian shape. Kavendish recoiled. The clown entity's face. You shall not pass. You shall not pass. The hum in the room gathered its volume again. He would have run if he could, but there was nowhere to run to. There was only the box. The box and Kavendish. He placed his arms reluctantly into the cauldron and pulled out the final artefact.

It was a book. Reeking of soil and decay. The cover was thick and unyielding. Constructed from tree bark. On the front was a knot of thorny branches cut into the wood. Above the carving were words. Barbaric, unruly, useless words. Drawn by a faltering hand.

The Tangle.

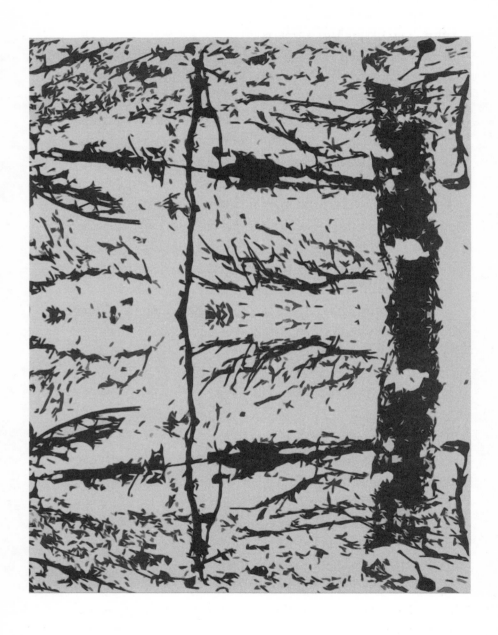

In Caxton Wood

In Caxton Wood the branches rattled together in warning
as the swarm approached. Their torches flickered through
the thicket. Muffled cries and angry shouts. A grim echo
of their impotent fury. In their hands they carried cudgels,
pitchforks, shovels, broken chair legs and a variety of other
ersatz armaments. Objects repurposed from everyday use to
bludgeon and beat the enemy. They were seeking scapegoats
and sacrifices to appease their vengeful god. In a forest of
obstinate indifference.

As the rain poured through the crown of trees, Elizabeth
Duncan trembled under the spreading oak. There was
nowhere left to run. She had been selected as an offering
to the flames. A solemn oblation to insure against another
poor harvest and the return of the pox. The villagers did not
care for her kind, or any other outsider. She lived alone in
the woods; it wasn't right. So as the first sores of the plague
began to weep and the stock market crashed, the villagers
looked for reasons for their bad luck. Some pointed towards
the woods and the humble cottage of Elizabeth Duncan.
She must be a witch. A concubine of the devil. Sent to bring
down ill fortune on the people. Her appearance counted
against her: a stooping frame that was bent from a lifetime
of misuse. She had a random cluster of blood vessels on her
face. These were the marks that set her apart. These were
the unmistakeable signs of the devil. Scars left over from

their unholy congress. The blemished must carry the weight of their sin.

Jeremiah Cavendish urged the mob on. His sombre clothing matched his puritan beliefs and rendered him virtually invisible in the darkness of the wood. Only the dull glow of his torch lit his righteous grimace. He was the law. County magistrate, managing director, diligent administrator, temporal and spiritual. He abhorred the criminal, the sinful and the blasphemous. He sought out the pickpockets, the thieves, the traitors, the rogue traders, the witches. He applied techniques of persuasion, learned in the trenches where the rules of engagement were forgotten. He never failed to get the confessions he sought and would apply the maximum penalty on every occasion. Death. The purifying flames, the snap of the noose, the salvation of the axe and sword. Hell would soon overflow with the worthless. Only then could the elect flourish.

'Come, my brothers and sisters! Forward my brethren, we have work to do.'

There was always work to do. Out here where no train ever stopped. A dot on the map on the way to somewhere else. A cry echoed around the density of the wood.

'Here, here, here!'

They came upon Elizabeth Duncan under the spreading oak. They snarled and slavered. Surrounding her with a ring of righteous hate.

'Seize her! Hold her fast!'

Jeremiah Cavendish pushed his way through the company to where two farmhands were holding the weeping figure of Elizabeth Duncan. They grasped her thin arms with unkindness, causing bruises to rise on her broken skin. There was no need for such force. She was defeated and without the resources to resist. But the men feared the power of demons. They may yet rise and surge through her bedraggled frame, lifting her into the endless mystery of night, away from the pyre or the hungry noose. Jeremiah Cavendish feared it too. He slapped the captive hard. The power of the spirit fortifying his palms. The sting of flesh on flesh aroused the magistrate. The fire of punishment tingled on his palm like stigmata. The work was good. He slapped her face again. Her head turned violently. Her thin neck unable to offer any resistance. Blood bloomed from her cuts and stained the forest floor.

'Now we have you, whore of Satan! Prepare the fire! Build the pyre! Quickly now, quickly!'

The burly men tied Elizabeth to the trunk of the oak. The rope bit. Rough twine binding her with an excessive thickness. Three members of the local constabulary stood guard, shotguns held menacingly at her face. Elizabeth's fingers pressed against the bark of the tree. The bark seemed to yield to her touch as if it was trying to offer her some comfort. Her fingers sank into its ridges. She longed to sink into those ridges too. To hide in the cracks until the ignorant tide had ebbed. She was not of the Tangle, though she was sympathetic to its pulse. The roots felt the embryo of awareness growing in this unremarkable being. These were the allies it sought. Those it could send to the world of men. To find things. To act where it could not. She was not a stranger to the forest. Its fruits had sustained her, and its herbs had healed her. At night she had danced amongst the trees to the impalpable melody of silence. But for now, she must face the flood. Some industrious villagers had gathered up a pile of brush wood. While others, hoping to impress the magistrate with demonstrations of zeal, had begun to snap the branches from the oak tree to add to the pyre. The tree groaned and thrashed in the wind as the steady deluge of rain fell. Elizabeth could feel the tree's complaining pulse through her fingers. Sympathy flowed between them.

The ridges of bark were scars on her arms. Branches were arms covered in scars. Torn from her sockets as the villagers snapped. Her fingers were twigs, bent as they fell. The sticks were the fingers pointing to hell.

The mob worked hard as the cold rain mocked them. Like one great excited organism they built their altar. Ties were loosened. Jackets discarded. Sleeves rolled up. Saws and axes chewed and bit. The sap dripped into the soil.

Under the loam the fluids combined, joined by the flow and the surge of the flood, into the roots the blood and the muscle, torn from the witches born in the mud.

Elizabeth closed her eyes and drifted into the trunk. Her blood seeped into the pith, into the veins of the leaves, and down. Down into the roots. The intimacy of fluids combining. Deep in the wooden heart of the forest. In the clearing the villagers lit their brands. Sparks leapt from flints. The lessons the lightning taught, made deadly by human hands. Tied to the trunk, the husk of Elizabeth Duncan waited to wither in the flames.

The villagers took her body, punching, slapping and poking at it with lustful fists. They dragged her across the ground and tied her to the stake. The rain spat contempt through the leaves, forming into black pools around the place of execution. Jeremiah Cavendish walked to the pyre with his sputtering torch raised high.

'In the name of all that is holy, I cast Satan out of this village. With fire I cast you out! With fire I send you to hell! With flame I cast you out! With flame I cast you out! With flame! With flame!'

His sodden suit weighed heavily on his shoulders. His black city brogues were claggy and sucked in the muck as he strode. His hair hung like miserable curtains over his temples, the pomade too diluted to stick. But the fire in his belly could not be so easily quenched. He thrust the torch into the kindling. It would not burn.

'Bring me the oil, quickly now, quickly.'

An eager lieutenant carried a pitcher. Jeremiah Cavendish sprinkled the oil over the sticks. Every fibre of the broken forest resisted the flame. Here and there the fire would catch hold. The flame struggling to a peak before collapsing into a blue pool, then finally vanishing. Jeremiah Cavendish cursed and threw on more oil. But the sap dowsed the flame again. Around the glade, the wood groaned as the tempest grew. The rain hammered the people of the village. In the damp their blood frenzy was subsiding. Rumbles of discontent broke out. Fears of the demon's revenge. The beast has sent the rain to drown God's flame. Some began to cower from the woods as it pressed in around them.

'Hang the witch!'

An enterprising bank clerk spoke up. Murmurs of approval amongst the villagers. Nods, shrugs, hideous grins.

'Hang her! hang her!'

'Take her down, if you please, Mr Wheeler.'

A stern-faced sergeant stepped over the steaming faggots and cut the ropes. Elizabeth's battered body was dragged from the pyre and taken back to the tree again. A rope and noose were flung over one of the oak's high branches. Inside the tree, the hybrid soul of wood and woman watched. They began to hoist her broken body up. Her legs kicked in feeble protest. Awful spasms jolted through her empty frame, making her body twist in unnatural directions. One last dance in the thick darkness of night. Then she was gone. The face of Jeremiah Cavendish was caught in the guttering torch light. He looked like a gargoyle melting in the rain. In the grain, the cells of a woman became cells of the wood. Senses dissolved to be replaced by nameless perceptions. These undefinable faculties studied the magistrate. They read the grim satisfaction in the subtle upturn of his lips. The crack of a branch as the lightning struck. Jeremiah Cavendish froze. He was in the Tangle now, not the boardroom. His pious cruelty had no meaning here. The tree creaked and swayed, shaking the useless shell from its bough. The body of Elizabeth Duncan crashed to the floor at his feet. The villagers scattered. Leaving cudgels and kitchen knives behind. The constables, no more than criminals with badges, waved their shotguns at phantoms. The sergeant drew his service revolver from its holster. Jeremiah Cavendish closed his eyes and prayed. He stood before the Kaiser's demon cavalry in Flanders Fields. He nursed his father, rotten with pox. He watched his dead son eaten by rats. He watched as the graves filled with the flood. He saw the rain and the lightning flash.

The Tangle sensed their passing. Through leaf and root, it marked them.

Ten summers passed in Caxton Wood. Flames burned bright in its dark interior. Gallows swayed and heads rolled. The ranks of the dead swelled under the spreading leaves. On the oak tree, the green shoots of repair hardened into sturdy boughs. Elizabeth was not yet nothing. She was a wraith, a phantom, still residually connected to the human frame.

Bit by bit, all that had once been her would be liquidated and transformed. She drifted through the soil like a vapour. Curling through stems, visiting the stamen of flowers as she merged with the bright corolla of summer petals. Not yet nothing. Waiting. Waiting. Waiting to perform her final human obligation. In the Tangle, time was already a concept to which she was no longer shackled. Patience was its own reward. She had almost forgotten the creaking rigidity of her former human existence. But still she carried the burden. The reminders were never too far away; the clearing, the chopping, the hacking and burning, all steadily diminished the forest. The hands of the villagers were always ready with the axe and rope. She would never forget the rope.

In the village, things had settled into the familiar pattern of semi-feudal life. Regimes changed with regularity in the far-off parliament. But out here, nothing had changed. In Caxton, tithes were paid, their children got sick, and livings were scratched from the land. The facades of modernity were evident: electric lights, motor cars for those who could afford them, tractors, banks, a hospital, and even a telephone or two. But for most it was still the scythe or the quarry. The local flint was prized in the city and a minor aristocracy had grown up around its exploitation. Gold pocket watches and Savile Row blazers. The river would carry the flint down to the docks. The boatsmen never tarried in Caxton's zombie port, where vessels were loaded by silent men with suspicious faces. The land remained in the hands of a few wealthy landowners, whose disdain for the lower orders was worn with pride. Breeding and the divine rights of birth held sway. Suffrage was not suffered here. Around the village, the tides of atheism broke on the rocks of their faith. Long ago church and state had gone their separate ways, but in

Caxton, the Lord's word was still the law. They praised him as they always had, with blood. With sacrifice. But the great depression had bitten hard in the world beyond the village, and now rumours of war began to percolate through the populace. Still, those brewing storms were of little concern out here. Here the conflict took on a different dimension. Some heretics who'd placed their faith in stocks and shares had been inconvenienced. Some had chosen the fall from Ardlington viaduct or deliverance by shot and gunfire. Some had perished in the flames. The pyre in Caxton Wood. The pyre and the rope. Others would burn soon.

As the world prepared to be torn apart, there was a great feeling of unity in the village. They had all played their part, and now they worked together to build a new church. For the elect. For Caxton. The old church had recently burned down, victim of an unfortunate lightning strike on another fateful night. The vengeance of demons was the rumour. The Tangle's languid timetable of retribution had been set in motion.

Eyes without sight, vision or focus. No lens or pupil, motion or locus.

What was once Elizabeth had felt the church burn from the crown of a sycamore tree. Patience was its own reward. The villagers worked tirelessly to restore the temple to its former glory. They sang hymns to fortify themselves against the elements as they placed stone upon stone. It would rise again greater than ever, that was their solemn vow.

The spectral residue flowed through the trees, down through their trunks and out into the bushes that formed the limit of the wood. The last fragment of Elizabeth settled into the budding fruit of a bramble bush. Aware of the villagers

going about their work. By scent, by vibration, by senses with
no name. The remaining pillars of the burned-out church
had been torn down and building work on the new structure
was well underway. The frame of the building was rising,
the outline of its form beginning to take shape. It was to be
a modest church, in keeping with the austerity of the times.
A simple church for righteous people. The church would be
made by sweat and sacrifice. By hand and muscle. No lathe or
machine would spoil its beams.

> *Eyes without sight, vision or focus. No lens or pupil,*
> *motion or locus.*

The residue sensed the carpenters gathering with their
long logging saws and double-handed axes. The magistrate
pulled into the site in his Hillman saloon. He consulted
with the architect and the foreman. They bent over plans
and diagrams. The needs of the structure were debated.
Instructions were given. The carpenters gathered their tools.
They stepped on the path to the heart of the forest. They
came to cut. They came to claim a trunk. The last fragment
of Elizabeth. The last sliver of the absurd entity she once was
flowed back through the forest. Sensing her chance had come.

The phantom seeped back into the trunk of the old
oak, settling deep inside the grain of the wood. She waited.
Absorbing the movements of the men through the filaments.
The carpenters had marched in ragged procession from the
village and were now entering the clearing. One of their
number slapped the trunk of the oak tree, as if he could divine
its provenance by touch alone.

'This will do the job, Gilbert. Let's get her down.'

'Right you are, gaffer.'

The carpenters chopped a wedge into the trunk to direct its fall. Each notch sent a spasm of sorrow through the forest. The last fragment of Elizabeth felt the disruption as she clung to the cells of the wood. Then came the agony of the crosscut saw as it bit into the trunk. Like an amputation without anaesthetic. She screamed inside. The horses they had brought to carry the severed trunk whinnied nervously and scratched the floor with their hooves. The woodland birds took flight. Only the disconnected and oblivious carpenters continued their rhythmic hacking. Soon the oak was down. It crashed into the surrounding forest, the branches of the neighbouring trees brushing against its rough bark as it fell. The carpenters loaded the trunk onto the cart and headed back to the village. The last fragment of Elizabeth waited patiently inside.

Within a few weeks the carpenters had skilfully honed beams from the trunk of the oak. The beams were then hoisted into place for the roofers to add their slates. The remaining planks were carved into benches, rough enough to keep the congregation alert to the sin of comfort. The minister and the magistrate inspected the work. God be praised, it was a fine building. A humble pulpit and simple nave. The ideal place to receive the word of the Lord. Honest wood cut from the Tangle.

'Will you and your wife be able to attend the opening on Sunday, Mr Cavendish?'

The Reverend Molin's obsequious smile was somewhat out of place on his habitually stern face. It was a stupid question, posed only to maintain the momentum of their conversation. The reverend basked in the light of the magistrate's attention.

'But of course, reverend, I would not miss such a holy occasion. God continues to work his miracles in Caxton, reverend, praise Him. The family and I will certainly add our voices to the choir, though sadly my boy is detained elsewhere, in service of the empire.'

'Ah, yes, of course, brave lad, doing his duty no doubt. Let us hope war does not come, Mr Cavendish. We will say a prayer for the boy's safety, and his swift return to the bosom of his family, on Sunday.'

Jeremiah Cavendish fixed the Reverend Molin with withering eyes. They burned through the layers of his platitudes, exposing him for the weak, stupid man he was.

'The war is already here, reverend.'

The last nails had been hammered home as the congregation gathered outside Caxton parish church. Jeremiah Cavendish and his family stood at the front, next to the other notable local dignitaries. Crisp shirts, sober ties, brushed broad-brimmed hats. The glinting chains of office. The villagers in their Sunday best stood behind them in pious ranks. The butcher. The baker. The old undertaker. The smell of moth balls and rose water drifted from the cloth. Bright scarves and spit-shined shoes disturbed the monochrome. Hard earned pretty things were quietly flaunted. The minister delivered an overly long and pompous eulogy to the holy labourers of Caxton. The mayor cut the ribbon. The Reverend Molin led the congregation inside. The last fragment of Elizabeth crouched in the rafters. Jeremiah Cavendish directed his wife and two young daughters to the front pew before positioning himself on the aisle. The church was at capacity, as it always was. The minister mounted the steps to the pulpit.

His sermon was not from a gospel anyone would recognise. It was a creed of fire, gleaned from faded scrolls long since lost. The Reverend Molin called for vigilance.

He called for vengeance and purifying deeds. He praised their fellowship and the magistrate's wisdom. He called for the gallows in the mud and the leaves. Find the sin that hides in the village. Root it out. Bring the accused to the place of judgement. Let the magistrate interpret the word. A beam creaked. The minister paused his sermon. They all looked up. It must be the building settling. The minister continued. Be mindful of those who would spread blasphemy, for they seek to undermine all we have built. Pray for our king. The king of the village. A nail dropped at the feet of the magistrate. The minister stopped, too distracted by the tumbling spike to continue. The magistrate picked up the nail. He examined it, and then turned around to fix the carpenters with his furious gaze. They in turn stared at the floor, hats held between shaking palms. They looked mortified and confused. There was devotion in their work. Pride, too, though it be a sin to show it. Every nail was driven home true and proper. The beams creaked again. Another nail fell. The congregation began to stir. Concerned glances were exchanged. More nails fell. Bolts too. People began to panic. The minister urged calm. The beams began to creak and sway. Plaster and daub now fell with the fittings. The magistrate grabbed his wife and children by the hand and tried to move towards the aisle. A large wooden beam swung down from the ceiling, blocking the way. People ran. People screamed. The air filled with dust and a shower of nails. Sharp pricks pierced skin and skull. Beams creaked and cracked. Splinters cut through cloth and burrowed into limbs. In the beams the wraith slid through the grain.

The essence writhed in the weave as the congregation came apart. But she felt nothing. She was of the Tangle now. Her compass turned on a different circumference. Pity?

What pity did they show her? She began to expand, warping the wood, changing its structure until it shattered. The splinters fell like the shells of the Somme. All around the humble pews they trampled each other in their panic. The last fragment of Elizabeth flowed into the door, tightening its frame until it was wedged into the stone. None would escape. The congregation fell on the door. Clawing and hammering. They piled up, clambering over the fallen. Faces squashed and pulped against the flagstones. Jeremiah Cavendish snatched the ceremonial scissors from the dying hand of the dusty mayor. He stabbed at the bodies that stood in his path. Slashing wildly with open blades. The Reverend Molin stood in his pulpit. Debris clattered around him. He caught the frenzied eye of the magistrate as he cut his way through the faithful. All they had built had come undone. The final splinter of what was once a woman loosened a joist from the transept and sent it across the developing ruins. It impaled the reverend through his chest. Jeremiah Cavendish caught the sound as the reverend gurgled through bubbles of blood. A wild toneless murmur. It ricocheted around the building, rising above the cries of the dying. Could no one else hear it? He tore his eyes from the corpse of the cleric and tried to move through the desperate muddle of people. The murmur turned to a moan. It bent through the frequencies. First a creek. Then a crack. Jeremiah Cavendish looked up. He thought he saw a face looking down from the buckling beams. A familiar face from a hangman's noose.

The ridges of bark were scars on her arms. Branches were arms covered in scars. Torn from her sockets as the villagers snapped. Her fingers were twigs, bent as they fell. The sticks were the fingers pointing to hell.

He remembered the crack of the branch as the lightning struck. Crack. He stood before the Kaiser's demon cavalry in Flanders Fields. He nursed his father, rotten with pox. He watched his dead son eaten by rats. He watched as the graves filled with the flood. He saw the rain and the lightening flash. Crack. Then the roof fell in.

It took four days to dig out all the bodies from the debris. It was the nails, they said. Poor quality fittings, they said. The blacksmith from Appleton was to blame. He was a drinker, they said. They hanged him. Cut his bollocks off too. The king himself came to inspect the wreckage. He said a prayer over the broken beams. Some say he cried. Caxton church was no more. Only ghosts lived there now. In the years that followed, the world made its own ghosts as the bombs fell. When the debris and dust had settled, the soldiers came home. A new world was promised, free of horror and the rule of tyrants. There was work to be done to fix all that had been broken. In Caxton, a young man dressed in the uniform of an army captain took his kitbag from his shoulder and unlocked the door of his old family home. The master was coming. A new flock would follow in time. They would work the land again and prosper. They would build their church on the foundations of the ruins. They would fear the Lord. They would be vigilant. In Caxton Wood the branches rattled together in warning.

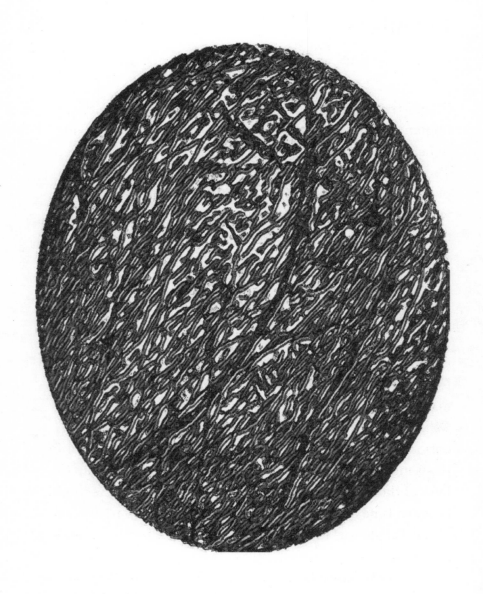

Furniture

Elizabeth Duncan had long since ceased to be. Her petty
human grievances had been erased. She was nothing. And
in her nothingness, she was complete. Now she was of the
Tangle. She was of the roots. A zephyr flowing between the
plants of the forest. Everywhere. Nowhere. Like God. Age
was not something that was measured here. There were no
beginnings to mark. Everything was now. Everything was
nothing. But, by human reckoning, thirty-five years had
passed in the wizened wood. This May morning in the year
of their Lord 1974, cells that were once human drifted in the
spores of a fungus. The fresh spring breeze carrying them
over the forest in search of a place to grow. In Hamble's Dell
the spores settled on a human bag. This was a popular spot
for people to discreetly discard their domestic waste, old
mattresses, broken sinks, piles of pornographic magazines.
Cells that were once human detected fragments of old
curiosity stubbornly clinging to the membrane. It was not for
the Tangle, the grotesque parade of events that made up the
lives of those outside. Here in the roots such concerns would
decay in time as all human concerns do. But an obscure layer
of the Tangle was itself still human. It contained its essence.

*Under the loam the fluids combined, joined by the flow
and the surge of the flood, into the roots the blood and
the muscle, torn from the witches born in the mud.*

That occult essence now stirred. Curious and wary. It sank into the discarded bag.

Inside, the heat of decay was beginning to swell, but had not so far grown so potent as to destroy the contents. The essence drifted amongst them, examining each item carefully. Clothes. Women's clothes. It detected a scent clinging to the weave. A perfume designed to imitate the fragrance of a forest flower. Wild approximations of nature. It found an item that looked like a journal. The cover was covered in drawings that suggested daydreams and a potent imagination. Bizarre hieroglyphs like the illuminations of a gospel. Stick figures entwined in exotic relief between the marks. The essence slipped around the words, turning in the curves of the letters to find their meaning.

> I am a stranger here. A traveller washed up on the margins of God knows where. This town is like a museum. The locals are polite enough, I guess. Quiet. Andrew? He was charming. Friendly. Like a blank slate. Nothing seems to have stuck to him at all over the years. I'm enjoying showing him. Books. Films. Life. Love. Is it love? We are heading to London for a weekend of dusty bookshops and dangerous dive bars. That's what I'm in for. He says he's never been. He knows so little. I have so much to tell him
>
> We spent the weekend in town. Bed. Plans to elope.
> I worry I might be happy.

It curled into a full stop. Love. What was love? When the essence was human it had experienced some unwanted attention. Intimacy forced, but never shared. But they were all under the earth now. It had seen them rotting in the mire. Here in the woods, here in the roots, here in the Tangle, feelings were not named. No love, no anger, no disappointment, no happiness. There were no feelings. Only the sensation of an endless riddle unfolding. The essence slipped around the bag looking for tags and labels. Agatha Denholm. It found her name stitched into the lining of a coat. Names. Names would soon be forgotten. It passed the heart-shaped doodling, the education of a trivial man. The love given freely and the passion for knowledge shared. Now Agatha's words took on a darker weight as the entropy of human relationships took its course. Disappointment, prevarication, betrayal.

I really don't know what I was expecting, I feel so stupid. Of course, he's married. I spotted the family out at the seaside. Kids too. He's just like the others, all those men with their hollow words and empty promises. The vain, shallow sack of a man. I'm such a fool.

This town is hell. I can't go anywhere without pointing fingers and wagging tongues. The atmosphere here. It's suffocating. If only I'd seen through it all. The lies came so easily. Andrew? That's not even his name. He's a Cavendish. Timothy Cavendish. That family. If only I'd known. So charming. So skilled at subterfuge. His father saw to it that I lost my job. That clan. The Cavendishs are trying to destroy me inch by inch. I hear rumours. I should be careful.

Cavendish. When the essence was a human he had hung her from a tree. The magistrate, the magus, the managing director. These were his progeny. If Agatha was in his power she would burn and dangle, just as Elizabeth had.

I just don't think I was made for these times, this town, this time warp. Tradition like a tourniquet. There is no one to turn to. The family rule like tyrants. No one will say a word. No future, no love, no hope. I just can't. I won't. Timothy has agreed to meet in Caxton Wood. Away from prying eyes. I'll tell him what I think. He can't get away with treating me like this. I want nothing from him or his family. Just my reputation and a chance to get out of this stifling prison.

But there was no way out of Caxton. The essence began to decay. Its identity collapsing as another took her place. She had fulfilled her obligation the day she brought the roof down on the parishioners. It was time for her to mutate. The essence drifted out of the bag like smoke. Sliding into the roots. Into the cells. Becoming nothing. Along the knotted highways. The essence. Losing its singularity. Multiplying. Searching for Agatha. The forest sensed a disturbance. An expectant chatter spread; psyche joining body. A new ghost for the wood. The essence bent through the fibres of a young ash tree, travelling along its branches, along the rough bark. It met the fibrous knot of a rope. At the end of the rope, in the mouth of a noose, a body swung like a grim pendulum. Once full of hopes and dreams, but now a simple husk. At her feet was a familiar face. He had changed. This was not the body he had occupied all those years ago, but it was him nonetheless. Another hangman, another Cavendish.

*

Minutes, seconds, hours, days. Pointless notches on the continuum. Meaningless markers set out by humans to convince themselves they were getting somewhere. Agatha stood at the threshold of a new dimension. Her body hung undiscovered in the woodland glade; her assassin had returned to the town. With her death the curious fragment died too. The last splinters of a human consciousness had been tidied away and absorbed. Now there was only the Tangle. Agatha stood in her place. Newly hatched, uncertain and anxious. She had been a woman of the city, of bricks and doors, of couches and beds, roads and traffic lights. She had seldom visited the woods while she was alive and always felt uneasy when she had. Too much muck and the chance of rain. But she was welcome now. In time she would forget the seduction of things, but for now she hovered in the flux between two worlds. She was not yet of the Tangle. She could not pass over the threshold until the bitter anchor she carried was discarded and her duty to the Goddess discharged.

The ridges of bark were scars on her arms. Branches were
arms covered in scars. Torn from her sockets as the cruel
man snapped. Her fingers were twigs, bent as they fell.
The sticks were the fingers pointing to hell.

The machine had replaced the fallibility of human craft, but a few artisans still plied their trade in the town. Their faulty notches came at a premium for those seeking authenticity in their furniture. A group of these artisans were out scouting for materials. Just like their ancestors, they were looking for trees to cut into planks and spokes. Agatha hadn't gone far since her demise, but she was already decaying. Her body had been gradually consumed by the entities of the wood. Bugs. Rats. Microbes. This was the funeral sacrament of the Tangle. A becoming. To nothing. To nowhere. Yet Agatha still was.

She was in the knots of trunks. She was in branches and leaves. She was in the glade when the craftsmen came.

Eyes without sight, vision or focus. No lens or pupil,
    motion or locus.

She studied the forms that stood in the clearing. She knew the young Goodridge boys from around town. They were a family of whittlers. So when they arrived in the forest with their axes and chainsaws, she knew their purpose. This was the chance to travel back to the world of men. Back to the town. To step once again on its broken pavements. To find young Tim and do him in. To satisfy the debt he owed. For all the knots. For all the lives cut short. As the Goodridge boys cut, she flowed into the severed trunk and waited.

Bartholomew Goodridge & Sons were Caxton's finest cabinet makers, where the fruits of the forest were turned into works of art in their workshops. They were best known for their beds. In their dextrous hands the wood was carved and bent. Topped with mattresses of exquisite comfort and generous depth. 'You'll feel so good in a Goodridge bed, you'll never want to get up' was how the advert went. The picture was of a laughing woman holding a steaming cup of tea, with an anxious-looking boy in his school uniform about to miss the school bus as his father languished in the comfort of his Goodridge bed. Private schools. Traditional values. The message would have been a calculated slap in the face had it been meant for the world outside. Three-day week. Power cuts and strikes. The country was struggling. But these beds were not designed for outsiders. These beds were not for the sinful backs of city folk. Goodridge beds were for the new aristocracy. The rural plutocrats directing their vassals from remote offices in Caxton's holy shire. Their brokers bought Panamanian bonds while they lived out lives of isolated feudal harmony. That was the way of things. Goodridge beds. For the elect. The summit of the social pyramid, like owning a Rolls-Royce. Roger Goodridge ran his finger over the smooth varnished headboard of their 'Golden Sleigh' model; it was a popular design amongst the country elite. Cavendish senior. A royal stamp of approval. Once he was satisfied that everything was in perfect order, Roger nodded to the foreman to begin preparing the bed for delivery.

'Well, this is marvellous, isn't it, darling?'

Timothy Cavendish patted the mattress like the neck of a horse. Karol Cavendish smiled thinly, holding a neatly folded pile of sheets. Timothy returned her smile with an unconvincing smirk. Their game continued. Gaoler and prisoner. She got what she could for her children, that was her only comfort. Divorce was unthinkable. In these days. In this place. Once the trap was sprung, you were held fast with bonds stronger than the ropes. Just like the ropes he favoured. She could not leave. This town had taken it all: her hope, her money, her will. Patrols kept them safe and the sinful at bay.

The magistrate, the magus, the managing director.

Karol placed the linen on the mattress and patted it wistfully. She knew not to get too attached to it. It would all have to be replaced soon. This was the third new bed in five years. They both knew why. Offerings. Sacrifices. She couldn't face occupying the same space afterwards. Every wrinkle and draft-blown feather was a reminder. A new bed and no questions. No one ever asked questions. In any case, the police would be no help.

The magistrate, the magus, the managing director.

She had never asked him to drive Agatha out of the town.
He said she had left and that he'd never see her again. She
never wanted anything bad to happen to any of them. But
bad things did happen. She sensed it. Her suspicion grew with
every muddy track on the carpet, every late-night bonfire,
every cut on his hand. He did so hate inconvenience.

The sunlight sliced through the gloom, playing over
Karol's face like a nagging child. She stirred, managing to
crank open one eyelid, which lifted like a reluctant garage
door through her Valium haze. Her husband's ill-defined
form lay still beneath the sheets next to her. He must be
asleep, which was strange as he was usually an early riser.
She was dimly aware of his face pointing towards the ceiling.
She wouldn't try to wake him. Time spent without him was
time well spent. Karol gathered her jelly limbs and quietly
shuffled out the door. In the bed, Timothy Cavendish lay as
still as a corpse, his arms and legs frozen and unbending.
His breathing had stopped too. His blood no longer flowed
through his veins, no pulse, no metabolic functions at all. But
he was not dead. He had merely been paused.

Eight hours ago, Timothy had slipped into the fresh new
sheets. Tired after fresh exertions in the wood. Another
escape from the mundane world of respectability he so
despised. He had enjoyed his fun with Agatha, and he was
sorry it had ended. But once the game was up there was
nothing for it but to pack her in. Clean up the mess. Tie up
loose ends. His father would expect it. As he nestled into
the duck down pillow, he thought of her. Her presence was
apparent. He could detect her scent in the smooth wood of
the bed frame, its grain like the soft warmth of her skin.

Agatha's face, too, was as clear as day. It was almost like she was in bed with him. But the film he had so carefully constructed from his memories refused to play. No matter how hard he tried to capture the image of her nakedness she would slip out of his grasp. Instead, she was clad in leaves, her garments the boughs and blossoms of the forest. Flowers sprouted from her eyes; shoots flowed from her fingertips. But her voice, her voice, her voice.

The ridges of bark were scars on her arms. Branches were arms covered in scars. Torn from her sockets as the cruel man snapped. Her fingers were twigs, bent as they fell. The sticks were the fingers pointing to hell.

'Timothy, Ti-mo-thy.'

Whispers.

'Timothy, Ti-mo-thy.'

Agatha floated from the grain of the wood, forming into a mist that drifted over and into him. Into his mouth, into his brain, through the pores of his skin and into his lungs. Timothy Cavendish tried to say something. Something witty and charming. Something seductive and sensual. A vision of a Mayfair hotel room flashed into his consciousness; two naked people in bed smoking. Smoking and fucking. Smoking, drinking and fucking. His silken words replayed at quarter speed like a demonic incantation.

'Room service. Your champagne, Mr Cavendish.'

The waiter's sing-song voice sounded like a dirge. He couldn't move. The mattress began to tear as branches forced their way out of the springs. He tried to jump out of the bed. To break the spell. But he couldn't move. The branches held him down. Agatha's wispy presence twirled around his

ears, his eyes, his mouth. The branches curled back into the
mattress. Now he was alone in a dark room. It was cold. It
smelled of decay and the must of damp earth. He could not
move. He tried to scream but his jaw set tight in a grimace.
Agatha turned into a whirlwind inside his veins, freezing
him in that exact moment, with all hopes of redemption
withdrawn and salvation rescinded.

It was nearly midday and Timothy had still not risen.
Karol thought she should probably check on him. She had
got the children ready for a day out and they were growing
restless. Better tell him they were leaving. He liked to know
where she was. At all times. But it was strange that he still
slept. Had he slipped out during the night? Would they be
needing a new bed so soon? Karol climbed the stairs and went
into the bedroom. She threw back the still-drawn curtains.
Springtime sunshine poured in, illuminating the bed. Timothy
was in the same position she had left him in. Head pointing
at the ceiling. But now, as the sun strafed the room, she saw
his face. His eyes were wild and wide open, with a strange
luminescence around the cornea. Karol leaned over him and
looked into them.

Karol, it's me! Oh, thank God! Help me get up, I've had
some kind of seizure. Bloody awful dreams all night, and
now I can't move.

She bent her ear to his slightly open mouth, listening for his
breath. But there was none. She moved her ear to his chest,
searching for his heartbeat. But there was none. Her fingers
sought his pulse. Nothing, not a flicker. He was dead. Karol
clicked her fingers in front of his eyes. Nothing.

It's me for Christ's sake, Karol! Can't you hear me?
Stop fucking about and help me!

She shook him, gently at first, and then more vigorously so
that his head rocked back and forth like a rag doll. No doubt
about it, Timothy Cavendish was no more.

'Oh, thank God.'

She leaned over him again, staring hard into his pupils.
She thought she saw something, a hint of a figure swinging
from a tree. It must be a reflection from the outside. Karol
closed his eyelids with her fingers. She had looked into those
treacherous pools enough for one lifetime.

No, Karol! Please, please my darling, I'm here. You can't
leave me like this! Karol! Karol!

The doctor confirmed the diagnosis. A seizure, he said.
Timothy's heart must have stopped in his sleep. He tried
to reassure Karol. I'm sure he felt no pain. Her face was
contorting in what the doctor took to be grief. But it was
rapture she was struggling to contain. His father must not
know. Not until she had time to escape.

The magistrate, the magus, the managing director.

Dr Harris, look at me! Surely you can see me. I'm alive for
Christ's sake! Where are you taking me?

The ambulance arrived to take the body away.

'There shall have to be a post-mortem I'm afraid, Mrs
Cavendish.'

The doctor said it should be a formality as no foul play
was suspected. No hint of a scandal would ever be allowed

near the Cavendish name, they could all be assured of that. The post-mortem was noisy. The pathologist sliced and sawed. Timothy was finding it impossible to articulate his pain by that point. It was really just one long strangled scream. All his parts thrashing about, undulating like a rollercoaster as the doctors cut and scooped. Agatha had long since flowed out of his malign frame. She had passed through the streets one last time but found they had lost their fascination. Instead, she followed the roots. Back to the woods. Back to the glade. Back to the Tangle. There she decayed.

Come walk with me to lilac glade, through woodland,
    stream and knot.
Come stand beneath the gallows' shade till all weeping
    is forgot.
Leave the tears and terrors to the mischief of the town.
Come walk with me to lilac glade, to the oak tree's
    shady crown.

In darkness now from darkness born, circumference,
    length and span.
In lilac glade the wreath and thorn, wove mockeries
    of man.
In lilac glade beneath the earth, in death's ecstatic bond.
Come walk with me in lilac shade, to the emptiness beyond.

The mouldering scent of dark, wet soil filled his nostrils. He had heard that people's senses were often scrambled during bouts of illness. It should pass in time. He opened his eyes. He hoped to God he'd never have to experience such agonies again. Christ, the hallucinations! The pain, like he was being cut open. Timothy stretched out his fingers, feeling the reassuringly familiar grain of smooth wood; there really was no mistaking a Goodridge bed. They always used the finest trunks to make their furniture. He could feel the quality. Timothy patted the wood again and tried to raise himself up from the bed. It was awfully stuffy in the room; he needed some air. His head banged awkwardly against something hard and unyielding. He put his hand up to feel. The finest grain, polished to perfection, smooth and sturdy, built to last. They really were the Rolls-Royce of furniture makers. His eyes focused on a bright brass plaque above his head. Bartholomew Goodridge & Sons, manufacturers of fine caskets and coffins.

Hunts Up

The problem had been years in the making, centuries
maybe. Rapacious animals had been allowed to run wild and
unchecked. They were ravaging the countryside and spoiling
the last pristine enclaves with their malignant presence. They
had already devastated the indigenous wildlife. Populations
were depleted and their numbers were sinking to near-
extinction levels. They marauded at will, protected by ill
thought-out laws that had been pushed through the council
by do-gooders and bleeding hearts. Enough was enough.
Something had to be done about this awful plague. A cull.
A cull, that was what was needed. It wouldn't be pleasant.
It would certainly be a bloody affair, but the council had
decided to approve the action by the narrowest of margins.
It would not be cruelly executed. It would be professional and
proportionate. The young and the majority of females would
be spared. It was the males that were the problem. Vicious
things, fearless and brutal, always fighting for territory, never
satisfied, permanently hungry. The council meeting broke up.
The preparations for the hunt began immediately. Tomorrow
the great purge would begin.

   The horn blast stirred the village. Hunts up. Today was
the day for the chase, for the beating of the scrub with sticks.
A day for shooting, trapping, tearing and rending. Hunts
up. Caspar yawned as he pulled his boots up over his tweed
trousers. The thick material was irritating after a summer

of unusually high temperatures, but there was a chill in the early morning air, and besides, he needed something sturdy to protect his legs from the thorny bushes. He would be right in the thick of it today. Caspar had the look of an athlete gone to seed; a vague paunch was encroaching on his belt. Ruddy cheeks and a tousled, blond mop of hair that looked like it had been dumped on his head suggested an upbringing of public-school dinners and compulsory sports. A solid 'chap' one might say. He glanced over to the radiator. Caspar had put the heating on early this year, and he was expecting to see their rotund cat Beryl curled up next to it, but she was nowhere to be seen.

'Is Beryl up there, darling?'

Caspar shouted up to Elspeth, his wife, who was pressing her hunting tunic for today's meet.

'She was out the flap early this morning, funny old thing. Out late last night too. Why?'

'Oh, no reason, just thought she'd be lazing by the radiator, that's all. Do you think she's taken a lover?'

He could hear Elspeth laughing as she swished the iron over her riding clothes. She had gone from public school to Oxford University, into a position with a respectable financial institution, and she was heading for great things. But she had given it all up for a quiet life of rural conservatism. As she pressed the iron through the folds of fabric, she often wondered what might have been. Caspar continued his preparations. He unlocked the cabinet and took out his shotgun, the smell of its freshly oiled muzzle bringing a smile to his face. He turned the gun over in his palms, admiring its intricately tooled barrel. He looked down its length. It was a fine thing. His father had been a keen hunter too; he had bequeathed the gun to Caspar in his will. Caspar had coveted it since childhood, and now it was his most precious possession. Today he would do his father proud. Hunts up.

'Right, I'm off! See you at the Bull for drinks before the ball! Wish me luck!'

'Good luck, darling! Don't forget Johnny is riding with me today. It might be the day for a blooding now the ban's been lifted.'

'Oh, God! Of course, I forgot. I hope you catch a few to make up for lost time! I'm just sad to miss the big day.'

'Don't worry, darling, you have to do your duty. I hope you get a decent brace. Don't forget to keep count. I know what you're like when you get carried away.'

'I won't, I won't. It could be a record tally today. No more bloody quotas and those ghastly men from the council poking about with their forms . . . Oh, and please get a nice picture of Johnny if he gets blooded today. Love you both.'

'Love you too, darling.'

Caspar smiled. Picking up his cartridge belt, he stepped out into the morning mist.

Bly Stone was a beater. A wife beater. A child beater. A dog beater. Today he would thrash the thicket, chivvying out the birds for the hunters to pepper. The work was well paid, easy too. He used to be a farmer until his drinking got the better of him. The foxes got the last of his flock a couple of years ago. Fuckers. Now you could hunt them again, Bly would love to kill one of those bastards. He'd join the hunters in a heartbeat if they'd have him back. But he was sure the incident at the Boxing Day ball hadn't been forgotten. Cunts. He was one of them once: jodhpurs, boots, the lot. Now he was a beater. A man beater. An animal beater. A self-flagellator. He did odd jobs for those who'd trust him. Stinking of booze. Stained with neglect. Most avoided his resentful glares, though some

were only a few sherries away from the same state. Those
golf club bores. Those landed Land Rover-driving snobs.
The middle management team builders were the worst;
they came in squadrons at the weekend, jostling for position
like a pack of young bucks. Amateurs. Shooting wildly into
the air, swigging on fucking hip flasks engraved with stags.
Fucking cunts. Bly was one of them once too. He had settled
before his time in this rural backwater. Given up the high life
of the city to become a sure-fire success in the agricultural
business. But the promise of a new life had withered in the
soil. Those long nights. No lights. No life. Plenty of pubs.
Bly rattled the whiskey bottle to and fro in the weak light
of the kitchen window. A slither of golden liquid stained the
bottom. He could see it glowing through the green glass.
He threw back his head and tipped the bottle. The meagre
contents dribbled reluctantly onto his tongue. He closed his
eyes and swallowed. He fucking hated himself. Bly took up his
threadbare cap, adjusting it carelessly on his unkempt head.
A group of local tomcats sat on a wall watching him leave
the house. Bly was often roused from his drunken sleep by
their endless scrapping, but today it seemed like a truce had
been called. They were almost regimental in their stillness as
they watched him head up the back lane. Bly dragged himself
towards the gathering place with a heavy head full of malice.

Eugene Carlson exuded success, from his John Lobb
loafers to his Jermyn Street tweeds. But he couldn't hide
his bridge-and-tunnel brashness, as his diamond ear studs
testified. His aristocratic pals found him a little gauche;
he was an American after all, and a young one too. The
older yanks, the industrialists and media moguls, seemed
to have adapted a lot more convincingly to the strict social
hierarchy of the shires. These young disrupters were a loud

and unsophisticated bunch, all booming autotuned dance music and carelessly stolen street slang. One was certain they would be happy to use machine guns at the shoot given half a chance. But seeing as Eugene now owned the country club, it was deemed better to ignore his more vulgar habits. This was the third year he had booked out the whole place and flown the shareholders out of their Manhattan lofts for a weekend of shooting. But this year would be especially cathartic now the local council had lifted the quotas. Something about a cull? Eugene liked the sound of it. It sounded . . . excessive.

He had taken a full plate from the country club buffet. Force of habit, you know? Grab it while you can, right? Still, the coke had taken the edge off his appetite. A morning pick-me-up had been required. Last night had been wild, man. But he needed to stay sharp today. Keep those shareholders happy.

'It's been another great year, guys. Thank you for your faith in me. Thank you for your faith in the company! I gotta say, I am stoked as fuuuck to be here again!'

A small chorus of whoops and a modicum of fist pumping broke out. Eugene felt like a superhero, amped on coke and his own legend. He could do no wrong. He had slayed the competition, cornered the market, bullied the team out of unionising, cut costs to the bone. So what if there were a few lawsuits? He could pay off those attention-seeking bitches. Hey, so you took a bit of persuading to party with the boss. So what? Here's a fucking apartment in Malibu. You don't want it? Fuck you. My lawyers will crush you, drag your sorry ass through the courts until you're penniless. Eugene got what he wanted, when he wanted it. He raised his glass to his nervous-looking staff. There were hesitant whoops and a throaty 'Fuck yeah' from his most loyal lieutenants. Eugene turned to face the gathered shareholders, raising his arms wide in a messianic pose. He carelessly filled his glass, letting the champagne slop down the sides and onto the ancient rug. He downed the champagne and filled the glass again. He sniffed, enjoying the numbing residue that trickled down his throat. He made a speech. Inarticulate. Rambling words. He talked about money. He talked about power and profit. He talked about himself. He talked about killing. More whooping. More clapping. More sniffing.

As Eugene eulogised inside, a large flock of birds drifted in tight formation high over the village. Gilbert Lambeth shaded his eyes. Sixty-five years a twitcher but he had never seen such an odd sight. At this time of year large flocks were not unusual, it was migration season after all, but never would you find such a variety of birds flying together: starlings, rooks, chaffinches and blackbirds wing to wing. Gilbert took out his old notebook and jotted down his observations. His fellow birdwatchers would enjoy mulling over the puzzle at the Bull later, if the landlord would let him in. Today's activities were bound to cause some unfortunate divisions in the village. Now the council had approved the cull, good folk of conscience like Gilbert must act. He was hurrying to the Quaker's meeting house to meet his fellow saboteurs: an eclectic cadre of youthful anarchists, performative hobbyists, Christian animal lovers, aging hippies who had been stranded in the countryside since the 1970s, and those for whom the idea of massacring animals for sport was, well, just wrong. Gilbert was a veteran humanist, carrying the conviction that people might one day metamorphose into something good. As a young man he had marched to Aldermaston, longing for an end to war. He had protested on the streets of London against various forms of injustice, chained himself to fences, sat in front of police vans and military vehicles.

He had been arrested and detained and was on a number of
Home Office lists. But Gilbert was, at his core, a good man.
A kind and gentle man. Most people in the village loved him.
Even those who thought his views to be dangerous Marxist
nonsense found it hard to really hate him. He was regularly
banned from the Bull, they all were, but it was usually to stop
the younger hotheads from starting an argument with the
beaters, and things tended to blow over in time. But today
would be different. Today things were going to change.

Gilbert knocked on the door of the Quaker house. Young
Jack Devlin answered. 'The Devil' they called him. An anti-
establishment provocateur. He was against most things and
found himself in a near-permanent state of fury. The Devil
had been arrested innumerable times, breaking into research
facilities, gluing himself to machinery, throwing eggs at
political figures. It was embarrassing for his parents, who
were both local notaries. They had even diverted a proportion
of his inheritance into a makeshift bail fund. But like Gilbert,
Jack Devlin was essentially a good boy. He saw the world
with the clarity of youth, before disappointment and regret
tarnished his optimism.

'Morning, Gilbert! Ready for it? Most of the others
are here, just waiting on the lot from town. Josh's bus is
knackered or something.'

'Good morning, you young Devil.'

Jack's serious 'direct action' face cracked a little at
Gilbert's gentle humour. Jane Bradshaw appeared at the
Devil's side. She was his girlfriend. Resourceful. Local. Born
and bred in the village. She was less sentimental about the
countryside than some of her fellow activists, but she opposed
the hunt with just as much vehemence. To her it was class
war; against the backdrop of rural poverty and prejudice, she

had dragged herself through college, becoming politicised along the way. She wanted to be a lawyer. To take the fight to the powerful and the forces of corporatism that were turning the countryside into just another factory. But for now, she was a mechanic. From an early age she had helped her father repair various farm machines, and now she put her experience to good use at her uncle's garage.

'Ah, and good morning to you, Miss Bradshaw! I do hope the others make it. We will need the numbers if the plan is to succeed.'

'They'll be here Gilbert, no worries, and don't you fret about the plan, it's going to work. There's no way it can fail.'

As the sentence faded on Jane's lips, a rickety camper van lurched around the corner and sputtered to a halt outside the hall. Jane sighed, a sardonic smile playing on her lips as she shook her head.

'I'll get my tools.'

Gilbert and the Devil offered a small round of applause as a ragtag band of saboteurs spilled out of the van, yawning and stretching into the misty morning air. Hunts up.

*

They stood in serried ranks. Experienced hunters next to half-drunk dilettantes. Clashing patterns of country attire and a dull rainbow of gumboots, like a privileged platoon of irregular troops. A variety of weapons crooked over forearms or in the hands of loaders. Some of the city boy adventurers tarried by the outdoor buffet. Trestle tables covered with starched white cloths were filled with steaming tureens of breakfast fare, untouched fruit bowls and trays of chilled champagne. Toasts were loudly proclaimed, backs slapped and hip flasks emptied. Hunts up. Caspar was impatient to start. He looked back disdainfully at the pack of financiers and entrepreneurs. He took the hunt seriously. It was a tradition in his family going back generations. He would not let his father down. Caspar grasped the gun in his hands and looked out over the bracken towards the woods. Though much of the ancient forest had been cleared for crops, there was still a large swathe of the Tangle in this part of the country. Caspar had played there as a child, making camps and fighting campaigns against imagined aggressors in the dips and gullies. He let out a long sigh. His hot breath curling into the cold morning air. He was aware of his heart beating in his chest. Something was wrong. Incorrect. Jarring like a mismatched thread. He watched the beaters heading into the thicket. Off to stir the flocks with their sticks. He tuned into his pulse; he timed its regular throb. What was missing? Then it struck him. Nothing stirred. There was only stillness. He spun around to see the drunken group of Carlson employees balancing flutes of champagne on overflowing plates. Not one hand was raised to waft away troublesome insects. Because there were no insects. No wasps on the jam, no flies on the bread, no mayflies or bumbling bees. Not even the ever-present midges hindered their enjoyment of the breakfast buffet. Caspar knew that the use of insecticides had increased dramatically recently. Perhaps that was it? Everything was changing, too fast, too soon. He would have to change soon too. Change or wither to nothing.

Caspar was shaken from his dreary daydream by the sound of the hunter's horn sounding in the village. Hunts up. It would soon be followed by the clattering of hooves and the baying of the hounds. A venerable country tradition had been restored. An ancient sport that made him feel safe. Some things were worth preserving, he thought. But the expected hubbub was strangely absent. Again the silence began to press around him. Isolating him from all that was familiar with its mutating pressure.

'What are we waiting for . . . ?'

Eugene Carlson was corralling his half-cut employees to the front line.

'Where's Ralph with my gun? Yo, Ralph, let's lock and load, dude.'

A stoical local handed Eugene his loaded weapon.

'It's Robert, sir. Please wait for the signal before you shoot.'

'Thanks a bunch, Ralph.'

Eugene was keen to kill. He winked sleazily at one of his employees. The ranks were finally filled. The chatter and bluster ceased. Now they all became aware of the silence. Puzzled glances were exchanged. Even the most experienced woodsmen seemed uneasy. They focused their eyes on the edge of the forest, trying hard to ignore their apprehension. Soon the silence would be broken by the turbulence of flapping wings. Eugene belched and took aim. Caspar lifted the stock of his gun and took aim too.

'I see something!'

One of the Carlson employees let off a round.

'Wait, don't shoot!'

An alert gamekeeper managed to push the barrel of the gun skyward, leaving the round to sail harmlessly above the trees, just as a group of beaters emerged shrugging from the wood.

'What the fuck?'

Carlson yelled across the bracken as Bly Stone emerged from the treeline, clearing a path with his beater's stick.

'Nothing doing! Not a thing!'

'What's he saying? Fucking clown. What's this guy saying? No birds, what is this bullshit?'

Eugene was not accustomed to disappointment and would not tolerate further inconvenience. He lowered his weapon and took a discreet sniff from his silver cocaine capsule. Caspar rolled his eyes, watching the young entrepreneur make a mockery of country etiquette. Caspar shouted across the scrub.

'What's up, Bly?'

Bly was now only a few feet from the hunters. He stopped and spat on the ground. He hated these cunts.

'Like I said, there's nothing there, in the trees or on the ground. It's like they all fucked off on holiday. Maybe they knew you were coming?'

'It's those bloody sabs!'

Royce Cotterill, master of the hunt, came storming across the lawn from the direction of the village. The kennelman and Elspeth followed in his wake. They were extremely agitated.

'Is everything OK, Eli? Where's Johnny?'

Elspeth shook her head and grimaced, mouthing 'It's OK' to her worried husband. Royce's face was red with fury.

'They've really done it now, those fucking troublemakers! I'll have them all up in front of the judge by lunchtime! This is intolerable!'

'Calm down Royce, what's happened?'

'Those bloody saboteurs have only gone and stolen our horses! Must have broken in last night. Everyone one of them gone. They should be strung up! And that's not all. Oh, no, it's the hounds too! Not one of them left in the kennels. They even took the pups. They'll do time for this!'

The kennelman glowered. Royce Cotterill simmered with rage. He smacked his riding crop against his thigh with a penitent's zeal. Elspeth joined her husband's side, offering a reassuring squeeze to his arm. Her face wore the look of someone used to being around blustering men, a kind of resigned frown.

'I can't do much good here, Caspar. Johnny will be so disappointed if he can't ride with the hunt today. But it's a bit bloody difficult without horses.'

Caspar gave his wife a smile. They were blessed with an ability to see the funny side of even the most unfortunate situations.

'I think I'll just head back to the house, wait for Johnny there, and hopefully head out later. Once they find the bloody things.'

'OK, darling, hopefully see you at the Bull once this is all sorted out.'

She kissed him tenderly on the cheek, more like a mother than a lover, and headed off to find their child. He watched his wife walk across the lawn back towards the village. He felt fortunate to have such an understanding spouse. She was the cement in his carefully constructed life. 'A fine filly' his father had called her. Caspar wouldn't use that kind of language, of course, but underneath it all, though he tried so hard to appear modern, it was really what he felt too.

Royce Cotterill had barely taken a breath since he arrived. His face was like a purple balloon filled with indignation.

'That Jack Devlin and his crusty friends will be behind this, you mark my words. I thought I saw their clapped-out old bus outside the Quaker's hall this morning. Well, I've called the police, they won't get far. I suppose we shall have to just ride out after lunch now.'

A scream cut across the landscape. Beaters, shooters, hunters and waiters snapped their heads towards the woods. The silence was beginning to fracture. Caspar instinctively raised his gun; the others nervously followed his example.

Eugene took another sniff and raised his weapon too. He'd
kill the first fucking thing that came out of there. Some of
the beaters who had recently emerged plunged back in to
find the source of the scream. Bly headed past the line of
hunters, looking for a few stray flutes of champagne to pinch
from the buffet. The stillness was underpinned by a low
rumble, like a far-off storm brooding. Distant but getting
closer. Gathering in intensity. Another scream. Closer this
time. Eugene let off a round.

'Sir! There are men in those woods.'

Another scream, this time elongated and desperate, like a
drowning man at sea being sucked under by the current.

'Fuck this.'

Eugene fired again.

'Wait! For Christ's sake, wait!'

More gunfire. Sporadic and hesitant at first. Then
they all opened up at once. Muzzles flashing and smoking
with impotent rage. Round after round crashed into the
inscrutable heart of the woods. Trees splinted and branches
crashed as the projectiles tore into the dark interior. The
firing stopped. The stench of cordite and human bowels filled
the air. Caspar was shaking, staring wild-eyed down the
barrel of his father's gun. Never fire when there are beaters
in the field, everyone knew that; it was basic safety. He had
let his father down. Tears welled up and trickled down his
trembling face. He stared hard at the woods. The whole
forest was vibrating. A juddering motion that made the
Tangle tremble and shake with perverse ferocity. Then a vast
wave came crashing through the undergrowth. The bracken
lurched, its stalks pulled by the unseen undertow. Closer.
Closer. Hunts up.

*

Gilbert unscrewed his Thermos and took a refreshing sip of tea. Hunt sabotage was much like birdwatching in many ways: long periods of patient waiting with only the briefest flurries of activity to relieve the tedium. All things considered, he enjoyed the anticipation as much as the activity itself. Doing good was something to look forward to. To save a life was a holy thing. Gilbert was always prepared for those long hours; he had a full Thermos and a stout blanket on which to rest. He had chosen a dark weave so as to blend in more effectively with the shrubs. He didn't go in for camouflage and face paint like some of the youngsters, but he did at least attempt to look as drab as possible. He settled down on his blanket and pulled out his binoculars. He scanned the fields. Nothing. No movement. No visible signs of life. Strange. But he was pleased that the animals seemed intent on hiding from the riders. He smiled to himself. They would be greatly delayed today. The plan was working perfectly. He knew it would be unpopular in the village. They had broken a number of laws, both written and unwritten. On this occasion every rule of the game had been bent and snapped. Horses and hounds spirited away and let loose. They would do time for their crime, of that there was no doubt. But the cull must be thwarted at any cost. Phase two of the plan was about to begin.

Gilbert's attention was drawn away from the fields and into the brightening sky. A large flight of birds was wheeling above him in a dizzying display of ever-changing patterns. Gilbert put his binoculars to his eyes. The same odd variety of species that he had noticed earlier. They whirled together in the crisp morning air. He reached for his notebook, momentarily forgetting his vigil. He scribbled down his observations. Fascinating. This week's birdwatchers meeting would certainly be lively, there was so much to discuss.

He wondered if anyone else had noticed these strange formations. Gilbert raised his binoculars again. The dancing flocks were much lower now. As one, they swooped, diving down at great speed, almost touching the ground, before shooting up into the sky again. It was like the attack pattern of a hawk. Perhaps they were foraging? Or hunting. Now the flock was directly over him. Low and close. So low in fact that he didn't need his binoculars any more. Gilbert put them down and began to note each species as they swirled above him. He was struggling to keep up. His pencil scratched frantically on the page. Such was the variety of birds, he was forced to use awkward acronyms and initials to record them all. He recognised the plumage of a chaffinch. Very close now. It swooped over his head, almost knocking his cap off. Gilbert laughed in delight. These beautiful birds felt his love for them. He could sense it. There was nothing to fear from him. He hoped one might choose to perch on his shoulder for a while, perhaps let him stroke its delicate feathers. He watched the chaffinch shoot up into the sky. It twirled up, cresting the current before corkscrewing back down towards him. Gilbert's smile froze. It was going very fast, and he hoped it would not collide with him and hurt itself. He shielded his eyes against the glare of the sun as the bird descended. Closer. Closer. The chaffinch was falling.

'Slow down, little one, slow down.'

The bird stopped a few centimetres away from his face. Flapping its wings to arrest its descent. Gilbert could feel the gentle waves of air flowing from the bird's beating wings. It began to ascend slowly, its tiny black eyes focused on Gilbert's wonder filled pools. Now it was hovering a few metres above his upturned face. He breathed a sigh of relief as his eyes focused on its subtle plumage.

'How wonderful.'

He whispered as the chaffinch folded its wings and dropped like an arrow. He didn't even have time to raise his hands before the bird's beak pierced his cornea. A dull moan escaped the old man's throat. A long note of incomprehensible pain. The beautiful birds. The beautiful birds. The chaffinch withdrew its beak from Gilbert's eye, dragging out bits of vitreous humour as it slid out. The bird cocked its head and began to peck, drilling into the lens of Gilbert's eye before tugging the whole thing out of its socket. The chaffinch cocked its head again, then with one swift movement it severed the link and flew off with its prize. Gilbert fell on his back, stunned. In agony. His hand groped about. Already going into spasms as shock took hold and the threat of death approached. His fingers lingered in a pool of tea and blood. With his one good eye, he saw the black cloud of birds hovering above him. They swooped on the currents of air. The beautiful birds. The beautiful birds. Then, like a giant fist, they fell on him. Pecking and rending until all that remained was the bloody shadow of Gilbert Lambeth on the scrubland floor.

*

Beryl sauntered into the woodland clearing at the head of a column of village cats. Every variety of feline from feral tomcat to pedigree Persian in tight regimental order. They made their way to their allotted place deep in the heart of the Tangle. Beryl licked her paw and acknowledged Hector, pack leader of the village dogs. Hector pricked up his ears and nodded his greetings. The glade was filling up. The tall, graceful stags stood at the back. The birds filled the branches. Long columns of mice, rats and voles entered the clearing

and took up their place near the front. The insects emerged
from the soil. Midges hovered and fireflies lit up the glade.
The first council meeting in several millennia was beginning.
The horses came late, having been only recently freed
from their stables by a mischief of field mice. Their hooves
vibrated on the forest floor as they trotted into the glade.
Athena, dressage champion and queen of the equine herd,
whinnied and tossed her forelock. The wild creatures of the
forest twittered, barked, squeaked and hooted their greetings
to their liberated comrades. Tonight, the struggle for life
was suspended. Ancient relations of prey and hunter were
put aside. Instinct in temporary abeyance. Now they had a
common enemy. A contagion that had been allowed to spread
largely unchecked was threatening to kill them all. The
contagion had once been of the Tangle, just like all of those
gathered in the glade. But it had mutated into something ugly.
Until they evolved the wisdom to see, they would have to be
contained. The animals had done little to resist the haughty
blooming of this infant species. Trusting that soon they would
remember the roots and the humility of life. Only the aloof
and independent bacteria had done anything to frustrate
the misplaced sense of omnipotence these creatures felt. But
then, they were never too fussy about who they killed. A hush
fell on the glade as the owls landed to begin the meeting.
The oldest and wisest bird in the forest had no name. Names
were for the indentured creatures of the village. She hooted
a greeting, welcoming the gathered fellowship, and after a
eulogy for those now extinct, the meeting began.

*

Jane rolled onto her back, absentmindedly playing with
a stalk of grass. Jane and the Devil, well hidden in the

undergrowth, their camouflaged fatigues covered with twigs and leaves to render themselves invisible to the hunt.

'It was weird, Jack. They must have got wind of our plan or something.'

Jane's face scrunched up in thought. Last night's operation had not gone to plan.

'What, so there wasn't a single horse in the stable? Not one?'

'Not even a foal, but the weirdest thing of all was the fucking dogs, man! I couldn't believe they'd managed to smuggle them out of the kennels without us knowing. Fuckers! Still looks like the jokes on them. Whoever hid them seems to have lost them, judging by the angry faces outside the Bull!'

'Ha, ha, classic. I wonder what idiot they put in charge of that! Still, once they've found them, we'll be ready, the plans not fucked yet, not by a long way. I reckon they did us a favour. But where the fuck are they?'

'Fuck knows, man. All I know is that it was one of the strangest missions I've ever been on. There's me all commando-ed up, bolt cutters, the lot, and not a thing to liberate. Even the mice had fucked off.'

They both burst out laughing, rolling together in the long grass like two shrubs.

Some minutes later, Jack 'the Devil' Devlin perched on his elbows and looked through his field glasses.

'Fuck all happening, Janey. Looks like they've proper fucked it. You heard from Gilbert, by the way? I love him, but he's shit with mobile phones. I don't want them slipping through without us knowing.'

'Nah, nothing. I reckon they're still trying to find the horses.'

'They'll be out again soon enough.'

Jack tightened his grip on the binoculars. He wanted this. The plan was too good to fail. Even though he knew some people in the village would never speak to him again, it would be worth it.

'Where are they?'

The Devil was puzzled.

'Ouch, the midges are lively today.'

Jack scratched at a swelling insect bite as a haze of tiny flies darted around his head.

'Argh, little twats.'

He put down the binoculars, using both hands to swoosh away the persistent midges.

'They like you. Must be that aftershave your mum bought you for Christmas.'

Jane was giggling at the sight of her boyfriend trying to fend them off.

'Not a fly on me, mate.'

Jane showed him her insect-free sleeves.

'Must be because you smell so bad. Ouch, fucking hell, they're all at it now!'

'Cheeky twat, serves you right! Shit, look Jack, now the ants want a go.'

Jane was laughing as she pointed at a column of wood ants that had marched out of the broken earth and was now making its way up Jack's leg. He tried to sweep them off, scattering them into the grass. But they kept coming.

'Just what I fucking need. I haven't had a nip since I was a kid. Fuck off, you little twats!'

Jack flicked the ants into the bracken. It seemed his love of animals did not extend as far as the insect kingdom. In answer, the ground darkened as if it had sprung a leak.

A black wave of ants burst out of the earth. They scuttled from every crack and crevice, surging towards the Devil's horizontal frame.

'Fuck's sake! Shit!'

Jack brushed frantically, trying to turn back the tide. He must not give away their position. Not now that the plan was so close to completion. The mass of ants had grown into a thick, unguent wave covering his legs like an oil slick. Their pincers tore through his fatigues and nipped at his flesh. It felt like hot daggers. Hot stabbing daggers. Stabbing. Stabbing. Jane tried to sweep the growing swarm from her boyfriend's body. But her actions only served to excite them more. The tempo of their attack increased to a frenzied pitch.

'Argh!'

The sharp needle of a wasp's sting pierced the skin of his cheek. The wasps began to do their duty. They pierced the young man at will. Then came the hover flies and the bumble bees. They joined with their modest armoury to harry the prey. Hunts up. Jane became frantic. Tears flooding down her face, she swatted and brushed, blew and swept the insects from his tortured body. Yet she had suffered not a single nip or sting. This was a precise and scientific cull, not a massacre. Jack was soon paralysed. His blood flowed with a potent cocktail of venoms and necrotic fluids that dissolved and corrupted every cell they touched. As his insides began to turn to slurry, his swollen body was being consumed by the mass. Spiders wove webs in his wounds and sucked the fluids from his skin. Flies injected their eggs into the cuts; the maggots writhed in congealing pools. Earwigs entered his nostrils and began to mine. Biting. Biting. Biting. Jane tried to brush the insects from Jack's mouth, hoping he could catch a breath through the stings.

'Oh Christ, Jack! Hang on, baby, I'll get help! Oh fuck, get off him, get off!'

An agonised groan escaped the Devil's mouth.

'Oh Jack, I'll get help, I promise, please say something.'

She leaned in to catch his mumbled words, her face in the jumble of spindly legs and hard, armoured bodies. She could hear their clicking and sucking.

'What is it, Jack? Please say something, please, I love you!'

She wasn't sure if she really did love him, but it felt like the last chance she would ever have to say it. Perhaps it would be of some comfort. The groan came again, sounding like the rasp of an old man. She leaned closer to hear. His swollen lips parted and a faint hiss of air escaped like a slow puncture from a bicycle tyre. Then came the mandibles. Jane ran. She ran towards the village and the safety of buildings. Roads and bricks and mortar. She ran as far from the fields as she could. Away from the grass, alive with savage ticks. Away from the pitted ground that hid the caves of malignant arachnids and the many segmented fiends. She ran even as the insects finished their work. She ran as fast as her legs could carry her, leaving the desiccated remains of the Devil to the new masters of the scrub. Behind her, the insects marched across the shrunken frame of Jack Devlin. They formed into thick columns and headed towards the village.

*

Bly gnawed on a chicken leg whilst stuffing a bottle of reasonably fine wine into his coat pocket. It was his reward for putting up with these useless cunts. They were popping off at phantoms on the country club's lawn. He'd beaten these woods for years now, but he'd never seen anything like this. Nothing stirred. He thought it was quite funny,

all this fuss over the cull, all the excitement at being able
to kill again, and not a fucking thing to shoot at. Fucking
funny. He heard another random volley rattle across the
scrubland, but this time it mingled with a scream. Bly
turned towards the woods with only mild interest. The toffs
were getting spooked. Another scream, closer. Now even
the seasoned hunters started to fire wildly into the trees.
Something was coming. Bly put down the chicken leg and
swept up a champagne flute, downing the contents in one
gulp. In the pit of his stomach a feeling of unease began to
rise. A reckoning. Bly tasted a metallic tang in his mouth.
He wiped it with the back of his hand. Blood. He had bitten
through his lip. He felt his cynical composure crumbling as
if a long-postponed debt was finally being called in. What the
fuck was that? A fresh scream, more complex and unsettling
than the last. It pierced the morning air, rippling through
the blue towards the gathered hunters like an invisible belt
of disturbance. Bly steadied his half-pissed frame against the
trestle table. Something was coming. He noticed that posh
cunt Caspar letting off round after round into the wood. He
looked terrified. The rich yank had lost his shit too. If he had
a bazooka, he'd be using it. Bly wanted to run, but a morbid
fascination kept him anchored to the spot. Could this be the
purging wave he secretly longed for?

*

Beryl dragged her pampered bulk through the stalks. She
was carrying a few kilos but she could still move like a cat
half her age. Behind her came the other village cats, flanked
by the beagles and Hector's canine militia. The animal
collective charged. They must carry out the council's grim
instructions. This was the first wave, the stealthy, low-slung

assault squad. The rats, mice, cats and dogs. They flew beneath the tall bracken virtually undetected. Beryl could see the polished boots of a part-time huntsman as they approached the edge of the scrub. Only a small lawn to cross, then they would be upon them. She tensed her muscles and prepared to pounce.

Eugene Carlson was fraying like a pulled cardigan. The coke and booze mingled uneasily with adrenalin, making him feel woozy and nauseous. He tried to focus on his rifle sight.

'Fucking reload, man, fucking reload!'

Robert held the reloaded gun ready, his hand steadier than the frantic pulsing of his heart. Eugene fired at nothing. He threw up on the stock and took the fresh gun from Robert. Wiping the stock, Robert reloaded and waited for Eugene to spit another shot into the void. Eugene wiped the sweat from his eyes. This was not the weekend of bacchanalian excess he had hoped for. He scanned the treeline, desperate for a target. Nothing. Just the disembodied screams of men. Suddenly, too late to react, he noticed the bracken vibrating on the edge of the lawn. Rats, like a volley of torpedoes, shot out from the undergrowth.

'What the fuck, Ralph!'

'It's Robert, sir.'

The rats flowed around their feet, gnawing through their ankles like buzz saws through pine. Robert tumbled to the floor and was soon consumed. Eugene was somehow still standing, held upright by the mass of rats. His mouth hung open, unable to understand how a man of his wealth and position could be so horribly inconvenienced. He tried to blast a hole in the horde with his rifle, but it made little impression. His shins were now being whittled to the bone by razor-sharp teeth. His eyes stared unbelievingly into the scrub as Beryl launched herself from out of the bracken. Her claws glistened in the sun as they plunged into his face. Eugene fell. His head smacked on the earth. Beryl stood over him, her chubby tail swooshing behind her. With one rapid slashing movement she took his eyes.

*

Caspar retreated, using his father's gun like a club. Rats and mice flew off at tangents as he batted them away. He prayed he could hold them back, because if the animal horde was to reach the village . . . God knows. He thought of Elspeth and Johnny waiting for him by the fireside. Toes curling and flexing as the flames warmed their feet. His wife would bring out the biscuits and hot chocolate. Johnny would spoil his appetite. It was shepherd's pie tonight. They would turn to the window, surprised to hear the sound of feet. Was daddy home? Their fragile bodies ripped to shreds on the Chesterfield sofa.

'Bly, help me turn these tables, quickly man!'

Bly was hypnotised by the unfolding horror. He moved automatically, tipping the tables over. Some of the hunters had the same idea and a makeshift stockade sprang up on the lawn. The tide of rats broke on the fortress wall. Caspar was shaking uncontrollably now.

'Oh Christ, oh Christ.'

He fumbled to reload. He could hear his heartbeat booming fast against his ribs. Everything had gone quiet again. The silence pressed.

'Fuck, fuck.'

Caspar risked a glance over the parapet. The animals had gathered in silent ranks around the tables. Cats licked their paws or prowled the perimeter. Dogs obediently sat and sniffed the air, as if waiting for a treat from their master's hand.

'Fuck, fuck, fuck. What are they doing?'

Caspar scanned the gathered animals. Some had once been pets. He recognised many of them from around the village. He had tickled their tummies by the welcoming hearths of local pubs. Thrown them treats at a thousand drinks parties. Patted their muddy heads as he chatted to their owners in the park.

'Good boy, good girl.'

He whispered to himself, as Beryl, slick with gore, inspected the ranks. Caspar wanted to shout her name.

'It's your favourite tonight, girl, yummy mackerel.'

The words died on his lips, mingling with the dying moans of humans.

Bly just stared into the woods.

'They are coming.'

Bly stood up.

'Get down, for fuck's sake, Bly, get down!'

Everyone was shouting at him like he was a disobedient hound.

'What the fuck did you say?'

You cunts. You overprivileged turds. Think you're so much better than me, do you? Bly's face broke into a grotesque grin as he pointed towards the woods. The treeline exploded. Out of the Tangle came the horses, stags, deer, oxen, sheep and pigs. The sound of their hooves thundered over the manicured lawn as they came on across the scrub. Bly carelessly kicked over a flimsy section of barricade and walked towards the oncoming animals.

'Bly, what the fuck are you doing? Come back!'

The rodents made a path. Bly walked down it. In zombie order he staggered forward. The cats and dogs let him pass too. Their noses twitching in anticipation. His tear-filled eyes were transfixed on the stampede. He reached the edge of the lawn as the first horses broke out of the scrub. The deep, dark pools of the horses' eyes swallowed him as they locked gazes. Bly fell to his knees and raised his hands, as if the messiah had finally returned to judge them all. He began to laugh hysterically.

'Oh, thank God.'

Athena's hoof splintered his face. His features instantly rearranging like a distorting mirror. As her hooves connected with the ground, they pushed Bly's broken head into the soil. Hunts up.

Now the siege reached its inevitable climax. Tables were tossed aside, and their defenders dispatched by tooth, hoof and claw. The ground became littered with the disconnected fragments of limbs. Lying severed amongst the blood-stained tweed flotsam like a grotesque tailor's floor. The investors, hunters, weekend hedge fund adventurers, lawyers, advisors and ancillary staff were all carelessly strewn about. All dying by degrees. Moans mixed in with the sound of gnawing. Once the killing had stopped, the rats and pigs had begun to scurry over the corpses, chewing at the flesh of the fallen, even as some still breathed. The battlefield would soon be clear. The first stage of the cull was going to plan. Now they must take care of the village.

Caspar lay broken against the splintered trestle table. His legs jutted out like the useless limbs of a ventriloquist's dummy. Flattened flesh and shattered bone. His entrails glistened, exposed to the morning air through a gaping wound. Next to him a circle of rats and cats were lapping

126

at the bloody remains of Royce Cotterill. His scarlet tunic was soaked to a tone that matched his angry face. The top of his head was missing; the ridges of his brain poked out through his ill-advised comb-over. Caspar thought he looked like a discarded sausage. He smiled to himself. Always good to see the funny side. That's what Elspeth said. Caspar was struggling to breath. His nose was clogged with broken bone and congealed blood, so he gulped like a fish. Not long now, he thought. A comforting softness brushed passed his shattered cheek. The delicate bones of a cat. Beryl rubbed herself against him, her tail flexing and waving as she purred. They were back in the cottage. Hot toast and tea. Ready to open their Christmas presents. Johnny was very small, jumping about, remonstrating with his cruel parents.

'Can we open them now, daddy? Please, please! You said after breakfast!'

'Alright, you little monster!'

Beryl brushed against his legs. Purring. Purring.

'Should we give Beryl her present first, Johnny?'

His breathing was too painful to bear now. Beryl stepped onto his chest, tail swooshing, body vibrating.

'Hello old girl. Come to see your dad, have you?'

Beryl placed her paw on his lips to silence him. She turned to survey the horror around them. She cocked her head and brushed it affectionately against his bruised face. The purring stopped. Their eyes met. Her eyes were filled with tears. It is strange to see a cat cry, Caspar thought. Beryl's claws flashed from her paw, piercing his lips, top and bottom. She drew his lips together as blood poured down his clogging airway. Their eyes remained locked even as his last stuttering attempts at breathing faded to nothing. Beryl withdrew her claws. Caspar remained inert, propped up like a forgotten toy. She licked her paw before padding off to join her comrades. Hunts up.

*

Elspeth wasn't sure how, or why, she had been spared. The animals had poured into the village like an apocalyptic whirlwind. Down chimneys, up plug holes and drains, smashing through windows and doors. Every conceivable species and subgenus had swept through the village, killing almost everything in their path. They had stormed the cottage too. Swarming from every crack and crevice. They had pursued her around the house, finally cornering her in the loft conversion. The dogs were snapping at her legs when a fox strolled through their ranks. It climbed her torso, perching on her chest, with a set of snarling jaws only inches from her throat. The urgent hoot of an owl had risen above the clamour. Then as quickly as they had come, they were gone. Elspeth stumbled out into the midday sun. Nothing stirred. All the animals were elsewhere. She wandered in a daze past the village green now littered with the torn remains of her neighbours. She headed for the stream. The gentle brook where Johnny liked to play. Perhaps he was there hiding in a tree? Perhaps they had spared him too. A small boy child too young to hurt a fly. But the flies were in no mood to be hurt by boys, girls, women or men. Now they buzzed over the carrion. The splintered remains of an arrogant breed. Elspeth passed through the brambles, careless of their vengeful pricks. She stumbled through the nettles, but the stings barely registered. She must find her child. By the slopes of the riverbank, he would be skimming stones, he would be making camps, he would be making plans. Where was Johnny? Her beautiful, beautiful boy.

Today was to be his first hunt. His first taste of the chase. Today he would place one faltering step into the adult world. Today he would grow into a man, just like his father: sturdy, proper, correct. Today he would be blooded. Today. Today. Today. Hunts up.

Helen

A single rose on a grave. A barren patch. No grass grew.
No insect settled. On the stone a simple engraving. Timothy
Cavendish.

No motto. No epitaph. No one to mourn him. His father
had died years ago. The last of the patriarchs. The magistrate,
the magus, the managing director. Only one of his two
daughters now lived. Helen. Helen standing here. Brigitte had
married the vicar and died. Helen lived. Helen standing here.

She dropped the rose. As she always did. Every year
without fail. Not out of love. She had hated her father. But
for her mother. She came every year for her. Just to check he
hadn't risen from the grave to spite them. She was a woman
now, like her mother, but stronger. Free of the bonds of her
family and the spell they had cast over Caxton. She had
flourished in her later years. She had moved to the city and
forgotten the oppression of this place. Helen worked hard and
gathered accolades. She added initials to her name. Professor
Helen Cavendish FRS, FRSA, OOG. She was as happy as she
could be, but she never forgot the sadness in her mother's
eyes. That's why she had built the thing. The Happiness
Engine. Everyone would feel the benefits of its wisdom. No
one would have to look that way again. But she was wrong,
and she knew it. Happiness is everything.

God knows how she had ended up back here. But the
town had dragged her home. It was the work. She had been

horrified when the university had announced the location of its latest research facility. But somehow, she had expected it. This place. Brigitte married the vicar and died. Then the world went to shit, and now military flags flew on every street corner. Just another coup d'état. The new regime had taken to her work wholeheartedly. Helen tried to back out, to destroy the files. She told them it would not work. But it was too late. Tomorrow the president would come. Freshly installed as the glorious leader; the figurehead of their bright new future. He would cut the ribbon and the A.B.A.C.U.S. would begin its programme. She stared at the austere headstone and sighed. So much death and so much yet to come. Her sister lay nearby. Cut to ribbons in her potting shed.

Brigitte's death. That's when the doubts had been seeded. Even before she finished her work, she knew her project would fail. But she was already too far in to stop. Those woods. Her sister had been an awful human. But no one would wish that on anyone. The blood. The Tangle. Helen had studied the forest since that day. She had wandered its knotted paths. That's where she found him. The author. Matted beard and dirty clothes. Scratched lenses in plastic frames. Too long in the wild. He was looking for answers too. He had taken notes. Drawn sketches. Bound them all in a book. He let her read his findings. Florid prose full of fanciful conjectures. But there was something in them. They had become friends of a sort. They explored the forest together. She was going to meet the author after the ceremony. She was going help him add some much-needed rigour to his words. She couldn't think in wires and switches anymore. She could only think of the Tangle.

Pond

Under springy loam and layers of hot decay. In the filaments of leaves and the deep veins of trunks. In stems and roots. In the dense air of the forest. From the canopy to the core. The blood of life surges like an insolent torrent. Occasionally it will settle, forming numinous pools. Cool ponds of inscrutable depth or dank mires of putrid sludge. These enigmatic lagoons are an invitation to glimpse another world converging with our own. A viscous scrying dish to aid time travel and augury. The wriggling microbes that infest the morass remind the creatures of the land of their origins. But look closer and it is possible to see the future stretching out through the murk. Look closer, good pilgrim. Come closer to the shoreline, good pilgrim. Gaze into rippling waters. Can you see the happiness you seek? Are you not deserving of all you desire? Through will and good fortune, let the world bend to your needs. The haughty pinnacle of evolution. Staring into the congealing blood of life. Do my bidding, for I am man. But blood demands blood. The satisfaction of desire always comes with a price.

Paul Porter waved his phone in the air like a wizard conjuring the furies. There was no signal in the Tangle. He had been disconnected from Fuck Finder and his hook-up was now missing in the bushes and byways of the forest. Things had not been going well for Paul. He was on his last chance at work. He had stapled a colleague's finger to the office noticeboard last week, and he was certain that once his case went to the tribunal, he would be out of a job again. The boss would be sorry to see him go; he'd said that. I like you Paul, he'd said. You're a good guy underneath it all . . . it's just, you know? You need to calm down when things don't go your way, Paul. He'd said that. Standing there in his fucking office. He couldn't look him in the eye. At weekends he moonlighted as a children's entertainer. Pazz the Magnificent. Balloon animals. Sleight of hand tricks with cards and coins. His pet rabbit Doris pulled from a top hat. He was cheap, so he kept a passably full diary. But one tousle-haired youngster had become too inquisitive and had snuck under his magic table. The screaming, the hair pulling, the messy faces and cake fights were all part of the background hum of children's entertainment. He could tolerate all that. But this boy had spoiled the fun for everyone. He had violated the magic code. Without a code you were nothing. Pazz the Magnificent had delivered an instinctive clout to the side of the child's head, causing the boy to spill out from behind the magic tablecloth and into the middle of the birthday party. His dazed whimpering had swiftly blended into howls of protest. Angry parents had escorted Pazz the Magnificent off the premises before he had time to complete his act, leaving balloon animals deflating in the conservatory. He had begged the parents, with tears in his eyes. It was a mistake; it would never happen again. He loved his work, making the little ones laugh. Conjuring the wonder. Of course, I'm not sorry. If you had some control over your children, this would never have happened. I'm a professional. Can't you see? Can't you see? Why can't you see? He wasn't a violent man. But some people just couldn't help breaking the spell. He fucking hated them for it.

His ejection from the venerable guild of children's entertainers had left him with too much time on his hands. He spent long evenings alone, browsing ever more lurid material on his computer. Eventually finding himself walking the darker neighbourhoods of the World Wide Web. As he brooded, with his resentment gnawing at him, so his desire for unorthodox diversions began to blossom. Passwords and encryptions. Keys, pseudonyms and dubious avatars became his obsession. Pazz the Magnificent was reborn as a sexual adventurer. Fuck Finder was a really great app. User-friendly. A five-star operation. He had met some very interesting people on it. But though he had certainly been put through his paces, no one had really warranted a return visit. He rarely gave more than 3 stars. His rating was low too. Detached, too rough, morose, those were some of the more helpful comments. He was beginning to think he might end up with the one or two-star amateurs and borderline offenders. Then Pan1977 popped up. The notification he'd received this morning was so stimulating that he had forgone his usual caution and headed into the dark interior of the woods. There was a promise of erotic delights of a more specialist variety than he was accustomed to. He rarely found anyone willing to satisfy his needs. Even the most open-minded correspondents tended to baulk at his more outré requests. But not Pan1977. They had offered some of the most dynamic suggestions for pleasure he had ever come across, and without prompting too. Normally he had to deftly pirouette around the subject, looking for the right moment to up the ante. But Pan1977 had jumped straight in. It was as if they had read Paul's mind. There were activities on the menu he never knew had a name. Pan1977's profile picture was a little blurry. But somehow, the indistinct figure with the lively imagination simply became more attractive in the shadows. He pushed on through the bush. Hard and focused.

Paul trembled as he brushed aside the branches. Pan1977 was somewhere in the woods, dancing their delicate reels amongst the flowers. He was certain. Pazz the Magnificent aroused. Pazz the Magnificent, risen and ready. Pazz the Magnificent, the elemental force of passion. He snagged his lightweight cardigan on a thorn bush. He cursed, hoping that Pan1977 hadn't noticed his awkward entanglement. A crackle of twigs alerted him to movement ahead. He quickened his pace. Soon. Soon. The light in the wood began to intensify. The grey-green shadows taking on golden epaulettes. Rays of sunlight pierced the crown of the trees as the forest thinned. Paul found himself emerging into a clearing of flower-dappled grass. Bright and sumptuous. A shimmering pond nestled in its centre. He had lived in and around Caxton Wood all his life, but he had never come across a pond before. Not even in his most adventurous childhood wanderings. Maybe it was one of those bucolic features the corporation had recently added. Alongside the woodchip picnic area and the folksy neopagan carvings that dotted the paths. The corporation had attempted to entice townsfolk to the forest. To sell them expensive parking adjacent to their crude parody of nature. This must be one of those features. It was too perfect to be real.

He scanned the banks. This would make a delightful spot to fuck away the afternoon. It was well chosen. He smiled and stretched out his fingers, entwining them in a web as he bent back his palms. His knuckles cracked as a twig snapped. He thought he could hear laughter. Light and playful. A game? Oh, how wonderful! Paul tore off his cardigan, twirling it around his head like a demented helicopter, before carelessly letting it fly. The afternoon sun was reaching its zenith, bathing the clearing with a dazzling warmth that penetrated his pasty skin and soaked into his bones. He unbuttoned his shirt, leaving him in vest, slacks and sensible shoes. He extended his arms in a Christ-like pose and shouted.

'I am here!'

His voice echoed in the clearing. Spinning endlessly around the glade like a scream in a cave. Paul was surprised. It was a fearful sound. Not at all what he was expecting. His voice kept ringing and swirling, bouncing off the banks of the pond. The gentle laughter he had heard earlier skittered across the surface like a water boatman. Blending into his own mournful tone. Gradually his echo dissolved into the summer afternoon chatter. Birdsong and cricket clicks replaced the ghostly boom. He relaxed somewhat. A smile returned to his face as his thoughts again turned to sensual exploration. He stepped closer to the water's edge and began to walk around the circumference of the pond. Hoping to catch site of Pan1977 in the rushes. The corporation really had done a marvellous job with this pond. It was so idyllic it was almost ridiculous. The green saucers of the water lilies were crowned with bright pink blooms, over which kaleidoscopic dragonflies hovered. Thick grasses and exotic ferns bowed over the surface like obedient butlers, providing shade for the sleek water voles, who occasionally poked their twitching noses into the air. The water was crystal clear, like polished glass. Paul stared into it. Pazz the Magnificent stared back.

He threw off his shoes and pulled down his slacks. In vest and pants he stepped into the water. Pazz the Baptist. Into the cleansing waters he waded. The cool, cool waters. The sensation was breathtaking. He went further into the pond, letting the water creep up his thighs. He waded further in. The feeling of well-being ratcheting up in intensity as he pushed back the supple water. The water caressed his cock like a gentle lover. The sensation was unmistakable. Fingers, palms, pressure. Paul closed his eyes and let himself get carried further and further into the pond. Hands were all over him now. Rubbing, tugging. The water was soon past his shoulders, rising over his neck. Paul hardly noticed that his head had disappeared under the surface. The hands increased the vigour of their caresses. He thought he might cum in the perfect pool. He opened his eyes. He was at the bottom of the pond. But the water was so clear it was like daylight on the surface. The caresses of the invisible hands were reaching their crescendo. He realised in his ecstasy that he was not alone. A vague shape was forming from the bubbles of his breath. A figure of staggering beauty emerged from the bubbles and floated before him. Neither male nor female. Nor an amalgamation of both. But something new. He could not describe this apparition with his stunted human vocabulary. Was this Pan1977? A god? An angel? A demon? He reached out to touch the creature as it swam around him. But it was already inside him. Its hands were the hands of the water. The beautiful, beautiful touch. The exquisite lightness. The water hands suddenly tightened their grip, becoming more aggressive. Just how he liked it. The current swirled hard around his parts until it felt like his cock might be torn clean off. He gasped in pleasure as he came. His seed mixing with blood, as finally his member was uprooted like a leek. Spinning softly in the current before settling on the bottom. Blood blossomed from the wound. Paul's smile was so wide he thought his jaw might crack. The cool cleansing water rushed into him, filling his lungs until they burst. His eyes, wide with joy, were fixed on the face of the beautiful creature as he passed from the world of men into the next. As he stared, the creature's eyes turned from emerald green pools to beams of burning red fire. Still beautiful. But now it was a terrible beauty. He drew his last breath. Sucking in more water until he was full. As he inhaled, the water thickened to a glutinous tar, encasing every fibre of the unfortunate ex-children's entertainer. He tried to scream but it was too late. The water hardened in his cells. Petrifying him from the inside. The blood of life sucked back into the Tangle.

*

Hilda Wilton struggled to the nearest bench with her phone wedged between her chin and collarbone. Breathless in the growing summer heat, she hurriedly deposited her dry cleaning and medical bag. There was a do on tonight. Smart frocks and ties.

'Dr Wilton.'

She answered with as much professionalism as she could muster as her dress slipped from the hanger into cigarette ash and dust.

'Fuck, sorry, no, nothing . . . must be a crossed line.'

She winced. This wasn't the 1930s. A look of relief mixed with a resigned eye roll as she finally recognised the caller's voice.

'Sergeant Harker, yes, yes, no, I didn't recognise your voice, apologies, ye, ha, yes, erm, how may I help you this morning, sergeant?'

She removed the phone from under her chin and quickly sat on the bench. The blood drained from her face and a hint of discomfort flickered in her eyes.

'Yes, I understand, sergeant. I know the spot. I'll get to you as soon as possible. Don't touch the body, if you please. Yes, yes, sorry, I realise you know that, yes, OK, thank you . . .'

She absentmindedly cancelled the call, letting her dry-cleaned dress fall back into the dust and ash.

For nearly thirty years she had avoided the woods. A short stroll in the park, skirting the edges of the Tangle, was as near as she would get. Naturally there had been quite a number of cases in the scrubland. She would try to avoid those calls too. How she had dodged them until today was anyone's guess. She had a feeling that people knew not to call on her for those jobs. The ones in the woods. They were good like that. Occasionally she would catch a whisper, a glance or a sudden awkward silence when she entered the room. The girl from the woods. That's what the newspapers had called her. Thirty years ago. Dangling by her legs. Staring at her lover's bloodshot eyes as they swung in the branches. The scuttling sound of those things. Pinching and cutting. The blur of blue as a policeman ran into the clearing to save them. The screams as the scuttling things cut him down. Severed limbs and stretched sinews. The swaying of the branches. The DI, in her calm, resigned way, pierced and rendered so they might live. She remembered running through the woods, stumbling into the day and a thousand flashing lights. Cameras, questions, blankets and tea. No one believed them, of course. She had spent a year in a psychiatric ward. Her lover had thrown himself off Ardlington viaduct. Push it down, they had said. The hysterical delusions, the hallucinations, they weren't real. Tam Stamp had done them all. The harmless hippy of the woods. He had killed all those people. Cut them up and rearranged them in that hideous stinking sculpture. He had killed himself before the trial. That was good. Case closed. Except she knew he hadn't done it. The scuttling things, the woodland spiders, the creatures of the Tangle. She had been an exemplary inmate and had grown interested in medicine during her time there. It was something real and tangible, something she could understand. Perhaps if she studied hard, she could fix the pain, in others, if not herself. Years of study and heartache. Now here she was, Dr Hilda Wilton, attached to Caxton CID, trembling on a bench.

Hilda sat in her car, staring at the dials on her dashboard. The last anchor of the human dimension. The spindly legs, clicking, piercing, cutting. The neat uniformity of the fuel gauge. The blood and sinew ripped and pulled. The machined perfection of the steering wheel. The headless torso in the leaves. She shuddered, closed her eyes and gulped down the conditioned air. Trembling slightly, she stepped out of the car.

'Sorry for dragging you into this one, Dr Wilton.'

The DI looked embarrassed and uneasy. She didn't like having to adopt such a formal tone with a childhood friend, but at least it was her on this job and not one of her macho co-workers. Hilda offered her a nervous smile by way of reassurance and nodded decisively towards the woods. They began to march towards the trees, the doctor's strides disguising her unease.

'This is a strange one, doc. I don't want to pre-empt your findings, but it looks like the victim drowned in the middle of the wood. That's not all, but I'll wait until you see the body before I speculate further.'

'Very wise, Claire. Let me be the judge of the cause of death, eh?'

Hilda regretted snapping at her friend. Claire Hammond was a good detective and a better friend. The vision of another DI. In another time, imploring her to run as a branch pierced her chest. She placed her hand on Claire's shoulder. Claire placed hers on top, squeezing it gently. She understood that this was not easy for the doctor. They pushed back the flaps of the forensic tent and joined the team who were standing over the victim. As soon as she saw the corpse, every nerve in her body told her to run. Get out of the woods, it's happening again. She swayed slightly. Claire steadied her.

'Are you OK?' she whispered. 'I'm right here behind you, take your time.'

Hilda tried to smile, hoping to force some confidence back into her face. But the smile froze and contorted into a grimace. Claire squeezed her arm gently. The doctor turned, acknowledged the officers in the tent and silently went to work.

She had done her best to leave the forensic tent with dignity but had noticeably lurched through the flaps. She gulped mouthfuls of heavy woodland air as she tumbled into the glade. She had seen worse: car crashes, industrial accidents, victims of fire. No, a drowned man with a missing phallus was nothing to get worked up about. It was this place. This fucking wood. Miles from any water. No signs of the body having been dragged or deposited here from elsewhere. But she was certain it was a case of drowning. This place. Always there, on the edge of her consciousness, the edge of her every moment. She steadied herself on a tent pole and tried to regain her composure. The structure vibrated at her touch. She would be better off leaning on one of the sturdy trees that were dotted about the glade. But she wouldn't touch the trunks. Things dwelt in the bark that she'd rather forget. The trees towered over her, their uncanny presence like a terrible echo from a past she had hoped to escape. She had to get out. That terrible harvest. That gruesome workshop. That beautiful furniture. She looked nervously at the trunks, half expecting the creatures to emerge. Glistening pincers and sharp wooden claws. But instead, there was stillness.

She took her hand from the tent pole. But there was no tent. No police. No forensics. Just the body of a drowned man, and silence. Her breath froze in her throat as if she was being gently throttled. She looked at the drowned man prone on the leaves. Stillness. Like a tomb. The drowned man on a slab. The drowned man walking on arachnid legs. Click. Clack. A sound began to drone around the trees. At first the sound was nothing but a discordant hiss, barely discernible above her own internal hum. But the hiss began to swell, engulfing the frequencies of the forest until it was all she could hear. She thought she might be losing her mind. She clasped her ears, wanting to rip them off, to escape the cascading vibration. The sound began to change from hiss to harmony. The structure of the wood shifted. Layers were peeled back and exposed. Her breathing became slow and steady. Music replaced the static hiss. Delicate chords of simple beauty rang out in the treetops. Its soothing tones, reassuring somehow. This was the woodland of her childhood, before those scuttling things had taken her. A subtle shift in key alerted her to the movement of water. Between the branches of a spreading ash, she saw a waterfall dropping silently into a rocky pool. The incongruity of the sight didn't disturb her one bit. In fact, she expected it. She looked around to where the crime scene tent had once been. The drowned man was there. The drowned man stood and began to walk, brushing past her as he headed towards the waterfall. She began to walk with him, over the soft forest floor as the strange symphony continued to swirl around her. In the middle of the silent flow, she saw a figure. The water bent around the figure like the current of air in a wind tunnel. The creature was part human, part rock. It looked like the naked torso of the deceased Detective Inspector. Thirty years in the past, standing under the falling waters. The figure signalled with a stony hand. The drowned man walked into the waterfall and disappeared.

'Come on, Hilda, let me buy you a drink.'

Hilda Wilton turned around slowly as her friend emerged from the forensic tent. She had a look of concern on her face. She gently took hold of the troubled doctor, and arm in arm they walked out of the woods.

*

Pazz the Magnificent lay on the mortuary slab, his ribcage open like a Viking blood eagle. His skull was unscrewed, with his brain nestling in it like a bag of fossilised worms. Various organs had been removed to be weighed and examined. His cock was missing. Dr Wilton walked around the excavated corpse, tapping her pen against her lips in thought. Her diagnosis of death by drowning had been correct. But it wasn't water she found filling his lungs, but instead a kind of black pumice. It resembled the solidified volcanic material more often found in and around active volcanoes, rather than inside the bodies of ex-children's entertainers. It was flecked with glowing red streaks that seemed to indicate part of the rock had not yet fully cooled. Yet it was not only cold to the touch, it was freezing. This was unusual. But, in her way, Dr Wilton had expected this too. She was haunted. Haunted by a space that would never let her go. The vison in the forest. The silently dropping waterfall and the ghost in its midst were all signs on a journey. Spectral signifiers of something missing. Part of her lost in the woods, longing to return. She wanted it back.

*

Hilda scanned the local papers. Hilda scanned the airwaves. Hilda was looking for stories. Events that seemed out of the ordinary. Unorthodox occurrences. Anything relating to old Caxton Wood. She studied its history, taking out every book on the subject from Caxton library. She poured over cuttings torn from old magazines. She bookmarked scratchy videos made by amateur naturists and low-rent historians. The wood she had avoided for over thirty years became her obsession. She had said nothing to her friends. Claire Hammond had called to see if she was OK. That day in the woods. Everything was so fucked up. But the doctor had seemed unnaturally still. Claire was worried about her. I'm good. I'm good. She said nothing of her late-night ramblings, her daily incursions into the Tangle. For years she had politely declined the invitations, all those picnics and languid summer strolls. People knew not to ask the girl from the woods. But now she looked for every opportunity to wander the twisting paths of the forest. Holidays owed, lunch breaks stretched, weekend plans cancelled or rearranged. Time was for the Tangle. The rough stone hand under the silent waterfall. The drowned figure. She walked the paths, hoping for the visions to return. In that gloomy glade with the gelded man under the tarpaulin. The wood had spoken to her through its indistinct signs. It was an offering. A chance. She must subjugate her fear and surrender.

The days were long and the nights were cold. In the deep black interior, she crept. The forest was never the same. Each visit was different. Familiar routes changed direction or were obliterated by the shifting foliage. It was hard to get her bearings. She found herself going over the same ground again and again. Her impatience only made the task harder, as if every irritable blow to a dangling stem caused the density of the vegetation to increase. So, instead, she found herself quietly standing under the trees. Eyes closed and focused.

147

She would reach out her palms to touch the trunks. Just like Sarah did. Sarah, the sacrifice. As the capillaries of her palms penetrated her skin, she thought she sensed tiny vibrations pulsing through the bark. The pulse was weak, barely perceptible. But, bit by bit, the path became clearer. Until one day she found it. It was getting late. Darkness was coming. But the light still clung to the sky like a fading stain. She had gone through her ritual as usual, eyes closed, breathing steady, intention set. This time the tingling sensation seemed more pronounced, as if her fingertips were being pricked by warm needles. The pulse was clearer. Beating with a disordered syncopation. Click. Clack. Clack. She opened her eyes. Her pupils as black as Dante's well. She heard the chime of harmonic chords. She was back. She gently pushed the branches aside and stepped forward.

The ancient ash, scion of the original root, swayed in its glade. It noticed a human figure stumbling in the twilight. A vaguely familiar creature. It had been here before, years ago, or was it only moments ago? What was it doing? It looked lost, all its kind did. They were dying, slowly, and soon they would be gone. But that was for later. This figure seemed sympathetic somehow. Like some of the others who had since joined with the Tangle. The ash stirred as the figure pressed its hands on the bark. It was her. Once the ash had been a craftsman. She had been one of the components. But she was faulty. The ash had found a better fit. The ash had taken only what it needed. But there was a residue. A surplus. Hilda pressed her palm firmly against the ridges of the bark. This was the place. The glade where she had been bound and tied all those years ago. Moments from death. Hanging by her bleeding ankles as those *things* cut and sliced. Tears rolled down her cheeks and her breath came in rasping sobs.

The memories were too great to contain. They threatened to overwhelm her. But she wouldn't run this time. She pressed on the bark. Inside, the faint memory of DI Sarah Ward pressed back. Hilda looked for news, Hilda looked for stories, Hilda looked for signs. She had forgotten something in the bark. Something lost. But the connection was still too weak. The door remained closed. The ash stirred. At the boarder of the Tangle, another figure was staggering into the forest, looking for satisfaction.

*

Baxter Long watched the doctor lock her car and walk off down the track that led to the woods. He had met her on a couple of occasions. He had even been a patient of hers for a short time. When the Caxton Harriers' regular medic had been on administrative leave. He remembered her penetrating gaze. She was nice, but odd. She had sorted his ankle out, no problem. He had seen her here, at this exact spot, every day for the last fortnight. Different times of the day for different lengths of time, but every day without fail. He knew because he was here every fucking day too. He always waited until the doctor drove away. He didn't want there to be any chance of anyone seeing him. Not that anyone would recognise him.

His once-taught belly hung like a deflated rubber ring over his cargo pants. The fact that he was wearing cargo pants at all was testimony to how low his standards had fallen. Once, he'd worn tailored suits or box-fresh kit with a sponsor's logo. The Caxton Harriers had been heroes of track and field. Gold medal winners. The others were anyway. Faces in the papers. Baxter obscured. Blurred in the back line. Arms around celebrities. Baxter at the peripheries. Not quite. Nearly. Reflected glory. Gold traded for bronze.

Now he made unenthusiastic kids feel bad about themselves in his Saturday morning 'Sport can be fun with Baxter Long' sessions. He would shout words of discouragement from the sidelines, then give them the benefit of his insight on their shoddy performance. They were more like extended eulogies on how close he had been to fame than instructive lessons on fitness. He despised them all. Especially the parents with their autograph books. Ironic snaps for laughs at his expense. His bitterness was quickly consuming him. Booze and pills kept him going, but he had been close to calling it a day. Three weeks ago, he had taken a rope into the forest. He had trudged through Caxton Wood to find a tree worthy of his corpse. He had threaded the knot and was about to cast it over a branch when the waters had risen.

She was taking too long. Something must have detained the doctor. He couldn't wait any longer, his desire was too great. Baxter would risk it. The forest was large enough, so he doubted their paths would cross. Not if he was careful. He opened the door and stretched; his joints clicked painfully as he pulled himself out of the seat. He was wearing his Caxton Harriers kit. It was stretched over his torso like the skin of an overinflated balloon. The medal flapped on a faded ribbon around his neck. He closed the door, threw the rope across his shoulder and set off towards the forest. Baxter stepped stealthily through the undergrowth, watching for signs of walkers or fucking couples. The wood was deserted. He whistled the theme tune to a weekend sports programme that the Harriers had once featured on regularly. He stopped and looked around again. This felt like a good spot. It was never the same, but he always had a feeling when he was in the right place. It had to be deep inside the wood, well off the beaten track. Private and secluded so that his ceremony would not be interrupted. Not that he would be embarrassed if he was discovered, far from it. He imagined people would be very impressed if they came across him while he was in full flow. He just felt the time wasn't quite right to share his rebirth. People wouldn't understand. He wasn't sure he did.

Baxter threw the rope over the branch and held the noose in his hands, pulling it gently open. He placed it over his head, then looked for a place to tie the rope off. He had discovered that he had to fully intend to go through with it before the waters came. It was essential that the experience was authentic. Soon everything was prepared. He stood poised. His eyes closed. He tensed, ready to step. Sure enough, after a few seconds, he felt the cold sensation of water running over his naked feet. He let the water rise further and further up his legs until it passed his loins. Only then could he be sure. He cautiously opened his eyes. A broad smile spread across his face. Once again, the hidden reservoirs of the forest had risen from the soil to save him. He was soon waste deep in a radiant pool. The cold waters had warmed to a pleasingly refreshing temperature. He wriggled his toes in the soft mud, waiting for the transformation he knew was coming. He glanced around the shoreline that had formed around the nascent pond. It was beautiful. As the water rose, he watched the brightly coloured insects settle on the leaves. They turned their compound eyes towards him. Baxter Long waved at them. The insects waved back. Their mandibles were now mouths. The pads of their feet became hands. The chirruping of the crickets turned to roars of adulation, willing Baxter on. The lilies rose, forming towering stands filled with excited spectators. The water flowed over his shoulders. His toes were no longer wriggling in the mud. Instead, he could feel the soft inside of a running shoe and the firm surface of a running track. The water covered his head, and yet he could still breath freely. The crowd roared. Baxter approached the start, waving again at the crowd as he crouched. He readied himself to spring out of the blocks. A stickleback transformed into a portly steward. Sun hat and flannels. He raised his fin and fired the starting pistol. The crowd roared as Baxter ran. He had never moved with such supple ease; the rest of the ghostly field was left floundering in his wake. The crowd were on their feet as he crossed the finish line. A new world record!

Baxter had set several world records that month. His accolades accumulating in his psychic trophy cabinet. Every day he walked through the woods. Every day enacting the same grotesque subterfuge. Every day the waters came. Every day he ran, jumped and threw his way into the record books as the packed stands cheered him on. Baxter emerged from the pond, the water falling from him and returning to the pool like mercury skittering across a laboratory bench. He breathed in deeply and prepared to enact another round as the pond retreated into the soil, just as it always did. This time he would stun the crowds with his prowess in the javelin. He stretched out his arm and simulated a throw. But outside of the water his arm clicked awkwardly. He cursed and rubbed his shoulder. The ache lingered in his joints as he picked up the rope. As he was bending down, he thought he caught sight of a figure on the other side of the clearing.

*

Hilda was huddled on all fours in the dirt and leaves. The dust of the forest that had stained her cheeks was criss-crossed with dark valleys carved out by streams of tears. She reached up and clawed at the trunk of the ash tree, pulling herself to her feet. The vague tingle continued. Inside the trunk, the impression of DI Ward pushed against the bark. The time was approaching. Hilda's eyes began to focus through the multi-faceted lens of her tears. Before her eyes, the glade was transformed. The muted browns and dark shadows were now complemented by a rainbow of colour. Flowers bloomed in an impossible variety; their pungent bouquet filled the air. Pin-sharp tones blended, creating an unlikely harmony. A chaotic arcadia. A shimmering pond rippled gently in the centre of the clearing. It was magnificent. Across the far side of the pond, she could see the figure of a man. She recognised him but couldn't quite place him. Was it from work, or the pages of a magazine? He was dressed in ill-fitting sports kit. He was throwing a rope over the branch of a tree. His presence was jarring in the bucolic disorder. She saw that he had tied a noose in the rope. He put his head through the noose. He was going to hang himself. She called out to him, but her words rebounded. Ricocheting off an impenetrable membrane. Do no harm. She began to run across the clearing towards the pond, shouting noiselessly at the man as she ran. She reached the shoreline, waving her arms, trying to attract the man's attention. Close, closer, so close she could almost touch him. She reached out to grab the stranger as he adjusted the rope around his neck. He was preparing to jump. Her fingers glanced against the nylon material of his athletics kit, causing a tiny static charge to leap from her fingertips. Then he was gone. Hilda was left clinging to thin air, looking out over the gentle pond. The sound began to rise again. From hiss to harmony. Do no harm.

Under the water the crowds were silent. Baxter waved. He beamed, waiting for the swelling roar to engulf him. But there was only silence. He looked up at the stands in surprise. A thousand blank eyes stared sightlessly back. The crowd stood like a zombie horde. Crooked necks on withered bodies. As if hell had been emptied and dumped on the terraces. This had never happened before. Something was not right. But Baxter could not stop now. Perhaps when he launched the javelin and it again broke all records, as he was certain it would, the crowd would transform, as it had from insect to human. His kit felt awkward and tight. He looked down in dismay as his paunch poked out from under his vest. The crowd stared blankly. He walked across the stadium towards the marked-out runway. The firm track was beginning to lose its integrity. Pools began to appear in the asphalt. His feet squelched as his pumps took on water. He hastily grabbed a javelin from the competition rack and began to mark out his run-up. The pools spread and merged. Dark brown sludge and claggy slime mingled into a horrible ooze that slowly flowed across the field. Baxter drew back his arm. All suppleness was gone. Now only the desperate ache of regret remained clinging to his muscles. Tears welled in his eyes. He had asked too much of the Tangle. His desires would never be satisfied, he knew that now. But it was too late. He ran through the foul mud and let the javelin fly. For a few seconds it described a beautiful arc in an azure sky. The zombie crowd watched its progress. The faintest flicker of life cut across their decaying faces like a badly tuned TV momentarily finding its signal. But as the arc itself began to decay, so the crowd began to devolve into a host of gibbering shadows. Baxter watched the javelin's flight. There would be no world record today. His world was at an end. A terrible howl began to rise from the stands. The javelin stopped in mid-descent and began to turn. Through tears made thick by earth and mud, Baxter watched the javelin travel remorselessly back to the source. Guttural groans filled the dissolving stadium as the stands reverted to mud and silt. The jutting jaws of flies broke through the rotten skin of spectators. All around, the illusion was fading and a dark unreality was taking its place. The javelin seemed to meander through the gloom, travelling at a painfully slow speed. He could see its sparkling metal tip revolving like a satellite. Turning. Turning. The only bright thing in the thickening darkness. He closed his eyes as the tip of the javelin found its target. Burrowing slowly through the sinews of his neck. The revolving spike turned to the branch of the ash as it carried him silently into the black depths of the pond.

*

The blood of life seeped back into the forest floor. Its consistency stiffened by the will of the lost. Into the roots the glutinous ichor flowed. The ash. Queen of the forest. Ruler of the third lunar month. Scion of the original root. Sucked up the blood. Into the bark. Into the leaves. Take only what you need. There was a surplus. A residue. The shimmering drone faded. Hilda stared after its receding echo. At her feet was the body of a man. The will, the longing, the horror. She knelt down to feel for a pulse. But there was none. The ash stirred. The surplus. The residue. Hilda let out a sigh. He looked so defeated in his ill-fitting sports gear. She caught sight of something glistening in the dead leaves. She left the side of the dead athlete and went to study the source. It was a medal. She picked it up, turning it over in her hand. The will, the longing, the horror. She bent over the body and placed the medal carefully around the dead man's neck. She laid it out neatly on his chest. She bowed her head and tried to conjure solemn words. But words were for the living. She looked again at the empty shell of the man. The ash tree stirred. The will,

155

the way, the longing, the horror. Hilda touched the bark as
her eulogy died on her lips. The horror would never end, but
nor would the beauty. The surplus. The residue. Take only
what you need. A silent spark flew. The ash returned what it
had taken. The surplus. The residue. Hilda felt nothing as the
spark passed into her. She would feel nothing until it was too
late to feel anything at all. She would feel nothing, because
it gave her nothing. The void was her gift. The emptiness its
offering. She pulled her phone from her pocket and called the
emergency services.

'In the woods. My name? Oh yes, Hilda Wilton, Dr Hilda
Wilton.'

She ended the call and returned the phone to her pocket.
As she removed her hand, Hilda studied it with interest. She
noted the growing prominence of her veins and the subtle
shading left by the soil of the woods, which made her skin
look like parchment. She raised her hand to her face and
felt her faulty flesh, letting her fingers linger in the pits and
crevices. The hint of a smile formed at the edges of her mouth
as she turned towards the direction of the town. Take only
what you need.

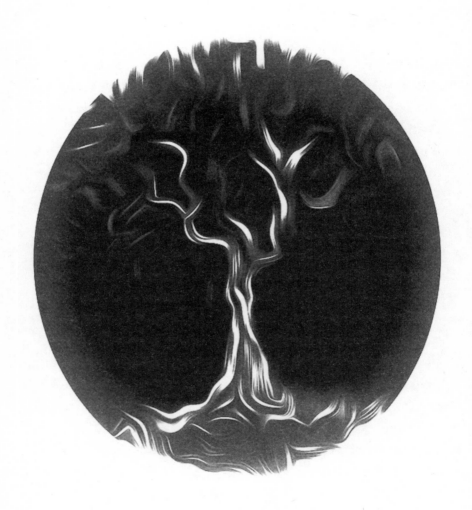

Apple Blossom

Uncle Tobias's hand gripped young Ethan's shoulders
with an inappropriate firmness. The odour of a dedicated
tobacco habit drifted from his fingers. A hint of a forbidden,
unwholesome world that Ethan's mother had tried so hard
to protect him from. But his mother now lay on the chiffon
lining of Lassiter Funeral Home's second-cheapest coffin.
A rough box of wood, six feet down and a short lifetime away.
Ethan stared down at the box, hoping that if he wished hard
enough, he could conjure up one last word of comfort from
his dearly departed mother. Something to make it alright.
Something reassuring like a game of windmills. He imagined
his mother spinning him around, his legs parallel to the
ground, her hands holding his arms as he flew. Round and
round. Round and round. Ethan smiled. Ethan laughed.
A sudden thud and the pressure of Uncle Tobias's reeking
hand snapped him out of his happy dream.

'Stop that, boy.'

Ethan looked up at his guardian, his face falling into a
mute blend of grief and fear. Uncle Tobias was big on respect.
He demanded strict adherence to his decrees, though the
boundaries for transgression were so fluid that you could
hardly call them rules. They were more like whims. A
constantly shifting set of demands, deliberately designed to
be impossible to fulfil. Only the punishments had a terrible
monotonous predictability to them. His mother had hated

Uncle Tobias. A second thud drew Ethan's attention back to the grave. Flowers were falling on his mother's coffin. Thud. Bright flowers on freshly cut stems, sundered from living plants, sacrifices in this strange human ritual. They would decay in the tomb too. Thud. Thud. White petals covered the lid of the coffin like forlorn confetti. Apple blossom. His mother's favourite.

One by one the mourners cast their blooms into the grave, pausing to nod awkward condolences at Ethan and his unwanted foster parents. Uncle Tobias returned their condolences with a curt nod of his own. His hand momentarily left Ethan's shoulder to direct his wife. Aunt Janet. An almost invisible presence in the household. A vague spectre who only materialised when called by his tyrannical uncle. She too was subject to his arbitrary brutality. Isolated and cowed. Soon he would do the same to Ethan. Uncle Tobias pushed his wife forward. He wanted to show a united front. He wanted to show the world that he was the master of the family now that his sainted sister-in-law was gone. She was always scheming, pouring poison into his wife's ear, trying to undermine his authority, trying to prize her away from him. Well not any more. Aunt Janet shuffled forward, acknowledging the mourners with an uncertain smile. Her hand brushed against Ethan's. She glanced down at his confused face and, for a few seconds, a tender look played across her features. The tar-clogged voice of Uncle Tobias broke the conspirators' bond.

'Time to go home. These parasites will be getting pissed at my expense, I suppose. They'll be no wake for us. She's dead and buried and that's that.'

He attempted to guide them back to the car as the gravediggers began to fill the pit. Grubby topsoil shot through with broken masonry and plastic bottle caps tumbled onto the cheap coffin. Thud. Thud. Ethan shrugged off his uncle's hand; he didn't want to leave his mother in such a disgusting hole.

'Wake up, wake up!'

Ethan ran to the edge of the grave. The gravediggers stopped their shovelling and bowed their heads, unsure as to what action was most appropriate. Uncle Tobias grabbed Ethan by his arm, dragging him away from the lip of the grave.

'Come here, you little swine.'

'Don't let him take me!'

'I'll have none of your nonsense, you little shit.'

Uncle Tobias cuffed the boy around the ear. Ethan let out a cry. Some of the departing mourners looked back with anxious faces. Then headed in the direction of the Bull, mumbling to themselves.

'No, I won't go! You can't make me.'

Uncle Tobias slapped the boy hard around the face. His head lurched viciously. Stars sputtered and flashed before his eyes. Such violence. Another cry. But not from Ethan's mouth this time. A mournful note that seemed to stretch and elongate, extending to the point of impossible intensity until it splintered and faded into the early evening air. But no one turned this time. Only the gravediggers seemed aware of the rupture. They looked from the grave to the man and back again. Ethan struggled free from his uncle's grip and ran to the grave. The scream had come from there, he was sure. Why could no one else hear it? He looked down into the pit. Apple blossom blooms peaked out from beneath the soil. Their sweet odour mixing with the damp decay of the earth. He was in an orchard on the edge of a pleasant meadow. His mother chased him around the trees as he giggled and ran. 'I'm going to get you, I'm going to get you, the tickle monster is coming, the tickle monster is coming.' The monster is coming. He fell, he floated, he drifted into the darkness.

Ethan was face down in the soil. Ethan was at the bottom of the grave. His small body flat on his mother's coffin. In his hand he grasped a twig of apple blossom. He looked up, resting his chin on the wooden lid of the coffin. He twirled the stem around between his fingers. The blossom seemed to sparkle in the gloomy surroundings, its perfume pulling him back, back to happier times. Ethan felt a soothing warmth emanating from the coffin. The grave became a womb. Suddenly he became aware of rough hands thrust under his arms as the gravediggers dragged him up. He caught sight of their sympathetic faces as they hauled him to the surface. His uncle waited at the edge. His face had no sympathy; it was red and furious. Uncle Tobias unfolded his arms and snatched Ethan from the gravediggers' embrace without the courtesy of a thank you. Wrenching the apple blossom from Ethan's hand he tossed it on the floor and dragged him towards the car. Aunt Janet followed a few steps behind.

*

The punishments were severe and frequent. In Caxton town's charmless suburbs. Behind the walls of the 1920s detached house. Beyond the off-road parking bay. Inside the pebble-dashed walls. Torture was undertaken with an obsessive attention to detail. Tasks were long and repetitive. Failure to complete them satisfactorily was certain. Even the slightest inaccuracy in the outcome would lead to further repetitions. Tasks, chores, duties. All were gateways to Uncle Tobias's real pleasures: torment. He was a skilled and ruthless operator, running the house like a gulag. Weekends were particularly difficult for Ethan. With work put aside, Uncle Tobias could really indulge himself. There was rarely a let-up in the cycle of punishments, and Ethan would often flop into bed sore and exhausted. As the sun went down and the neighbourhood made its way to bed, Ethan would pull the covers up close, waiting for the creak of the stairs. The sign that his uncle was paying him one of his frequent night-time visits.

Breakfasts were fraught. Uncle Tobias liked to leave the house promptly at 7.25 a.m. He had timed the journey to work perfectly: thirty-five minutes door to door. His routine never altered. But Ethan was a new and unwelcome obstacle to his daily timetable. He was chivvied relentlessly from the moment he woke until his departure for the school bus at 7.20 a.m. No slacking. No dawdling. At 7.23 a.m. Uncle Tobias would lock the door, leaving Aunt Janet imprisoned inside. She had access to the garden, of course. He wasn't a monster. Besides she could keep the garden nice and tidy. Just the way he liked it. The talk of the cul-de-sac. The beautiful garden behind the house of infamy.

Ethan's route to the bus stop never varied. He would walk steadily along the neat footpaths, past the prim and proper flower beds of suffocating ordinariness that bordered the unremarkable gardens of unremarkable people. This was a suburbia of bitter, thwarted ambitions and disappointment. On the way to Long Lane the path opened up into a grassy verge, rising on each side and dotted with shrubs. At the crest of the slope was a small copse of trees. The sentinels of the Tangle. The edge of the matted woods. Ethan used to play there, beyond the borders of the known world, deep in the twisting domain of living things. Every day as he walked past, he could feel its nagging vibration. Under the asphalt, in the cracks of crumbling paving stones. The roots.

At 07.10 a.m. precisely the Bakelite phone clattered into its cradle. This had never happened before. Uncle Tobias looked more than surprised. He hated to be inconvenienced. Fury contorted his jowls, but his phone manner remained faultless.

'Of course, Mr Barrowman, I understand. It's never happened before. No, of course, that's no excuse. I will leave immediately.'

Uncle Tobias replaced the receiver. He continued to utter a steady flow of foul invective as he gathered up his jacket and briefcase. Ethan had never seen his uncle look so uncomfortable. The beast was rattled. He struggled to keep a smile from his face.

'You.'

Uncle Tobias jabbed his finger at Aunt Janet.

'You, you don't . . . don't do . . . just don't do anything. And you.'

In lieu of instructions, Uncle Tobias clipped Ethan around the ear as he headed towards the front door. He watched his uncle's bulk slide across the hallway like a malevolent shadow. The door slammed, causing the teacups to chime against each other as the house shook with his uncle's transmitted fury.

For a few seconds, a dense silence settled in the kitchen. Ethan and his aunt were momentarily free. The kitchen appliances hummed, their electrical cadence absorbing the pair's attention for want of a more familiar focus. Aunt Janet broke the silence.

'I have something for you.'

The sound of her voice surprised Ethan. Like the faltering sentences of a small child, or the cracked dialogue of a hermit recently returned to civilisation. A fresh sentence formed on her lips, but she sucked the words back down. She went out into the hallway. Ethan could see her reaching into her outdoor coat. She pulled an object from the inside pocket. He could see a faint smile play across her pale lips. Aunt Janet was holding something in her hand. He could just make out its spindly silhouette in the ochre glow. It was a sprig of apple blossom. His apple blossom. Aunt Janet returned to the kitchen holding the sprig in front of her like the cross at the head of a pilgrim's progress.

'I went back to get it for you, the day of your mother's funeral.'

His mother's funeral had been weeks ago, and yet the sprig of blossom looked as fresh as the day it was cast into her grave. The petals were firm but delicate. They looked like eyes. His mother's eyes. A drop of water dripped from one of the petals like a tear. It hovered in the static between leaf and floor. Inside its delicate membrane Ethan could see his mother's face smiling back at him. He floated through the static, sinking through the membrane. A whisper drifted across the distance. Words of comfort. Words of prophecy. The teardrop hit the floor.

'You best get to school, Ethan. You don't want to be late.'

*

Ethan's days became uncharacteristically eventful. Not that anything happened. It was more that his moods shifted and pitched in a way that he had almost forgotten. Since his mother's death he had existed on a blank plane of numbness. It was best to press his feelings down. But now he felt something. His sorrow hadn't diminished, but now, at least, he was experiencing something akin to hope, that most human of illusions. Ethan kept the blossom close. He felt the twigs against his torso; they felt like comforting fingers, stroking. Stroking. Often he would take the blossom out and examine it. He took in every detail, every knot, every curve of every shoot. It remained unchanged. Even in the tight confines of his pocket, with all the attendant clutter pressing around it, the blossom never diminished in any way. It was constant, like his mother's love. But the laws of entropy were clear: the apple blossom must decay. As the days passed, his anxiety grew. Decay or discovery, one was inevitable. If his uncle was to find the blossom, he would lose it forever. He must find a safe hiding place.

Monday morning. A dread day for most children, but for Ethan school at least provided a few hours away from the cycle of horror. Breakfast had proceeded with the same military precision. The rustle of his uncle's newspaper, the occasional clink of knife on porcelain, the randomly barked orders, the habitual hum of the morning. Ethan had been somewhat surprised to see his aunt when he returned from school the day the blossom came. He thought she might have taken the opportunity to run. But she had stayed. She had stayed for Ethan. They exchanged the briefest of glances as he left the house. A conspirators' nod.

The walk to the bus was routine enough. Monday held as little surprise as any other day. As he walked, Ethan took the sprig of blossom out of his pocket and examined it again. Every day it somehow seemed fresher and more fascinating. He held it up to the sun. The light caught the petals and radiated out. He paused on the path where it opened out into the green valley of grass. He looked from bough to bank. The soft sound of the grave drifted down the verge. It came from the Tangle. It was a melody, like the songs his mother used to sing to him.

Come walk with me to lilac glade, through woodland, stream and knot.

166

Come stand beneath the gallows' shade till all weeping
*   is forgot.*
Leave the tears and terrors to the mischief of the town.
Come walk with me to lilac glade, to the oak tree's
*   shady crown.*

In darkness now from darkness born, circumference,
*   length and span.*
In lilac glade the wreath and thorn, wove mockeries
*   of man.*
In lilac glade beneath the earth, in death's ecstatic bond.
Come walk with me in lilac shade, to the emptiness beyond.

Ethan left the path. The soil seemed to writhe as his feet
touched the grass. Like the rippling tide in the shallows.
Like a shoal turning on the currents. He neither walked nor
climbed. He was carried. The bent back of St Christopher, the
torn arms of Simon of Cyrene. The nameless saints carried
him. The Tangle carried him. Ethan reached the top of the
bank. He was no longer in Caxton's drab suburbs; he was in
the borderless hinterland of nowhere. He entered the wood.
As he stepped, the jumble of roots parted. His sense of time
was forgotten, his location became irrelevant. Further and
further. Until he was deep inside the Tangle. The path grew
wider, flowing like a river into a bright clearing. Shafts of
sunlight penetrated the canopy in mottled columns. Ethan
was deposited in the glade. It felt cloistered and safe. Around
him the chatter of birds was tuned to the melody of the
forest's conjuring rite. Rise sweet child. Rise sweet boy. He
felt the blossom in his hand turn, as if it were attempting to
escape his grip. It was unmistakable, the bough was moving.
It was drawn towards the soil. The sprig of blossom began

to writhe, its bark no longer soft and comforting, but harsh. Biting. Covered with thorns. Ethan dropped the sprig as if he'd been stung. Tears welled in his eyes. His blossom. His beautiful blossom. The blossom drifted slowly down to the forest floor. When it hit, he knew. His tears stopped in an instant. A smile, like the grin of the happy child he once was, shattered the sadness. He began to run around the glade in an ecstatic circle. Ridiculous, stupid, without reason or purpose. Alive again, if only for a few moments. He fell, breathless, to his knees, next to the fallen blossom. He began digging in the soil with his small boy hands, clogging his nails, staining his school uniform with dark streaks. Soon he had created an impressive hole. Ethan planted the blossom inside. He tidied the loose earth around the stem. The earth hugged around the stalk. The trees of the glade bent low over the bough, then sprang back to create a perfect circle in the canopy. The sunlight poured in. Ethan stood and smiled. This would be a good place. The blossom would be safe here. Time spun back to its recognised pattern. The dimensions shimmered, shrank and vanished, retreating to their former concealed locations. Ethan was alone on the path. On the road up ahead, he could see the bus pulling out of the stop. He would be late.

That night was the longest in Ethan's short memory. A grim procession of punishment, belittlement and abuse. But he did not cry. He made no sounds of lamentation or sorrow. He was not there. He thought of the beautiful blossom, even as his uncle misused him.

Ethan ran for the bus the next day, he must not be late again. The dull throb of his bruises offered their counsel. There is no time, Ethan. There is no time. He sighed and dejectedly dragged his sore, battered body along the path. He reached the bus stop. But no one was there. Not one familiar uniform, not one classmate or fellow student. Had he missed it again? Had the school changed the timetable and not told him? He stood for a few minutes looking at his shoes, trying hard to think of a way of escaping the horror he knew was coming.

'Ethan, is that you? Oh, my dear boy, whatever are you doing waiting here?'

It was Mrs Krebbs, the drama teacher, driving past in her mini. Mrs Krebbs pulled the car over and shouted theatrically to Ethan from across the other side of the road. She was a 'fun' adult, an actor in her youth. She lived a few doors down from his uncle's house. Ethan had seen her pruning her privet. He looked embarrassed and continued to stare at his shoes.

'Why, the school is closed for the morning . . . I thought everyone knew . . . Asbestos removal in the science block . . . You best get home . . . We are starting after morning break today, though I don't know for the life of me why we don't just have the whole day off . . . That would be lovely, wouldn't it!'

Ethan managed a shy nod. Mrs Krebbs sensed she was wasting her time and skills on the young boy. She waved, wound up her window and drove off. It took him a few seconds to appreciate the opportunity that this unplanned break presented. His uncle was at work, his aunt wouldn't expect him home for hours. He turned towards the path and headed for the glade.

Ethan ran up the verge and hesitated. The scenery looked commonplace and derivative. His heart sank. He must find the path across the threshold. His mind sought the summoning spell.

Come walk with me to lilac glade, through woodland, stream and knot.

Come stand beneath the gallows' shade till all weeping
    is forgot.

Bit by bit he began to see the landscape fold, becoming richer
and more complex. Colours multiplied. Variety blossomed
on the edge. The gateway opened before him. A smile broke
out on his face as he entered the wood. He was carried along
the path in the same way, but something was different.
This time the sound of the forest was muted like a lullaby.
The hush was oppressive. The welcome he had felt the day
before was not as warm, as if his appearance was somehow
ill timed. As he went deeper into the Tangle his feelings of
awkwardness grew. Eventually he arrived at the glade. It too
was different. Disturbed. As if it had been hastily rearranged.
He remembered his mother running around frantically, trying
to plump up cushions and hide the dirty teacups when his
granny turned up unannounced one afternoon. She did that
a lot before the end. Ethan stepped into the clearing. The
trees had closed their crown once more. The light was soft
and subdued. The sound had dropped to a hum. His eyes
began to widen. Everything was upside down, back to front.
Wrong. Wrong. Where was the blossom? It had gone. He
looked around frantically. Nothing. The young bough lost.
Stolen, broken, dead. Gone. They had promised to keep it
safe. The trees. They had promised. He began to feel anger
swelling inside. He had never been so angry. He had been
betrayed. Abandoned. Ethan sank to his knees. He would lie
here and wait for the end. No one cared. Not a single person
alive or dead. A branch creaked. Ethan started. Had his uncle
found him? Let him come, there was nothing left for him to
take. But it was only the trees that stirred. He studied the
gnarled branch that swayed and groaned in the breeze.

Its movement was unnatural. Here in the heart of nature, far from the regularity of men, this branch was pointing. It was unmistakable. The sticks, the bulbs, the leaves, all pointing. Pointing to a spot on the forest floor. Ethan wiped his eyes with his dirty sleeve and followed the line. A subtle light played across the figure of a plant. A sapling. An apple tree. Ethan clapped his hands and began to laugh. This was no tomb; it was a nursery. He approached the delicate plant. It was stretching and flexing its stems, feeling its growing potency as the sap rose. Ethan pressed his hands on the young bark. A whisper echoed around the glade. A voice as familiar as his own.

> Come walk with me to lilac glade, through woodland,
>   stream and knot.
> Come stand beneath the gallows' shade till all weeping
>   is forgot.
> Leave the tears and terrors to the mischief of the town.
> Come walk with me to lilac glade, to the oak tree's
>   shady crown.
>
> In darkness now from darkness born, circumference,
>   length and span.
> In lilac glade the wreath and thorn, wove mockeries
>   of man.
> In lilac glade beneath the earth, in death's ecstatic bond.
> Come walk with me in lilac shade, to the emptiness beyond.

The day went quickly. All he could think about was the apple tree. Nothing could dislodge the joy from his heart. At 4 p.m. the bell sounded for the end of the school day; he ran for the bus. He jumped out at the top of Long Lane and ran down

the path. The verge rose up to meet the Tangle. He rose with
it. At the summit the gate opened, and he stepped inside.
He glided through the undergrowth until he reached the
glade. His own sacred grove where the spheres intersected.
The clearing chimed with the chatter of living things. At its
centre was the miraculous sapling. It had matured and grown.
Sapling no more. Here was the tree. Somehow, though he
knew it was impossible, Ethan was not surprised. The forest
floor wore garlands of blossom that gathered in bright arcs
where it had fallen. On the branches of the tree, the flowers
had been replaced by sparkling green apples. He marvelled
at their perfection: their skin was taught and shiny, with
the slightest hint of dew glistening on their unblemished
roundness. He reached up and plucked one from a low-
hanging bough. The trees seemed to ripple around him as
he took a bite into the apple. It was the most delicious thing
he had ever tasted, a subtle sweetness that insinuated itself
into every nerve and cell. Just that one bite filled him with
a feeling of extraordinary well-being, as if the flesh of the
apple had been transubstantiated. He took another bite. The
flesh contained a code. In its juice, a message that trickled
down his throat. As it seeped into him, the meaning of the
code was revealed. He was small, too small to understand the
shapes and colours of this new world. The voice, the pulse, the
beating heart. His mother guiding him towards his essence.
First steps, first words. Words coaxed from his developing
mind by his mother's love. He grew, mushrooming from the
sack of sinews and skin into a person. The voice, the pulse,
the tutor's hand. He was a boy, this boy, any boy, any girl,
neither, nor, nothing. He was nothing. As the juice reached
his heart he was erased and reset. He was Ethan, he was no
one. Now he was of the Tangle. The familiar whisper floated

around him. Dripping from the skin of the apple, flowing in the sap of the wood. The sound drifted into his small boy ears. The cipher decoded. The plan set in motion. He looked up into the canopy as it loomed over him, and he smiled.

*

Ethan tumbled through the door, propelled by his uncle's reeking hand. He was obliged to wait for his return every day, no matter the weather. He must be standing ready for his uncle to unlock the stockade. He had been talking to his aunt through the letter box, passing messages to her from the Tangle. He could see her fractured silhouette through mottled glass as she bent down. She had sounded delighted at his tale, though he sensed some incredulity in her hesitant replies. But now his uncle had returned, silence had descended once more.

'What have you got in your pockets, you little shit? You'll ruin that coat and I'm not buying you another one!'

Uncle Tobias clipped him around the ear in a thoughtless reflex and stuck his hand into Ethan's pocket.

'Apples?'

Uncle Tobias's face momentarily broke from his usual scowl.

'I like apples, oh yes. Apple pie with custard, oh yes, yes indeed. Janet, I shall have apple pie after the meat.'

Uncle Tobias licked his lips, letting a globule of saliva roll down his chin.

'None for the boy. That'll teach him for mistreating his clothes so appallingly.'

Uncle Tobias clipped him again. But it lacked his usual accuracy and merely ruffled Ethan's hair.

Ethan's stomach complained. Protesting with a low frequency rumble. Uncle Tobias clouted him again. His uncle had made him watch as he inhaled a vast plate of greasy

meat and potatoes. Ethan had nothing. This was merely
a warm-up for later punishments. Uncle Tobias belched
and farted simultaneously, a skill that Ethan had always
marvelled at. That lumbering turd. Clout. Ethan's smile was
undimmed. Clout.

'What do you look so fucking happy about?'

Uncle Tobias bellowed, his foul breath smothering Ethan
as his uncle's furious face hovered inches from his nose. Clout.
But his smile remained undiminished. Uncle Tobias looked
confused. He raised his hand to strike again, but the scent of
a freshly baked apple pie stopped his swing. Ethan and Uncle
Tobias both turned their heads towards the oven. Trails of
perfumed steam drifted across the kitchen. Uncle Tobias's
mouth flopped open, drool cascading down his grotesque jaw.
Ethan's smile widened, his cheeks struggling to contain it.
He turned to look at his uncle. His gaoler. His tormentor.
He took in every detail of his face, every foul crevice and pit.
Ethan's smile straightened as he concentrated. He looked
more intently now. Into his sweat-filled pores. Into his greasy
follicles. Ethan studied him like a specimen of putrid fungus.

'Oh my, Janet, that sm—sm—smells . . . Oh my.'

Uncle Tobias struggled to form the words as the pie
made its way to the table. His yellow eyes bulged. His flabby
tongue flicked. He loudly cleared his throat, preparing the
passage for the coming pie. He clipped Ethan around the ear
absentmindedly. Ethan felt nothing. Ethan was still studying
his pustulant uncle.

'Not a crumb for you, little shit, not a fucking crumb.'

He wanted to clout him again, but the scent of the pie was
too much. Uncle Tobias grabbed his spoon in his grubby fist.
He plunged it into the golden crust.

'Oh my.'

Uncle Tobias's voice was no louder than a whisper. His faced glowed in the light of the exposed fruit that lay hidden beneath the golden crust. Sumptuous and glistening in the embrace of his aunt's best Pyrex. The ambrosial scent peaking in intensity. A subtle vibration pulsed through Uncle Tobias's flabby frame as he dug his spoon into the pie. His eyes widened. His first bite. The juice seething in the crust. The taste. Too much. Too profound in its depth and variety for any pallet to make sense of. Ethan stared intently; he could see his uncle's synapses sparking as he chewed. His brain struggling to process the signals. There was the briefest of pauses after the first mouthful, as if Uncle Tobias momentarily sensed the nature of the fruit. But he was not of the Tangle. Greed was the maxim that guided his kind. There was a blur of spoon and hand. Uncle Tobias shovelled the pie into his corpulent maw with mechanical diligence. Ethan thought his uncle might suffocate, such was the rate at which he filled his mouth. A series of stuttering snorts kept his lungs full as he continued his relentless binge. The pie dish sat empty. Not a single crumb remained. He had claimed the prize. He could savour the victory. Uncle Tobias lent back in his chair and let out a long, elongated belch. Ethan relaxed too. The flat line of concentration bent back into a smile.

His uncle was breathless and bloated. His nose had started to run. Uncle Tobias produced his handkerchief and blew hard.

'Damn itchy nose, must be the dust. Don't you ever clean up around here, Janet?'

Aunt Janet looked at her husband with a newly discovered defiance. The whispers at the letter box. The childish babble of Ethan's fantastic story. She sensed prophesy at work, even as she stewed the apples. Janet had kneaded the flour into the perfect disguise. The crust was the sheath. The apples the dagger. She was an assassin. Uncle Tobias let out a belch like the chorus of hell.

'I said, don't you ever dust this fucking kitchen?'

Uncle Tobias grabbed at her arm as she was collecting the empty dish. Aunt Janet wrenched her arm from his grip.

'No.'

One word. With all the power of a sermon. The pie dish clattered to the floor. Ethan laughed. Uncle Tobias's eyes darted between Ethan and his wife. What was this? Mutiny?

'What the fuck are you laughing at, little shit? Pick that up! Pick it up this instant!'

'What's wrong with your nose, Uncle Tobias?'

Ethan enquired through stuttering laughter. Aunt Janet's hand went to her mouth as she saw the joke begin to reveal its punchline. Her laugh harmonised with her nephew's.

'Oh, yes! What is it, Tobias? What's wrong with your nose?'

Uncle Tobias began to unravel. His power over his captives waning fast. His hand shot up to his left nostril. Something was growing through the mucus. He tugged at the blockage. A slender green shoot sprouted from his nostril, unfurling in the yellow light of the kitchen. It writhed and thrashed in the air like a new-born serpent hatched from the egg. Uncle Tobias tugged at the shoot. It kept coming. He let out a groan. Ethan laughed again. Now a second tendril was sprouting from his right nostril. Uncle Tobias's voice became a congested snarl.

'What's haaaarrrgpening!'

Ethan was on his feet now. Laughing and clapping as he jumped up and down on the spot. Janet tilted her head and enjoyed the view, like a proud parent at the school nativity play. Uncle Tobias went to punch them for their impudence. A branch exploded out of his thigh. Uncle Tobias screamed as the gnarly frond entwined itself around his leg and fixed him fast to the chair.

'Do something! Get a knife, cut me out! Cut me out!'

His last words were strangled in his throat as a thick branch crept out of his gullet. Small twigs edged across his lips, clamping his mouth shut. Ethan stopped jumping and clapping. He watched in fascination. The whisper in the woods played in a loop. Aunt Janet's arm reached out over Ethan's shoulder, pulling him into her side. He buried himself in her embrace. They stood in silence, as if they were watching an eclipse or a beautiful sunset. Uncle Tobias's eyes were wide with ignorant indignation. Too late had he realised his fragility and weakness. A thin branch flicked his eye out, stretching the optical nerve taut until it snapped, leaving Uncle Tobias's eyeball skewered to the stick like a strange fruit. His chest burst. His trunk became the trunk of a tree. Roots where his legs had been, spreading across the lino floor, burrowing into the soil beneath the suburban hell. Uncle Tobias's features were barely discernible through the spreading foliage. Contorted with confusion and disbelief, defeated, broken, stretched and smashed. At last, his skull snapped. The canopy spread out across the ceiling, broken fragments of skull and flesh hung from the twigs. As the flourishing of the tree slowed, small green buds emerged from shoots. One by one, they opened. Into blossom. Apple blossom.

Janet sighed. Cupping a flower gently in her palm, she inhaled the delicate scent.

'What a beautiful tree, Ethan.'

'Yes, Aunty, what a beautiful tree.'

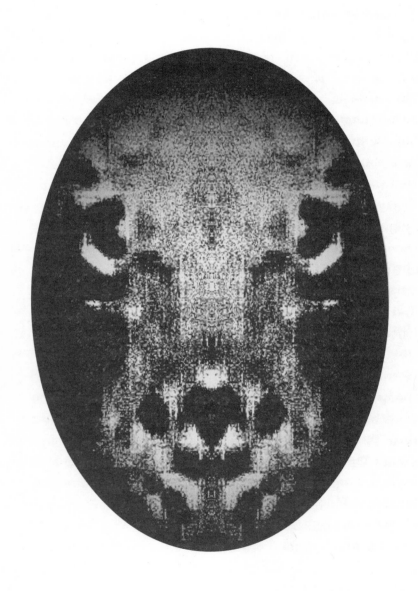

Hector Starts a War

Hector was a hound. A hybrid. A variety chocolate box of strains and blood lines. A mutt, a mongrel, a mixture. A good boy. Dumped in the Tangle by a pack of ridiculous humans. As a puppy, his early life was difficult, but not without joy. He tumbled in the leaves and found food in the forest. Friends too. Many of the animals living in the wood were helpful. Those not intent on eating him anyways. But he was no wolf, and he struggled to survive in the rough and tumble of the Tangle. Nevertheless, he found a way to grow into a reasonably robust dog. His fur was matted, and his muzzle was a mess. But he had learned wisdom from the woods: how to hide, how to hunt, which berries were good to eat, and which ones would kill him. But the first lesson was a warning. Avoid men. They were the deadliest of all the animals. Killers, the lot of them.

But Hector was a dog. His species had grown attached to these mean bipeds. Back in time, humans had lived in the Tangle too. Hector's ancestors had watched them from the bushes. The humans would gather in small groups around burning piles of wood and leaves. They would incinerate the animals they had killed over the fire. They were rapacious, slaughtering beyond their needs. They inhabited the skins of their prey and polished their bones to decorate themselves and their dwellings. The dogs watched them. They seemed cruel and taciturn, they seldom mixed with the other animals, and often killed simply for pleasure. But a few of them seemed nice enough. Some of the dogs ventured down to the humans' nest. Probing the perimeter. At first, they were met with a flurry of stones and angry grunts. But as time went on, they were gradually accepted at the burning piles the humans huddled around. It was warm there. There was food too. Bones too big to wear as ornaments, or too small to make effective clubs, were discarded around the fire. Perfect for the dogs. Over time, a symbiotic relationship began to build between them; the dogs would guard, fetch and kill for the humans, and the humans would in turn provide a degree of comfort for the dogs. It was a good deal. Most of the time.

Hector knew something of humans. Some were kind, at least some he had met. They would stroke his fur and tickle his stomach, giving him treats or playing games that they seemed to take great delight in. Endlessly throwing balls was one thing humans seemed fond of. Hector would run and drop, run and drop, over and over again. They were very sweet, but, by and large, pretty dumb. Their senses were stunted. Their bodies were weak. They blustered about blindly breaking things, never noticing what it was they were breaking. Most of creation was closed to them. As they enjoyed their daily strolls, Hector would take in all the fascinating scents along the path. He could travel through time by smell alone, sensing all the animals that had passed that way before. To him, each scent was a gateway to enlightenment. A message, a signature. He felt the great web of life flowing through the air, and the possibilities of future events encoded in the olfactory flow. While he immersed himself in the richness of experience, the humans would jabber dumbly to each other, carelessly thwacking broken sticks on the surrounding foliage. His first humans had been physically faulty too. Microbes had found them wanting and they had perished. The next humans he encountered were fucking horrendous. By some unfortunate happenstance he found himself passed like some bound chattel to this benighted family. Brutal, arrogant, corrupt and even more stupid than the last lot. Though he was only a small puppy he was far wiser than these idiots. His short time with them was unpleasant; he was bashed and abused, starved, beaten and eventually dumped. That's how he found himself in the Tangle.

On a clear day in spring Hector was playing in the long grass that sprang up in disorderly clumps in the woodland clearings. He was sniffing the recently blossomed flowers, sensing the patterns of the coming months, when he was alerted to a familiar scent drifting on the breeze. The scent of carbolic, compounds, components and manufactured things. The scent of humans. Hector froze. What variety of Homo sapiens was trudging through the woods? Hector ran to the safety of a thicket and sniffed the air. His ears pricked up. The sound of laughter. Soft and joyous, without a hint of malice. The naïve chattering of simple creatures. They sounded harmless enough at least. Hector sniffed the air again. Food. Humans called it a picnic. Hector was starving; his ability to hunt was impaired by his inexperience and inappropriate colouring. Filth could not hide his yellow fur. Hector made a tentative step out of the thicket and whimpered to get their attention. Sympathy was one emotion humans possessed, though only in its most unsophisticated form. The human chatter stopped. He could smell them coming closer. Hector barked uncertainly, having not uttered a sound for several weeks. The human chatter started up again. Hector detected concern in their tone. He barked again, this time with more urgency.

'Oh look, Mummy, it's a little dog! Oh my, poor thing, look at the state of it.'

'Must be starving. Give it something from the hamper, Dad.'

So it was that Hector found himself in the spartan surroundings of the St Hamilton Street Municipal Dog Pound. The first few days felt like a continuation of the indignities he had suffered as a puppy. Their first act had been to cut off his balls. The operation left him in a stupor for days, but after time the pain of loss faded somewhat. Hector would deal with the now; there was no point worrying about might-have-beens. In the pound the possibilities for interesting scent experiences were limited, but the food was good, and the other inmates were pleasant enough. They were a ragtag pack of strays and abused canines who had been rescued from the clutches of various unsympathetic humans. Barely understandable, but sadly familiar, tales of neglect and violence formed the backstory to most of the residents, but strangely few felt any lasting resentment. There were, after all, still a few good humans. The ones that helped and the ones that needed the dogs' help in turn. Hector was hoping for a place to lay his paws. A soft couch and a warm fire. Just like the fire his ancestors had gathered around all those millennia ago. On a late spring morning, the Tangle provided.

He was woken early by the swoosh of a broom and the scraping of a ladder on the concrete floor of the cell block. The good humans were scrubbing the whole place top to bottom with more vigour than usual. Hector and some of his fellow hounds poked their noses through the bars to get a better idea of what was going on. They were putting up bunting and flags. Very strange. Next, a crew of gruff-looking humans came in. They ran thick cables which snaked along the floor to anglepoised lamps. A man came in with a large camera and positioned it to focus on the area where the beams of light met. Hector barked across the central walkway to one of his comrades. A flustered-looking guy with a clipboard cocked his head in Hector's direction.

'Hope these mutts keep their yaps shut when the big man gives his speech.'

A group of serious-looking men joined the flustered-looking man. They were wide and stocky, with dark shades, dark suits, stony faces. They started to check the place over, shining flashlights into the shadows. He sniffed their scent. Military, cordite, sweat and boot polish. Guard humans. After a while they all filed out, except a couple of the serious ones who stood in silence with their chests puffed out. Their fists, hanging at crotch level, balled into their palms. Occasionally one of them would put his hand to his ear. Hector could make out the buzz of chatter in the guard's earpiece. He was receiving commands. Stay. Fetch. Good boy.

'Big Bird is in transit. Standby.'

'We have visual. Unit 2 standby.'

'Roger, roger.'

'Big Bird arrival imminent. Standby.'

'Groundhog, we are go. All units stay sharp.'

Hector could smell the wild gaggle of humans before they had got anywhere near the kennels. They gave off a confusing stench, ranging from obsequiousness to violent overconfidence. His ears pricked up as the rabble approached. Some of the former guard dogs began to alert out of habit. A member of staff and the flustered human ran ahead of the pack and tried to calm them.

'It's OK, boys, nothing to get excited about. It's just the president.'

The president? Hector snaffled up the treats the flustered man had thrown into his pen as the mob of humans burst into the kennel. Cameras flashed and voices clashed. The dogs barked in unison.

'Mr president, will you be increasing funding to animal welfare groups in the next budget?'

'Mr president, did you have a dog growing up, sir?'

'Mr president, will you be letting the kids name the dog?'

'Mr president, is there a poop scoop in your briefing room?'

Laughter skittered around the group like a wasp at a window. All their bodies seemed to be focused in one direction. Hector couldn't quite see the subject of their attention, but he could smell him. He had the scent of frailty and misplaced hubris. He smelled of fear. The pack of reporters, bodyguards and the bigwigs from the dog pound charity began to move along the kennel, stopping to inspect each inmate in turn. The artificial click-clack of camera shutters stuttered down the line of cages. They were getting closer to Hector's pen. He could see the arched backsides of the reporters as they reversed along the row. Then there he was. The president, apparent leader of the ecstatic technocratic regime.

'This one is very special, Mr president. He was found living in the woods all alone, poor thing. He was a terrible mess when he was brought in, but as you can see, our team did a marvellous job fixing him up.'

Hector cocked his head. Who me? They're talking about me. The president came closer to the bars. Hector could see him clearly now, and his first impressions had been correct: his looks matched his scent. Around sixty years old, with a sadness about him that lingered behind his eyes, seeping through his veneer of confidence. He was conservatively dressed, as were all the humans in his pack. But he looked like he would be more comfortable in a fishing vest and plaid shirt. He was a simple man, dull even, and any spark of vivacity or charm was superficial. He looked scared. Hector felt sorry for him and put up his paw to comfort the frightened human.

'Aw look, he likes you, Mr president.'

The president broke into a smile.

'It certainly looks that way, hey boy.'

He locked eyes with Hector and offered him his hand to sniff. So the president knew dogs, it seemed. Hector sniffed. Mid-price cologne. A faint smell of tobacco. Probably a secret smoker. A woman's fragrance. Traces of childish things. Maybe two or three children, one quite young, the others just shy of their teens. He married late, or maybe remarried? The stale sweat lingered on his pores. He was busy: the fading odour of hand soap meant he hadn't had time to adequately rinse. He perspired a lot due to the effort expended supressing his uncertainty. Out of his depth. A political patsy controlled by more self-assured operators. Hector licked his hand.

'Hector! Don't lick the president!'

'That's OK, I like the little chap.'

The president scratched Hector behind the ears. He wagged his tail and rotated his head in a semi-circle to get the full effect of the presidential scratching. The president definitely knew dogs.

Flashbulbs popped like corn in a pot as the president held Hector up for all the world to see. Hector dutifully licked his face to the rapture of the gawping humans.

'Will he get his own bodyguard, Mr president?'

'What about his security clearance, Mr president? How can you be sure he isn't a spy!'

More laughter from the press pack. Hector wagged his tale, happy to see the humans happy. The flustered human hurried them out to a waiting convoy of limousines as the gaggle of reporters continued their chatter. The door of the president's limousine closed with an airtight thunk. Hector was now government property.

*

The presidential palace was a wonderful place for time travelling. The accumulated scents of centuries clung to every cushion, cornice and skirting board. Fascinating to think of all those generations of leaders and their followers who had deposited their memories in the fabric of the building. Hector sniffed everything, intoxicated by the complexity of the place, so much grander than his previous homes. They had smelled of defeat, anger and resignation. This place smelled of power. But under the top note was the acrid odour of misplaced confidence. Almost all human dwellings had it, but in this building it was overwhelming. Hector pretty much had the run of the place and enjoyed checking in on the various departments of government to see if they were happy. He would pad into offices, tail wagging. Most were glad to see him, but some were too glum to raise a smile. These humans seemed to be suffering terribly. Hector thought it cruel and unfair that they had to be so afflicted. He wished he could help them. Sometimes he would claim a small victory; rolling on his back or raising a paw seemed to crack even the steeliest of malcontents. Those moments were heaven for Hector. To see the curl of the mouth and the light twinkling behind the sadness. Even the most brutal humans could be capable of love, he thought.

Some of the humans were a particular mystery to Hector. The ones with the medals lashed to their tunics like Pantone strips. The ones with tombstone teeth and permanent suntans. The ones with the impersonal statistics and growth forecasts. They loved Hector. They ruffled his fur. 'Good boy, good boy.' But they hated other humans. The president was forever banging the table when they came around to visit. Hector would hide under the desk. Inhaling the conflict as the pheromones darted across the Cabinet Room. The vice president and his coterie of advisors would often be called in to steer the argument to some kind of conclusion. But Hector sensed the president wasn't always convinced by the outcome. The familiar scent of defeat and uncertainty lingered in his wake as he paced the presidential quarters. Occasionally he would slump down on the sofa. Hector would hop up, doing his best to coax a smile from the unhappy man.

'Hey boy, you don't know how lucky you are. Not a care in the world, eh boy?'

Hector humoured the dumb commander-in-chief by wagging his tale and licking his face. He really had no idea. Hector's life was full of worry, but he never let it overwhelm him. To say he lived in the now was too simple. In the Tangle, all things lived in the past, present and future simultaneously. Aware of the ebb and flow of events, but never confident of their outcome. Life was more pleasantly surprising like that. Humans were a perplexing anomaly in the flow of all things. They were forever disrupting the balance. They were heedless of warnings, however dramatic. They had invented a universe for themselves. Setting parameters of their own invention. Creating subdivisions, charts and categories that always placed them at the apex. Like precocious youths who won't be told, they swaggered and tutted their way to disaster. Still, he liked them. Perhaps these humans would mutate into something more benign in time.

These thorny issues were beginning to play on Hector's mind as he scampered along the corridors of power. Everyone here seemed so stressed and unhappy. One afternoon in high summer, when they should all have been out taking in the air, a particularly stern group of humans entered the presidential offices. Curtains were closed, and all but the president's closest confidants were ushered out of the room. Hector curled up under the desk as usual, listening to the cascade of chatter. He sniffed the air to discern its meaning.

'Mr president, we believe this will be an important addition to our arsenal and a major deterrent for the hostiles. Our intelligence suggests we are years ahead of them with this particular technology, sir.'

'OK, OK, I've read the briefing, Colonel Hyacinth. I know you guys at defence are keen to green-light this project . . . project . . . what are you calling it again?

'Project Good Boy, sir.'

Hector's ears pricked up.

'Good Boy, I understand. So, like, be a good boy or you're all gonna get it, right?

'Something like that, sir, yes.'

One of the group of very stern-looking men had a metal briefcase handcuffed to his wrist. The colonel clicked his fingers and the briefcase man inserted an odd-looking key into the lock. A dim light emanated from inside. The colonel continued.

'Project Good Boy is a pathogen delivery system that will dump a virus designed to nullify the hostiles' geno-specific capability to offer battlefield countermeasures, or, for the non-combatant component of their possible response vector to coalesce into a coherent resistance module, right down their gizzards, sir.'

Hector smelled confusion.

'Thank you, colonel. Perhaps you could clarify a few points for me.'

188

'It kills them, sir.'

'All of them?'

'Yessir, every last one of them.'

'That sounds very effective, colonel. How does this weapon work exactly?'

'The genome specificity is modulated . . .'

'In layman's terms, if you please.'

'Yes sir, sorry sir. Project Good Boy targets the specific sociogenetic make-up of the hostiles, splitting them apart at the subatomic level, rendering them inert, sir.'

'Inert, eh? Sounds nasty. How do we know it won't do the same to us, colonel?'

'Well sir, our scientists assure me that the hostiles are different from us, sir, like a different species. More like animals than bona fide human beings.'

Hector smelled bullshit and rolled onto his back. He began to groom himself, paying particular attention to the scar where his ball sack had once been. *'More like animals.'* He licked his paws and tuned into the chatter again.

'Are you sure about that, colonel? I've met a number of the hostiles and they seemed pretty similar to me. Are you sure this race bomb will work? I'd sure hate to wave that thing around if it ended up killing us all.'

'Absolutely, Mr president. They've run the numbers and conducted all the tests. It seems we are superior in every way to the enemy. We have nothing to fear from these patriotic germs, Mr president, sir, of that I can assure you.'

'That *is* reassuring, colonel. What do you make of it, Newt?'

The president turned to the vice president, who was listening patiently in the shadows.

'I recommend green-lighting the project. The science is clear. We cannot afford to slip behind in the pathogen arms race, Jack.'

'Very well. Keep me informed of your progress, colonel.'

The stern humans saluted and marched out of the office. Hector emerged from the desk and sniffed the floor as they left. The odour of overconfidence clung to the carpets like tobacco smoke on a woollen jumper. He detected the scent of the pathogen too. Despite their best efforts, the germs could not be contained. Their faulty human senses had failed to detect the subtle depths of the microbes' being. They were safe enough. For now. The quantity was too low to cause any significant harm. Hector was happy for that. He sniffed the air. Just as he thought. Bullshit. In fact this particular pathogen, though rare, was not unfamiliar in the Tangle. It lurked in the hidden substrata of the forest. The other animals acknowledged it and left it in peace. But somehow the humans had chivvied it out in their eagerness to find fresh ways to kill. The pathogen was not happy about the disturbance and had mutated into its most aggressive form in response. Hector barked a warning. It was deadly. They should put it back where they found it.

'You need to go outside? Hey Jasper, can you take the dog around the grounds? Poor guy probably needs a pee.'

'Certainly, Mr President. Come on boy, do you want to play catch outside?'

The ball was fun. He'd done his best. Hector followed the aide into the gardens of the presidential compound. He looked like he needed to play fetch. Hector wondered if he'd ever really understand these creatures. If only they could just say what they wanted.

*

The following year was a difficult one for the president and his friends. The hostiles had been doing things and going

190

places the president wasn't happy about. There had been threats issued and people had been killed. Hector heard it all, curled up under the president's desk. He wanted to help them, but so far they hadn't listened to his advice. One morning the sternest of all the president's staff ran into the meeting room, smelling of panic.

'Mr president, our intelligence suggests the hostiles are massing on the border, sir. Satellites confirm a massive troop build-up at their forward bases. We are advising you move to a safe location immediately, sir.'

'Initiate the Carthusian Complex.'

'Yes, sir, isolation at a secure location for all key staff. We recommend urgency, sir.'

Hector ran across the lawn as the president waved to the group of photographers who were permanently camped outside the compound. A flurry of indistinct questions drifted across the lawn. The words were scattered by the rotation of a helicopter's blades, making them sound like the script from an experimental theatre piece. The president fixed a smile and waved, as various aides flung important government documents into the chopper. The stern man with the briefcase handcuffed to his wrist stood a few metres away. He had become a permanent fixture in recent months, since Project Good Boy had been successfully completed. The president ducked his head as the draft of the helicopter blades sucked up his hair like a family of curious snakes coaxed from a basket. He sat between two burly guards. Hector jumped onto his lap and licked his face reassuringly. He knew how much the president hated flying.

The bunker had few scents of interest. No history, fully sanitised, vacuum sealed. But it did have one advantage: its seclusion. The Carthusian Complex was situated in the remotest part of the country, housed deep within the rock of a mountain. The secret hatch opened up onto a rolling green meadow, dotted with wildflowers and low shrubs. At its boarder the Tangle blended into the lawn. Bush became thicket became forest. Whilst the president strolled with his advisors, deep in conference, Hector would run into the woods. It was a relief to be amongst the chaos of nature. The wild proliferation of scents and the stories those perfumes told. Hector made enquiries whilst he was there. What was the best way to help his troubled human friends? How could he make them happy? They were suffering terribly. The Tangle would know. He found answers in the roots and in the secret places where the microbes dwelt. Some decisions were very hard to make, he thought.

'So the hostiles haven't agreed to any of our terms? What does that mean, Newt, in terms of our response?'

'The hostiles aren't happy, that's for sure. We need to be decisive, Jack. The gloves are off now, I'm afraid.'

'I have to agree with the vice president. We must take action, sir, and, of course, we always have Project Good Boy.'

Colonel Hyacinth nodded at the stern man with the briefcase. The stern man returned his nod with a whip-crack nod of his own.

'I'll hear no more talk of Project Good Boy, not until every possible angle has been tried, and that's an order, Colonel Hyacinth!'

'Yes, *sir*!'

Colonel Hyacinth offered a salute to his commander-in-chief, whilst giving the vice president a sly side-eye. *'The hostiles aren't happy.'* No one was happy, Hector thought. He felt sad.

The following days took on the same familiar pattern. The bad news mounted, and the threat of conflict loomed ever larger. Hector padded around the sterile corridors. His visits to the Tangle were becoming less frequent as security was stepped up at the base. But the diagnosis had been painfully clear.

'Mr president, I really must urge you to deploy Project Good Boy, sir, before the hostiles have a chance to overrun us. They have a nearly two-to-one advantage in battle tanks and a three-to-one ratio in heavy bombers. We just can't sustain the losses likely in a conflict situation, sir.'

'Thank you for your advice, Colonel Hyacinth, but we are not actually at war.'

'For now, Jack, but how long can this stand off last? There's happiness to think of, happiness is everything, God damn it!'

The vice president banged his fist down on the conference room table, disrupting the plastic models of ships, tanks and aeroplanes that were dotted about a map of the world. The humans looked awful. Pale yellowing skin, dark rings and heavy bags like refuse sacks, dangling under blood shot eyes. They had barely eaten. Once corpulent men now looked like withered scarecrows dressed for Halloween. Jackets had been long discarded, revealing shirts stained with sweat patches and collars black with grime. Hector was as concerned as any dog would be. He had tried his best capering. Sit. Good boy. But he had only been greeted by increasing hostility. The humans were reverting to type. There was a limit to his patience. The Tangle had warned him. Back when he was only a pup, it had warned him. Avoid the humans. They were difficult. You couldn't teach them a thing. Don't waste your time Hector. It had warned him. They are too much responsibility.

'Mr president, the folks in the cities are in a bad way. One thousand dead today from lack of food, and another five hundred killed in rioting. Sir, we have to do something!'

'Hyacinth's right, Jack. It's time to deploy Project Good Boy.'

The president's eyes filled with tears. He hadn't slept for days. The pressure was just too much for a simple man like him. Hector saw him in his plaid shirt, casting a line into a woodland river. Hector scampering over the rocks looking for sticks to chew.

'I'm so tired, Newt, so fucking tired.'

'OK, OK, Jack, you get some sleep. We'll make the decision once you've had a chance to rest.'

The vice president shot Colonel Hyacinth a conspiratorial look. Hyacinth in turn nodded to the briefcase guy.

'Get the president a sleeping pill, won't you?'

The vice president clicked his fingers. An aide appeared with a glass of water and a white tablet. The president took the glass distractedly, took a sip and swallowed the pill. The bodyguards snapped to attention and escorted the president to his quarters. Hector lingered under the briefing room table.

'Right, you, get that thing over here.'

The stern briefcase human clicked his heels together and gave an inappropriate salute.

'Jesus, Hyacinth, where'd you get this guy?'

'He's a patriot, sir.'

The stern, patriotic briefcase guy placed the briefcase on the table, just above the spot where Hector was curled up.

'Who's got the key?'

'Fuck. The president has the key, around his neck, sir.'

'What, there's only one key?'

'No sir, but you need two keys to arm the device . . . the other is in the base commander's safe.'

'OK, Hyacinth, fetch me that key. I'll try and get the other one off the president's neck. He's gonna be in la la land right now, those pills are strong. Get to it, Hyacinth, and take the briefcase guy with you in case anyone starts any funny business.'

'Sir, yes, sir.'

The angry humans left the briefing room, trailing their angry scent behind them. They went looking for the launch keys. But they would not find them.

Hector padded over to his place of precious things. He nuzzled the items he had acquired during his time in the bunker. A couple of tennis balls, the drill sergeant's slipper, a bone from the canteen and two Project Good Boy launch keys.

*

For days he had watched the humans unravel. Their appearance becoming progressively more dishevelled. The mood turning ever sourer and more aggressive. He had done all he could, but the Tangle was right, there was little to be done for these troubled creatures. Hector pawed at one of his tennis balls, enjoying watching its erratic orbit around the place of precious things. He was putting off his decision. He had a responsibility. He knew that. Things would only get worse for his friends if he did nothing. Things had really begun to unravel in the bunker. Hector thought it wise to remove the dangerous items from the base and put them in a safe place, so his friends wouldn't come to any harm. Tennis balls were a terrible trip hazard. Old bones unhygienic. Launch keys? Well, they were the most dangerous of all. Who knew what harm they could do if he let them play with those? Removing the president's key had been easy; he was easily distracted. He had placed it over the chair in his room while he was changing into his last clean shirt. The president was so exhausted that he quite forgot he was supposed to be wearing it. The base commander was a little trickier, but still, simple enough. Hector had waited until the safe was open. The base commander was quite an amiable fellow. He loved Hector and had remained on good terms with him, even as the others became more taciturn. Hector had simply nosed his ball across the floor. Barked. Then lifted the key from the safe as the base commander went to retrieve the ball. Shutting the door of the safe and patting Hector on the head, he was none the wiser.

They would be back soon. The angry humans and the vice president. Hector tugged at the threads of the tennis ball. He rolled onto his back and wiggled about on the floor, enjoying the roughness on his fur. He sprang up, dropping the ball and letting it roll back to the place of precious things. He padded over and picked up the launch keys in his mouth. They clinked together, sounding like milk bottles in a shopping bag. He scampered over to the briefing table. He tried to pull himself up, but his legs were too little. He reversed a few steps and jumped. The briefcase was open, just as the humans had left it. The inside was sparse. Just two key holes with two green lights above them. A button in the middle. A red button. A big red button. Hector dropped one of the keys on the tabletop. Taking the remaining key, he padded over to the briefcase and, tilting is head deftly to one side, he pushed the key into the hole and turned it. The green light lit up. *All those pasty, sweaty faces, they looked so sick, what can be done? Thousands dying of hunger. Riots. Violence.* Hector picked up the remaining key and repeated the process. The green light went on. *The hostiles are not happy Mr president, the people are not happy Mr president, we must act Jack. Project Good Boy.* Now the red button lit up, winking like a sailor on shore leave.

There was nothing to be done. Everything had been tried. It was a mercy. A mercy for all concerned. What kind of life would they have? Those sunken, sad eyes. It was heartbreaking. Such a good boy. I guess we're all going to miss you, but when all's said and done, you wouldn't want them to suffer any more, would you?

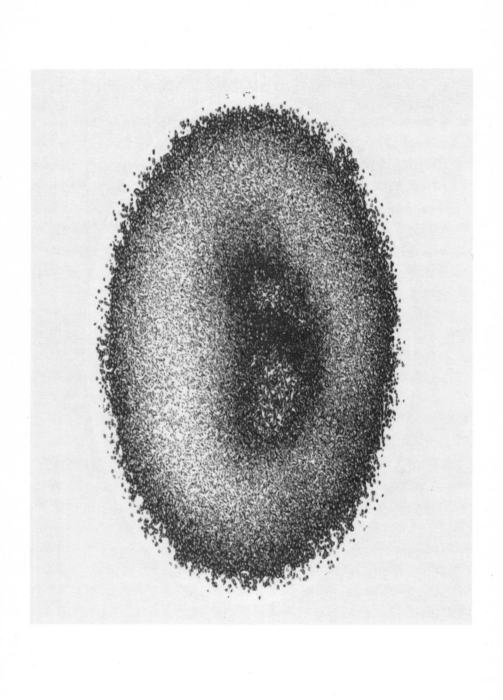

Water Holds Memory

A soft strip of pulverised rock. Dull yellow, blending to
grey. Where the rotting stems of stranded seaweed decayed
on the edge of land and sea. Forgotten by the tides. They
lay like wounded soldiers left to die on a battlefield. Picked
over by crabs and gulls. Staring into the foam through
lidless eyes, never to return. The beach. A soft strip of
pulverised rock. The beach was a graveyard for immutable
stone and the certainties of solid ground. Where the water
mocked the illusion of permanence. This was the front
line in a conflict that had raged longer than any human
memory; even the rocks themselves struggled to remember
its beginning. But no one came here any more. It was once
a place of pilgrimage for the animals of the land. Gazing
from the brink into the green folds of another world,
perched on the precipice of their habit. Wishing for fins
and gills. In the summer months the rites and the frolics of
the season used to fill the beach with laughter. Crowds of
people had broken the seal between soil and sea, splashing
over a charnel pit, an aeon in the making. But now no
one came. The council said it was an oil spill. Dangerous
chemicals they said. Local gossips offered more lurid
explanations. Nothing substantiated beyond idle chatter
over the market stall, but everyone knew someone who
knew someone who had heard from someone else about a
rumour. There was something uncanny about that beach,

whispers in the sand, a feeling of unease; that was what really kept people away.

Over time the beach faded from memory. The gossips passed away, taking their stories with them. Years turned to decades, the beach brooding in its isolation, untroubled by visitors or the eyes of man. It was a remote spot. No cafés or amusement arcades, no pubs or sea front restaurants. The few refreshment huts that used to cling to the humble promenade had long since packed up and moved on. The promenade too had gone, battered by storms, never to be repaired, its brittle skeleton finally sucked back into the sea. There was no sign of humanity now. Even the lane, once thronging with holidaymakers filing their way down to the water's edge, had been reclaimed by the forest. Now an ambiguous woodland trail was the only means of access. Trodden down by foraging deer, thin and indistinct in places, it wove through the woods, stopping just short of the bay where the beach crouched like a cornered stag. From the sea the beach was almost invisible, its shallow gradient hiding it from all but the keenest lookout. It rose in a gentle slope to a craggy chine, an uneven spine that looked like the work of a careless butcher. The chine, in turn, dropped down to a thin border of coarse grass where the promenade had once stood. The Tangle tumbled down to its edge, with its wind-blown trees standing like stern sentinels against the aggression of the waves. Beyond the Tangle the world of men began.

*

Vince rode his bicycle. He swept down the empty lanes. The lane morphed as his imagination transformed it. Perspectives of time and space were temporary borders to be shifted at will. Behind him was the town. Its bland avenues and decaying crescents providing only the dreariest of backdrops. Its predictable edges and crumbling cornices were nothing more than a faded tableau of misplaced confidence that was slowly decomposing. Vince peddled hard inland to escape its baleful orbit. As the town began to fade from view he felt a liberating lightness, like an acrobat whose partner has recently dismounted from their shoulders. He stood on the pedals, coasting along the quiet country roads, stretched limbs in other dimensions. He was no country boy. He was born and raised in the city. Ten years in the rough 'n' tumble. Ten years of postcode scraps and big lads with knives. The nearest he'd come to the countryside was the petting zoo in the city park. Tired-looking goats, threadbare chickens and a lonely llama. The currents of gentrification had carried his parents out of the city and deposited them in a coastal town that had seen better days. It was cheaper here, they had a yard too, but there wasn't much to do, even the pound shop had closed down. Outside the border of the town the greenery stretched into eternity. Vince had never seen so much open space. Even though large swathes of it were fenced off, marked private or under the plough, there was still room enough for his imagination to trespass. His agile consciousness filled the landscape, probing the layers that were hidden to older minds. Out here, in the controlled wildness, he was alone.

It was midsummer. It was hot. Very hot. The kind of searing heat that triggered government health warnings and kept sensible folk inside. These types of weather events were no longer rare or even surprising any more. Vince took them in his stride. He wore a cap, as his mum had insisted. It had his favourite band's logo stitched to the front; it had been his dad's, from his raver days. The sun battered him like a schoolyard bully. Drenched with sweat and panting in the thick air, Vince pulled his bicycle over to the side of the road and took a swig from his water bottle. Conditions were hard, but the thought of returning to the town seemed to place unwanted borders around his fantasies. He had further to go, more to see, frontiers to cross. He was far from home now, at the outer boundaries of his world. But he was tired and in need of rest. His parents would not be home for hours yet. The pot was yet to be stirred and the bread remained uncut. He had time before tea. Time. Time. Supressing the pangs of hunger and the nagging of weary limbs, he pushed his bicycle off the road. Vince noticed a wood. He hadn't seen it before. The wood was just there. Suddenly. It was as if it had burst out of the ground like the flourishing of an untapped well. The wood looked like an oasis of variety at the end of a series of monochrome fields. The shade would be delicious. He pushed his bicycle down a stony track. The wood shimmered like a mirage. From where he stood, it looked wild and deregulated, every conceivable species of tree and shrub jumbled together in a disorderly clump. It was hard to gauge its dimensions; the perspective kept shifting, as if the wood was hopping along the edge of the field, retreating to the horizon before surging back across the field. It reminded Vince of the waves on the seafront.

As he got nearer, the wood quickly expanded, taking in the whole horizon. The motion was fluid, silent, unfathomable. The movement was impossible to quantify. Try as he might, his perception was too faulty to judge it correctly. Distance, height, volume, all seemed like inadequate units of measurement for the uncanny flux of the forest. It was spreading out. Surrounding him. Branches and shoots spiralling in all directions. Until he was suddenly standing in the middle of its tight weave. Boy. Bicycle. Alone. The track he had been walking down was consumed by the vegetation. His bicycle tyres began to bounce over the roots that spread like veins under the surface. As he walked, the wood throbbed and pulsed like a lung. But despite this sudden change in the rules of nature, fear was entirely absent from Vince's mind. He was calm. The wood was peaceful. The wood was cool. The wood was full of soothing sounds. Time was moving at a different pace; he could feel it. The melodies of birdsong skittered around the trees in a harmonious sequence. The buzz of insects pitched down to a hypnotic drone as they described languid orbits around his head. Pollen, sparkling in the shafts of sunlight that pierced the canopy, seemed to hang effortlessly in the air, as if the laws of gravity had been momentarily relaxed.

Vince pushed on through the wood, finding the path easy to follow. Direction soon became meaningless. He had no idea where he was going, so he let his feet get carried by the path. He caught a sound. Familiar and yet out of place. The boom of surf. That was impossible. He had been heading away from the sea. He always made for the hinterland during the daylight hours. The seaside was for the evenings. The beach was quieter and more interesting in the twilight, when the contrast between land and sea was less pronounced. But here he was, pulled back to the shore. The sudden collapse of geographical logic was easy to understand; it often happened to him, only not in the tangible world of touch and taste. It was more an ease with the mutable nature of things that played out in his waking dreams. His parents too had once had the gift, though the ageing process had gradually eroded the wonder. But this was the first time he had seen the spell performed in the real world. It was beautiful. Vince noticed the trees beginning to thin before him, parting like the curtains at the start of a play. The sun streamed into the wood. The wood stopped abruptly on a ragged border of coarse grass. Hesitant trees recoiled from the grass as if they had skidded to a halt on the edge of a hidden precipice. Beyond the grassy border a ragged chine was the last defence from the sand. A band of brutalised rock merging with the sea beyond. This was the battlefront. Life on land may have crawled from those salty depths, but now that it had grown apart from the womb it would suffocate if it were to trespass any further, as surely as a child returned to its amniotic sac.

Vince shared none of the forest's reticence; like most humans, part of him wanted desperately to return to the sea. He pushed his bike over the border, bumping over the chine and onto the coarse sand. Looking behind him, he felt the forest recede, mirroring the movement of the waves. The tide was going out. The beach had a forbidding density. The hot air was heavy with anticipation, as if awaiting the coming of the storm and the ozone crackle. The pleasant coolness of the wood was forgotten in the cauldron of the bay. A demon heat rose and hovered above the sand in shimmering waves. Vince took off his T-shirt, kicked off his shoes and rolled up the legs of his trousers. He felt the hot sting of the sand on the soles of his feet, scorching like a penitent's spike. Vince dropped his bicycle carelessly onto the sand. He began to hop over the beach towards the coolness at the water's edge. Moving further and further from the certainties of the land. The damp sediment, dark grey from the lick of the sea, soothed his feet. Vince waited for the waves to return. The initial shock of the cold ocean as it splashed up his ankles; the transmitted snap as his muscles contacted; the simple pleasure of a contrasting set of uncomfortable sensations, confusing his equilibrium. Paddling in the sea was as close to heaven as anyone was ever likely to get. Evolution in reverse. The simple crossing of dimensions. The innocent refusal to be hemmed in by liveable terrain. The thrill of danger as uncertainty played its hand. One misstep, one unexpected surge, was all it would take to drag him under.

Vince focused on the approaching wave as it formed in the channel. A ripple, growing fast as the water was forced up and over the shallows until it became a thundering torrent of tumbling devils. Stretching their tangled limbs towards the land. They ran across the shingle, only to stumble as the beach asserted itself once more. Forcing the demons back into the sea, leaving only their withered aquatic arms to vainly claw at the sand as the ocean retreated. The wave stopped short of his wriggling toes. Vince risked a further step. A fresh wave was forming out at sea. He shuffled forward, hoping to feel the soothing sting of the water on his legs. The wave came on in the same old way. The white-flecked ridge grew again. As he knew it would. But this time it seemed to ascend faster, almost angrily. Vince felt the urge to run. But the sand had sealed around his bare feet like manacles. The serpent wave rose. Slipping rapidly up the shore. But as it was poised to strike, it slowed. It became almost static. He could see the wall of water above him. Frozen. The wave had none of the qualities of water he was familiar with, none of the sparkling froth one might expect. Instead, it was a viscid ooze. Glistening and malevolent, undulating along its length. Vince thought he could see faces bulging from

the surface like prisoners pressed against the bars of an
overcrowded jail. Fractures began to appear in his world.
Small glimpses into a hidden mechanism. He could see the
formless cogs grinding. Cold. Unconcerned. Relentless.
This moment of disconnection lasted only a fraction of a
second before the wave reverted back into its more familiar
form. It broke on the beach and scampered up the sand.
Slopping around his ankles and splashing up his shins. The
feeling was sensational. He quivered with delight as the
shock travelled up his body. The sun above him renewed its
attack. Vince splashed into the water, letting the waves dash
against his torso, tasting the brackish tang of the water on
his lips. He felt the weight of the heat lift from him. As his
body gradually became acclimatised to the chill of the ocean
he started to risk further forays into the surge. Rubbing
the water onto his shoulders, splashing it on his face until
it stung his eyes. As his confidence grew, so his desire to
explore the depths blossomed. The bottom of the ocean.
The undersea fiefdom of eccentric monsters and astonishing
things. He was diver. He was submariner. Vince plunged
into the approaching wave.

> Root of the land, hidden by earth, sown by the seed,
>   born by the flood.
> Drowned by the wave that sundered the rock, the sea
>   and the salt, the skin and the blood.

The sound of the world suddenly shrank away. As if all the
frequencies had been crushed under enormous pressure.
He was an intruder returning to the deep after an absence
of millennia. However, the sea was already familiar with his
kind. Long ago it had spat his ancestors out onto the land.

They had returned millions of years later in vessels that
floated on the surface. They had caused mischief in the sea,
as was their habit. The sea had been forced to remind them
that they were creatures of the soil now. It smashed their
boats and ravaged their ports. But still they came. Vince
pushed himself like a torpedo out of the foaming mess. As
he floated above the waves he thought he saw figures on the
beach. He tried to twist his body as he flew. But the forces
of attraction were too great, and he fell back into the swell.
He sank down, inelegantly writhing as water rushed up
his nose. Sudden panic overtook him. He was an imposter,
he could not function here. He pushed himself back to the
surface. Gasping and sputtering. This time he managed to
get to his feet. Steadying himself on the seabed, he brushed
the wet hair from his face. He scanned the beach. There
was no one there. He looked up and down its length. He
was sure he had seen something. Nothing. Still its presence
dangled there. Like a broken body in a gibbet, hovering
over the sand.

Those few moments above the waves made him shiver.
His body had adapted to the temperature of the sea, and he
found himself unwilling to leave it. Now it was the land that
seemed alien to him. That shimmering presence. Vince dived
back down into the water, neither fish nor boy. Trapped
between two worlds. The sounds of the beach retuned to a
womb-like frequency, but something had changed. The layers
peeled back. Molecules bonded in unfamiliar sequence. This
was the seldom glimpsed dimension that only occasionally
intersected with our own. Vince was held fast. Water. Not
water. This was how things really were. Thick. Clinging.
He thought he would drown in the clag. It clasped him tight,
unwilling to cede an inch. Instead he moved like seaweed,

finding himself rooted to the bed, his legs like stems bending in the current. This was how it would end. Stuck fast and drowning. His lungs cried out for air. The mechanisms of his body clicked and spun. Despite the precariousness of his predicament, his mouth opened, seeking the breeze. This is how it would end. But the flood never came. Instead he found he could breathe easily. The viscous liquid filled and nourished his veins. He swayed like a weed. A dark shadow passed over him. The keel of a boat. Sounds, slowed down to a wrenching grind, echoed around the gelatinous medium. Vince put his fingers in his ears, but he had no fingers, no ears either. The sound was continuing to bloom, growing steadily louder. He tried to translate the vibration into something intelligible. He thought he recognised screams. Grunts. Wailing. The noise of conflict.

Eyes without sight, vision or focus. No lens or pupil, motion or locus.

He looked up to the surface, though he had no eyes. He saw smoke drifting in the air. Vince's lungs began to ache, his throat contracted. He was human again. He fought his way back to the surface, the thick liquid thinning as he swam. His mind signalled caution, but his body demanded air. Vince pushed his face through the skin of the water. It was dark. On the beach it was night, and the beach was not empty.

A long, wooden ship was anchored in the shallows. It was of an ancient design, with a prow that curled up into a barbaric dragon's head. Vince recognised it from his history lessons: a Viking ship. Screams eddied across the waves, curling around his partly submerged skull. His eyes were frozen open, stinging with the salt but unable to close.

Figures milled around the shore. He could see unwilling women being dragged towards the longboats, their faces streaked with blood and tears, arms stretched back to the land as if grasping at some invisible thread that would secure them to their homes. On the sand, blood ran in black rivers that sucked the light from the risen moon. It flowed from the cuts and severed limbs of men. Monks dressed in their sodden habits were kneeling on the sand. Gruff warriors stood over them, sorting those deemed useful from those to be left in pieces on the shore. Axes swung and swords swept like scythes. Heads rolled. The lamentations of the monks spiralled into the sky. Waiting for a reply. The wrong question. Always the wrong question.

Vince's head throbbed. Part sea, part blood. The horror fascinated him; he was transfixed by the hypnotic swing of the axe and the mantras of despair rising from the victims. The vision was too compelling, too unbelievable. Those screams. Those fractured arias. They were real enough. He submerged himself further, hoping that the water would muffle the cries, but it only seemed to channel them all the more, until it felt as if the screams were inside his head. He had received no instruction from his parents, no guidance on how to deal with such matters. Spectres. Time travel. Don't talk to strangers. Call us if you think you are in danger. His telephone was in his trouser pocket, in a pile of his clothes lying next to his bicycle. This certainly felt like an emergency. He should call someone. Vince poked his eyes above the swell and looked to see if his bicycle was still on the beach. He had left it just short of the craggy chine, in the area where a Viking warrior was currently disembowelling an unfortunate cleric. The steam from his gushing viscera described an arc around where the handlebars should be. There was no sign of his bicycle. Vince hung in the ooze.

The current began to take him closer to the boat. The Vikings were hefting loot and battered captives into its shallow hull. He tried to paddle away from its looming form, but the current was too strong to resist. These irresistible eddies. They had sprung from the depths quite suddenly, dragging him along like the line of a fisherman's rod. He whirled helplessly towards the dragon boat, spinning around like a leaf, unable to reverse his course. As he got closer he could see a statuesque warrior emerging from the hull. His imposing frame raised itself above the gunwales. He was enormous. Vince sailed impotently towards him. The warrior raised his axe, dripping with gore and sorrow. Vince was close enough to see his face. An unholy beard carried fragments of skin and brain in its matted weave. His eyes were black, empty sockets in which only a demon light flickered. The warrior raised his axe above his head. His horned helmet silhouetted in the moonlight like Baphomet risen from hell. The stench of wet fur assailed his nostrils. The goat god is risen. The goat god is risen. Vince forced himself under the waves, pushing against the current with all his strength. His lungs burned. He pushed and thrust. Trying to move through the thick water. His body was weak. His body was frail. He needed air. He began to rise through the murk. Vince closed his eyes as he floated to the surface. He hoped for a swift end. A quick, sharp bite from the warrior's axe. It would be over in seconds. He awaited his fate. But no blow came. Vince opened his eyes, expecting to see the cloven hooves of the warrior devil above him. But all he saw was a wispy cloud dissolving in the summer breeze.

The wave broke the stone, the salt sowed the soil.
The wood fled the shore as the serpent uncoiled.

Vince was cold and exhausted. Had it been minutes, hours,
days, or years since he had stepped on dry land? With feeble
strokes and laboured kicks he approached the shallows.
His tired and bloodshot eyes tried to focus on the beach.
His bicycle and neatly stacked clothes were where he had
left them. He felt relieved to find objects occupying their
expected places. A gentle wave broke over his head. Vince
spat out brine and blew the sodden wisps of hair from
his eyes. As he looked up he could see translucent figures
parading across the sand. Glamorous ladies twirling parasols
on a ghostly promenade. Moustachioed gentlemen in striped
bathing costumes preening in front of modestly attired
girls. All shimmering and transparent in the summer heat.
Another wave broke over his head. A strangled cry rose
from the surf to his left. Close. Vince turned to the source.
A small child, no older than five, struggling, in trouble,
clearly drowning. The figures rushed to the water's edge
but seemed unable to enter. Vince was closer. Could he save
the boy? Vince was only a child himself, could he carry the
burden? He swam in a rapid crawl towards the drowning
child. He was so close to the boy now that he could see the
hope of salvation in the child's eyes. The boy reached out
his hand, his fingers stretching across the swell, trying to
connect with Vince's own outstretched hand. Their fingers
met. For a few seconds the barrier was breached, two worlds
fusing in a dreadful symmetry. An ectoplasmic shock darted
up Vince's arm. His eyes were the boy's eyes, scanning the
beach for his parents. Too young to be in this deep. Lacking
the skill to stay afloat in such choppy seas. They would never

forgive themselves, he thought, as the water cascaded into his lungs. The figures on the beach vibrated in the haze and began to spin. They spun faster and faster until they became tornados of sand, their features stretching in the torrent, pulling their bodies up into the sky. The spinning stopped. A fine mist of dust settled back onto the beach. The boy faded into waves. Vince shouted in confusion as he floundered in the tide. Spinning around looking for the child. Diving down again and again until his weak boy arms gave out. The waves pushed him up the shallows and deposited him onto the beach. He lifted his head from the sand, spitting out grit and seaweed. He was alone.

*

Vince woke from another night of fitful sleep. Tangled in his sweat-drenched sheets. Every time his eyes closed, the visions returned. He was hanging in the ectoplasm. Axes, blood, the screams of butchered bodies. The helpless fingers of a child slipping through his own. His body had only succumbed to sleep in the early morning, when his mind had momentarily paused. These snatched moments of sleep provided no rest, just confusing fragments of changing states. He caught his reflection in the mirror as he dragged himself out of bed. He was carrying heavy bags under his eyes, his skin looked grey, a winter tone on a summer's day. Vince avoided the sunlight. He avoided the beach.

His parents were worried. Why would a boy so young be so anxious? It was the summer holidays, a time for adventure, a time for fun. But for the last three weeks Vince had become quiet and withdrawn. At weekends he sat inside. Even as the temperature soared, Vince stayed in his room;

his friends would pop by, but all he did was shout down that he was not well and needed to rest. Never mention the sea. They knew that now. Vince had grown to hate the sea. Mum and Dad tried, but fared no better, though they attempted to coax him down with bribes and incentives. But Vince could not be persuaded. Perhaps they should call the doctor?

Three weeks became four. Four dragged into five. But, at last, the nightmares became more manageable. His mind had begun to file them away. Memories to be laughed at in later years as childish fancies or youthful illusions. His parents were full of such stories, shared fables that hinted at insights that had now faded from their memories. Haunted homes. Creatures in closets. Figures in the trunks of trees. All these stories were true. But such ideas were too inconvenient to be allowed to rub shoulders with more agreeable facts, so they were filed away as well. Vince began to make cautious trips into the outside world. He began with a visit to the backyard. All the phantoms were there, as he suspected they would be. The next day he made it as far as the shops; the ghosts on the high street clattered on their melancholy routes. Sightless eyes and spectral limbs. Endlessly looping. Vince became accustomed to the apparitions. He always suspected they were there, occupying the indistinct folds and creases of the town. He knew others could see them too but had chosen to blot them out. He wasn't troubled by these stranded spirits and lost souls; it was the beach that refused to let him go. Its cruel tangled net had wrapped itself around him. Vince hacked at it every day. Stay away from the ocean. Stay away. But the Tangle needed allies, emissaries, ambassadors to convey its message to the beach. It began to work its way back into the fabric of his world.

Who will carry the weight of the golden seed to the shore?
Who will brave the tide and the ocean's savage maw?
Who will pay the price the waves will surely ask?
Who will ride the swell in the tempest's icy blast?

These were the last days of the Anthropocene, when the
summer never ended. The Tangle lay low under the scorching
torch of the sun. Outwardly withered, but truly only resting.
Waiting for the heat death and the passing of the mantle. For
the evolution of sense or the funeral dirge. These were the
last days of innocence, when all the elements had gathered
together, fusing into something new, something terrible. In
these last days, Vince sweltered in his room or in the scant
shade offered by his yard. Anything. Any fraction of relief was
better than the beach. Between the cracks the weeds broke
through. Spreading invisible scents and seeds throughout
his home. They planted themselves in the dust of his room,
into the cracked toys of his childhood. The spores fused with
the fabric of his clothes and bore down into the fibres of the
food he ate. Time to rise young man. Time to hatch. One
Wednesday in August the pressure was too much to bear.
The mercury had popped off the scale, and his parents were
out at work as usual. Vince found himself alone with his
thoughts and the presence that surrounded him. These were
the last days of childhood; the urge to live was too strong.
The back roads and fields, the hedges and ditches, all needed
to be explored and occupied. The Tangle was calling him
back to finish the games he must play before weariness and
responsibility made them seem foolish to him. These were the
last days for good boys and girls. Before the mysteries of the
world sunk back into the bark, locked away for eternity. These
were the last days for Vince. For now, he must live.

Who will carry the weight of the golden seed to the shore?
Who will brave the tide and the oceans savage maw?
Who will pay the price the waves will surely ask?
Who will ride the swell in the tempest's icy blast?

Vince pushed his bicycle out of the garage, where it had languished these last few weeks. A few tenacious cobwebs clung to the spokes. The dozier spiders tumbled off and ran for cover into the flower beds as he wheeled the bicycle out. He began a silent countdown. He adjusted his rucksack on his back. He checked his route out of the town. Vince was using his father's old Ordnance Survey Map. He didn't want there to be any chance of ending up on the beach again, no quick routes to avoid roadworks or time-saving deviations favoured by the satellite navigation. He needed a dependable path inland. Vince selected winding B roads and seldom-trodden tracks that all led in one direction: away from the sea. 5-4-3-2-1. The countdown to a childhood's end. He supressed his nascent adolescent feelings and put his trust in the Fates. It would be good to be back in the folds of the forest again. Away from the oppression of the town and the cauldron of his home. Away from the thick air of his room. Away from the boom of the surf. Vince put his feet to the peddles.

The country lanes were like leafy veins criss-crossing the rolling landscape. They followed an ambiguous route. Old packhorse trails and eccentric shepherding paths were their templates. Along these winding byways the arms of roadside shrubs arched from densely weaved hedges. Reaching high above the road they embraced in the middle of the lane, forming dark tunnels that provided welcome shade from the glaring sun. In these spaces his mind was free to wander.

He peddled fast, his chin close to the handlebars. How like a blood cell he was, sucked by the current into the land. His imagination filled the cracks and peeled back the cataracts. He could see the tramping progress of carts and heavy horses, bent-backed villagers seeding the soil. He could smell the sweat of their labours and taste the juice of sweet fruits sampled as they harvested the crop. Timeless at last, he felt the occupants of long-lamented eras returning to their homes. Some joyful and content, singing and clapping down the lanes, others resentful for lives cut short or wasted on whimsy. He could feel the bones of highwaymen hung from gibbets of iron. He could hear the crows call as they pecked the last strands of flesh from their faces. Sightless, they called to him as he cycled by. Let him pass. He will never linger here again. Vince flowed, and in this silent passage the beach was quite forgotten.

He had cycled for maybe an hour or more when he came to a fork in the road. He stopped to check his father's map. He must not take the seaward route. He must not falter. The map was confusing, too many lines and bewildering gradients. He was tempted to try his phone, though he was suspicious of its intentions. But there was no signal out here. There was a sign, however. It was old and carved in wood, not a modern council sign, all fluorescent and eye catching. It was a wizened post. Weather beaten. It had a gnarled trunk that held two roughly hewn arrows at its summit, each with a name carved into them. The letters were in a spidery script, painted in black pitch, almost impossible to read against the knotted wood. Vince had to squint to make them out: right, Ambleton; left, Caxton. He checked the map, shaking it out in the thick air, trying to decipher its meaning. The road to Ambleton would take him back to where he began. It described a warped circle that joined up stranded islands of twee cottages until it was reabsorbed by the network of roundabouts and carriageways that ran back to the town along the coast road. The sea. He must stay away from the sea. In contrast, the road to Caxton was relatively free of interruption. It meandered through Caxton Wood until it reached the town on the other side. That would be the safest route. He had been to Caxton Wood with the school on a history field trip. Vince had found the trip fascinating, though the darkness of the wood had unsettled him; it was dense and full of shadows. Whispers rose in its glades and gullies. He could hear those whispers now, hanging in the heat haze. He must stick to the road. But that wood? On the other side was Caxton. An island of manufactured things. It wasn't a bad spot, a collection of villages that had blended together over the years. It had all the usual vestiges of old-world charm: Tudor cottages, the ruins of the old church and the remains of a roman fort. Generations of local youths had scrawled on the crumbling battlements, 'Trevor Hines is a twat', 'Caxton rucking machine', 'Barry loves Helen', with crudely drawn genitalia adding to the romance of words. There was the hint of the now too. Poorly translated, as the town planners tried to move with the times. Buildings that smacked of committees and compromise were hidden amongst the heritage, like the embarrassing results of an after-school craft lesson brought home by proud children. Function flexed in the Central Business District. There were car parks with supermarkets at their centre, mini roundabouts and bypasses, a shopping centre too. He could shelter there a while. Perhaps skim stones in the lazy river that ran under the medieval bridge. Add his notch to the wisdom carved into the stones of the fort. Then he'd double back through Ambleton and be at home in time for tea.

The climb was hard. Vince stood on the peddles to achieve the torque he needed. He slowly climbed the hill. Once he reached the crest, he could see the road slicing an incision through the vale, right into the heart of Caxton Wood. He paused at the top of the hill, looking down into the dark blob of the forest. It pulsed to its own rhythm. The trees moving to and fro against the breeze, even though he could feel none. The sight was mesmerising. Inviting. Pollen, seeds and spores, the genesis of flax, all the elements of reproduction and renewal, swirled in the air around his faulty frame. Doubts ebbed and flowed. His breath pulled the particles into him. They spread through his cells like a vaccine, increasing their potency with every inhalation. Doubt turned to senseless calm. The trees swayed against the phantom breeze. He turned to look at the world he had left behind. The road that led home. Beyond the hamlets and hedges, across the fields and farms, under the drains and pipes, over the roofs of houses clinging to the land was the sea. Vince pushed off and sailed into the mouth of the entity.

The descent was effortless. Like a helpless fly sucked into a whirlpool, Vince was drawn into the wood. He sailed closer to the edge. The sun's rays lost their strength. All light, all heat was absorbed and annihilated. He shivered as he crossed the horizon. Vince took his feet off the peddles and freewheeled along the dented country lane, separated from the seasons and the passage of time. It was cold, the muted chatter of birds and the soft creak of ancient trunks the only sound. The road was out of place in the wood, like a surgical pin thoughtlessly lost in an unwilling patient. Vince was a stranger. His mind wandered through the knot of branches.

218

There were no apparitions of humanity here. No wraiths called from their rest by his passing. The voices he heard were of a far more ancient vintage. Deeper and deeper he drifted, caught on the currents that drew him like a magnet to some hidden terminus. Vince tacked across the lane, careless of bends and blind corners. There was no human traffic here. He was alone. Vince knew from the map that Caxton Wood was not large, having shrunk from its former vastness over the centuries. It should take him no more than thirty minutes to cross it. Yet he felt like he had been in the forest for hours. He looked at his watch. It had stopped.

He felt uneasy. He felt separated. Separated from the tangible. His mind groped for anchors: his room, his yard, his parents. Here amongst the sticks, here in the Tangle, there was no place for parents. He must turn back. He had miscalculated; the journey through the wood was taking too long. No time. No time. No time to carve his name into the ramparts of the fort, no time to skim stones or explore the grey courtyards of Caxton town. No time. He stopped and swung his bicycle round in the dark lane. The canopy pressed around him, arching over his head, forming a black dome like a starless night sky. The heat began to rise. The cold tomb-like air began to thicken into a viscous heat. In front of him the road home was quickly swallowed by the forest. There was no way through. No chance of return. He spun around and peddled fast. He must get out of the darkness. The road bent and swerved around impossible angles and improbable inclines. Vince peddled harder. Sweat began to pore down his face as the thermometer climbed. The heat was crushing. His breath came in stuttering gulps as he pushed himself along the pitiless highway. Ahead, all he could see was an endless tunnel of trees. He concentrated on his feet, willing them to push the peddles faster. His white plimsolls blurred like pistons, laces snapping like snakes. His legs began to fill with lactic pools, corroding and painful. He tried to concentrate on the passing of distance by focusing on the road beneath his wheels. He imagined the darkness lifting as he exited the forest. He willed the sun to return to brighten the lane. Soon, it must be soon. As he stared, the road beneath his wheels melted, morphing from the hard, concrete certainties of tar and stone chip into a dark, forbidding liquid. He looked around him, trying to find some natural marker by which he could fasten his sanity. As his eyes penetrated the gloom, the dense knot of the forest began to unwind. Vince could hardly breath now, the air was solid. He thought he could see light up ahead. Was he out of the wood at last? He peddled faster, though he could no longer feel the peddles. The branches continued to unwind; the unbroken blue of the summer sky began to break through the melting canopy. He felt a breeze cooling his sweat-drenched brow. The relief was magnificent. He closed his eyes and enjoyed the sharp chill as the currents of fresh air broke against his body. It was like plunging into the ocean.

Who will carry the weight of the golden seed to the shore?
Who will brave the tide and the ocean's savage maw?
Who will pay the price the waves will surely ask?
Who will ride the swell in the tempest's icy blast?

His legs moved with the same regular, piston-like motion. But he was no longer connected to the peddles. His hands no longer curled round the plastic grips of the handlebars. His fingers no longer summoned the brittle ring of the bell.

He was no longer cycling. He was paddling. Vince's eyes
sprang open with sudden horror. He was in the ocean. He
floundered in the waves, eyes fixed on the endless horizon,
unwilling to look behind him. What strange vortex had
spat him out into this? He began to long for the terror of
the forest. At least it wasn't . . . *this*. This haunted pool.
He began to shiver, the cool refreshing sensation changing
quickly into a bone-deep cold. His clothes ballooned in the
swell, then clung to him like icy limpets as the air escaped.
His lips turned a corpse-like purple. His skin mottled. He
spat into the water and cursed. The maps had failed. He was
back. He was alone. He knew it would be there, even before
he finally plucked up the courage to turn around. The beach.
That haunted ribbon of broken, pulverised rock.

Vince pushed back the water and waited for the waves.
Deep inside him, the seeds and spores began to write their
message in the molecules of his body. Through pores and
glands it gradually seeped into the water to be collected
by the tide and carried back to the emptiness of the core.
Vince stared out to sea as the first wave formed. It came on
like a regiment of cavalry, slow at first, but then growing
in confidence as it approached the bobbing boy. It was only
a few feet away and already Vince could see the turquoise
lustre of the wave fade to a dour grey. The supple flow of
the water replaced by the dense solidity of a malignant
effluent. The wave hit, sending him under. Beneath the
surface the thickness continued. Strong eddies of churning
goo spun Vince around in slow motion, filling his nostrils
with slime. He held his breath, willing the rotation to stop
long enough for him to come up for air. The liquid turned
with agonising indifference, but at last he completed his
cycle. Vince spluttered to the surface as the wave rolled

past him. The sky turned from day into night. It was raining hard, and a gale of enormous ferocity blew as the rain lashed down. His instinct said live. At least there was a chance that way. He turned towards the beach and attempted to swim back to land. The storm surge kept pulling him back, pushing him sideways or dragging him under. Progress was difficult. The message reached the core. The emptiness considered its response.

On the beach Vince could see lanterns flickering through the gloom and figures running about on the sand, engaged in frenzied activity. A barrel floated past him, then a tea crate, fragments of broken wood. Vince grabbed at a piece of timber as it floated by. He clung on to it as the sea continued to rise and fall with a nauseating strength. The broken plank had the feel of a cured ship's timber, perhaps part of a damaged hull. A shipwreck? A body floated past dressed in the tattered uniform of an ordinary seaman from the eighteenth century, with ripped canvas pantaloons and a striped marinière. He recognised the costume from his history books. He followed the body towards the shore. He could hear shouting now. The lanterns were clearer too. The scurrying figures on the sand were forming ant-like columns, running from the shallows up the beach, then to carts yoked to sullen donkeys. The figures were loading barrels, crates and boxes into the carts. A cry rose to Vince's right, another sailor, but this one very much alive. Vince watched him swim with painful difficulty towards the figures on the beach. The figures paused their salvage as the exhausted sailor dragged himself ashore. Two men put down the crate they had been hefting and ran towards the desperate seaman who was attempting to raise his battered body from the surf. Vince was glad the sailor had made it.

One of the men took the sailor under the arm and pulled him up, steadying him against the breaking waves. The other man drew a knife from his belt and cut the sailor's throat. They let him fall back into the water as he gasped for air through the grim incision. Vince began to swim as hard as he could away from the shore. All along the beach, similar acts were being committed on floundering survivors. With knives, cudgels or the application of hands on exhausted heads, thrusting them back into the waves to drown, not one was to be saved. All that was to leave the beach that night was the wrecker's loot.

Vince trod water in the cantankerous swell as another wave formed out at sea. The wave rose in the same turbulent fashion. A haunted mountain of dull, grey sludge crashing over him. Sucking him down and spinning him about in its dark undertow. When he surfaced this time, the sky was shot through with the lilac hue of dawn. The sea was calm and still. There was an unnatural silence pressing down around him as he floated uncertainly offshore. In the atoms of the sea the council debated. Treaties and compromises. Looking for a balance. Vince wrinkled his nostrils as an acrid smell drifted across the waves, invading his throat with its corrosive vapour. He recognised the unrefined odour of gasoline. He began to notice the surface of the sea; it was covered with a film of oil. Great globules of thick crude floated like ponderous jellyfish in the contaminated brine. He began to swim cautiously towards the shore, the oil gathering on his clothes and skin as he swam. He became heavy with the clinging load and was struggling to move his limbs as the current carried him further in. Vince wanted to free himself from the reeking sea. But that beach. That beach was death. On the sand there were no spectral figures or phantom bathers, but something worse. The dying squadrons of seabirds, their feathers coloured black with bitumen, struggling to take flight, away from the horror, away from land. Oil saturated the waving claws of suffocating crabs, their shells caked in clotted tumours of spilled crude. Gasping fish poisoned by chemical waste, struggling for life on the polluted shore. This was hell. Hell for all things living. The idiot waste of a childish race littered the oceans and scarred the land, leaving carrion rotting in the wastes as its only monument. Down in the deep, the spores joined with the drops of the ocean. New formulas were spliced in the cauldron and sent back into the world.

The wave broke the stone, the salt sowed the soil.
The wood fled the shore as the serpent uncoiled.
Now the sea is calm, its fury spent at last.
The land has brought the sacrifice, broken sail and mast.

The wave rose in the dark to claim the sacrifice.
The gift was wisely chosen, the land must pay the price.
The broken bones of sailors, from vessels cruelly torn.
Their souls sing incantations, in emptiness reborn.

The reckoning rose in the gathering wave. This time the swell swept in a vast wall of black water, higher than any building, temple or folly. Vince resigned himself to the end. He thought of his smiling parents, of sunny days laughing in his pram as they pushed him around the park, feeding the ducks, licking an ice cream. He thought of his friends, he thought of their games, their stories, their comforting arms lifting him from the gravel when he fell, their encouragement when he tried new tricks. He remembered his parents' old flat, his neighbours waving as he walked past, him waving back, their eyes meeting in a bond of unbroken community. He remembered the cruelty too. Then the wave hit. He had expected to be tossed about by the undertow, to be cruelly battered and tormented before finally succumbing to the tide. But there was no movement, no current. There was nothing. The blank emptiness of pure absence. It was as if the water was now beyond all comprehension, in a dimension where the contradictions of being and nothingness were settled in a void of complete indifference. The relation of all non-relativity. In this place, though it had no location, laws, rules and equations meant nothing, and all mankind's absurd fumbling was annihilated and reborn. This was the divine dimension.

The laughter of a seagull woke Vince from a dream. The dream of life. He lifted his head from the sand and pushed his soggy locks from his eyes. He was on the beach again. But not the beach. It felt like an exorcised space, with all the ghosts finally laid to rest, mingling with the particles where they belonged. The day was warm, but a pleasant breeze gave it a freshness that made it close to perfect. He sat up and examined himself. No bruises, no cuts, he felt strangely rested and whole. He noticed that his clothes had gone, but he wasn't unduly concerned. He got to his feet and began to walk along the shoreline. The water lapped up the sand in a gentle cascade. Azure blue, clear, clean. Vince felt a vibration from the land and turned to its source. The Tangle blended effortlessly into the beach, as if the sea and land were two different states of the same substance, its limits impossible to determine. It was green and lush, spotted with dots of colour from a thousand exotic flowers that exploded in the thick canopy. The vibration was life. The chatter of the forest, a chaotic symphony with no key, filled the air with its disorganised music. Vince walked up the beach, drawn by the strange melody. The sand, soft beneath his toes, gave way to grass-covered loam. His nose twitched as it registered the scent of the extravagant blooms. Unfamiliar species with unfamiliar fragrances. He entered the Tangle. Vince was an emissary, a pilgrim, absolved in the waters, no longer in need of redemption, no longer seeking the way, for there was no path to follow, no maps to guide him. He was nowhere.

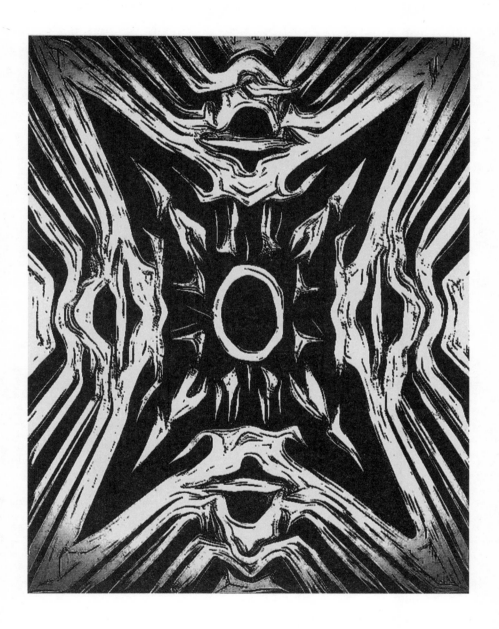

Send Us a Thought, Oh Dark Lord

Ageing fingers bent by the cruelty of time curled around the heavy glass. Ageing hands wrinkled into ridges lifted the glass to a thin, furrowed mouth. Ageing gums with an absence of teeth sucked at the liquid. Nectar or poison, she could not tell. It was just another glass. Like all the others. She placed the glass back on the table and stared into the fire. The flames licked over the hissing logs; smoke blossomed in the grate. Hilda Wilton was old once. Perhaps it was now? She had worked here as a young girl. Pulling pints. Breaking up fights. She had met her first and last boyfriend here. They were lovers. Then he died. Cut into components for the ash tree's beautiful furniture. It was too much, he'd jumped off the viaduct. Then there was the Tangle. Now she was here.

The Bull was buzzing. The large television screens that had been recently installed to the annoyance of the older clientele were the subject of the whole pub's attention. A local girl done good. There she was on the screen. Professor Helen Cavendish. From a long line of Cavendishs. Caxton's most ancient clan. She drank in the Bull, so the landlord said. Nice girl, he said. They all did. Not like the rest of that cursed line. Not like her father. He'd died young. Good thing for him they didn't have the death penalty then or he'd have swung for what he did. That's what they said anyway. Those bold enough to whisper. She was a scientist. Local girl done good. Head of a team of scientists. They'd cracked it.

Made a computer, better than all the other computers. She was going to watch the president of the new regime switch it on. Everything was going to be alright when he did. The A.B.A.C.U.S. they called it. Here he is now, the president. Quiet everyone. Like the fucking moon landing this is. That's what they said.

Hilda stared into the flames. She had sat here for hours, or was it days? The comfortable Queen Anne chair, one of a pair. A permanent fixture in the Bull public house. She had just arrived. She had just this minute sat down. No one ever saw her come in, no one ever saw her leave. She was always here. Always now. Don't let her glass run dry. It's unlucky. That's what they said. Hilda stared into the flames. She turned her head slightly. Her friend was there. He was always there. She tried to smile, but she'd forgotten how. Erwan turned his head towards her. Their black eyes locked, and a silent message was passed. On the screen the crowds waved as the president's motorcade arrived. Flags with crooked insignia flew. The president addressed the crowds and glad-handed dignitaries. The president mounted the steps of a grand building reeking with overconfidence. He strode with purpose towards a brighter future. He had ribbons to cut.

Erwan sucked in the liquid. Don't let his drink run dry. It's unlucky. That's what they said. They stared into the fire and waited.

Eyes without sight, vision or focus. No lens or pupil,
*   motion or locus.*

The broken body of an astronaut lay in a crumpled pile at the foot of the stage. His neck had been twisted 180 degrees. His glassy, dead eyes gazed at the vaulted roof of the Museum of Ignorance. An old man dressed in eccentric attire skipped down the steps. He wore the peaked military-style cap of a museum employee on his head. Two tufts of orange hair jutted insolently from the sides. On his feet he wore a pair of mismatching shoes.

'Oh, what a shame,' he said, closing the astronaut's eyelids. 'He was such a dainty thinker in all matters scientific. Quite a curious sort too, though he obviously wasn't looking in the right places on this occasion. We shall all miss him terribly.'

The old man smiled. The smile grew into a laugh. Then a scream that spiralled into a piercing shriek filled every corner of the museum.

They'd keep the pub open late tonight. Everything was on the up. The new regime was harsh but fair. They all said so. You can't make an omelette without cracking a few eggs, they said. Besides, this new A.B.A.C.U.S. would sort everything out. No problem. The Happiness Engine, that's what they were calling it. Happiness is everything.

The old man's cap began to tear. His clothes split. His shoe leather ripped and buckled as the wiry malignance burst from his wizened frame. Blood and sinew dangled from his skeleton. The dripping figure stretching to its full height, flexing its talon-tipped limbs. The Mesmeriser gathered up the broken corpse of the astronaut in its wasted arms and began to ascend the dais. Once at the summit it absorbed the essence into its core, leaving an empty skin at its feet. The Mesmeriser sat on its throne, gazing down at the exhibition hall of the Museum of Ignorance and all its dusty trinkets.

There she was. The local girl done good. She was showing the president the flashing read out. The A.B.A.C.U.S. whirred. The president was delighted. Medals were pressed on chests. The drinkers in the Bull cheered. I knew her when she was a little girl. I knew she was destined for great things. That's what they said. Despite all the tragedy. They said. Her father. She was so young. The ropes in the woods. They whispered. The name Cavendish had death hanging from every letter. She was different. That's what they said.

Hilda and Erwan. Sucked at the liquid. Don't let their glasses run dry. It's unlucky. That's what they said. They watched the flames fuck up the wood. Its fiery tongue lashing the grain. They watched the fire and waited.

A lost dandy glided between the exhibits. Citizen Kavendish Jeremiah, looking for thrills. The Mesmeriser pulled a thought from its skull and twirled the archaic script around in the air. The words revolved. Faster and faster until they merged into one solid black ball. The Mesmeriser spun the globe on the tip of its foul nail. Suns, stars and galaxies began to form around the spinning globe. Vast, infinite expanses of cosmic objects spread out around a single point. Then the spinning stopped. The Mesmeriser flicked the thought out into the vastness it had created. To become just another speck.

The president cut the ribbon.

Outer Town Dissolution

His Sensory Nexus Mask lay discarded on the museum table, a muffled ping the only discernible sign that it was still functioning. Kavendish stroked his bare skin. Taking the time to reacquaint himself with his own flesh. His skin felt rough compared to the celluloid certainties of the mask. It felt flawed, faulty, frail.

In front of him was a book. Its pages were full of stories. It was empty. His hands felt the rough wooden surface. The words nagged at the edges. It was as if he had uncorked an intoxicating poison. Its complicated vapours were now drifting into him. The slow exhilaration began to seep into his veins. The figures from the photograph mocked him. Her face. His face. You simple fool. You pointless fraud. Kavendish tried to turn his eyes away, but a taloned hand grasped his cheeks and forced him to look. The questions rose like smoke. Somewhere there was night. Somewhere there were moons and stars. Somewhere there was trouble, violence and disturbance. Somewhere there were unruly roots. Somewhere there were mysteries.

Kavendish worried; he never worried, he hated it. He felt divided. Professor Helen Cavendish. A scholar. A creator. The creator. The A.B.A.C.U.S. Yet her doubts had flourished. Something had fractured her certainty. She had found it in the woods. But by then it was too late. There were secrets in this book, secrets that would disrupt the Great Equilibrium and leave it in a garbled mess. Kavendish's world of unrestrained pleasure was a dank, windowless prison. But now, after reading these few tattered pages, it seemed as if a great crack was forming in the walls of his cell. Illuminating his confinement. He was curious. It was electrifying. Kavendish gathered the book and loose photographs and stuffed them into his pockets. He was committing the first crime in centuries.

The pavement was warm and clean, bathed in the light of the never-setting sun. The rays bounced off the sparkling glass of a neighbouring building, projecting the reflection of the Museum of Ignorance onto its surface. Kavendish felt the museum loom behind him. The stolen book weighed heavily in his pocket. He felt confused and unhappy. The most dangerous emotion. The only crime. The only possible act of sedition. He glanced up again at the reflection of the museum; it wasn't too late to return the book. The burden was too much. He just wanted to be happy. He turned to return. But the reflection was gone. There was no museum. Just an endless piazza surrounded by absurd fuck pads. His Sensory Nexus Mask pinged back into life. He was transparent once more. The screen filled with vast plumes of data. Kavendish blinked furiously. His Kudos Quotient was low. He had been away too long.

He needed to think. What a horrible prospect. Kavendish began to walk slowly across the piazza. His face frozen in an unconvincing grin. His Kudos Quotient showed some modest improvement. The Service Citizens who had been so diligently tending to the sidewalks were returning their brooms and sanitation equipment to the storage facilities and heading for the transports. A Discipline Drone monitored their progress.

I hope you have had a productive day, Citizens. I hope your service has brought you happiness. I hope your leisure time will be joyful. I hope you had a productive day . . .

The drone's voice faded into the distance as it shadowed the line. The visions of the twisting roots still lingered in Kavendish's mind as he watched it disappear. The city suddenly seemed ridiculous to him. All this energy, all of mankind's ingenuity, squandered on vacuous projects and funnelled into ludicrous architecture. All these vulgar buildings cluttering the skyline with their demented spires. Behind their elaborate frontages was a decadent, duped population wanking itself into oblivion.

Kavendish found himself by the river again. The pneumatic pavement following its path toward the glass bridge and the park at its terminus. Kavendish took some solace from the river. It flowed outside of time. Separate from the follies of the city that it bisected. As civilisations rose and fell, the river continued to carve its way to the ocean; and when all our ingenuity was exhausted and our buildings had returned to the soil from whence they sprang, the river would keep flowing. Relentless and unimpressed.

The hoots of a monkey troop announced Kavendish's arrival at the park. He entered through an arch of lush foliage and took the anti-clockwise path. The genetically modelled animals moved amongst the foliage. Their chatter diminishing as they alone sensed the onset of darkness. It was only humans that gibbered and frolicked in their artificial day, though there were no Aristoians to be seen at present. The Service Citizens were returning to the transports. Kavendish would soon be alone. Something caught his eye. A twisting pillar, like a drill reversing from the ground. A rough tower was emerging from the manicured lawn of the park. It was a tree. The same tree. Unfolding in the vanquished twilight. Casting shadows where none should fall. Its canopy sprang open like a magician's bouquet.

Kavendish was no longer on the path. Though he hadn't moved a step. He was under the canopy. It was dark. The bright, trimmed lawns of the park had vanished. In its place was a rugged floor of broken twigs and dead leaves. He was in a forest. All around him. The Tangle. Thick with trees and tightly meshed shrubs. It was uncivilised and inhuman. He felt his face. His Sensory Nexus Mask was gone. Quotients were irrelevant. The sounds of the modified animals had tuned to the cautious chatter of wild things. The rustle of creatures running for cover added an unfamiliar cadence to the warning calls. In this dimension the animals feared man. Kavendish stepped gingerly on the uneven surface. This was not the way of things. He approached the gnarled trunk of the monstrous tree. It resembled a bent, malignant figure. Its branches the tentacles of a great leviathan. His impulse to touch the black bark was uncontrollable. His manicured fingers crept from his tense, balled fist and made contact with the skin of the tree.

The face of the professor. His face. Her face. So like his own, and yet not him. The mouth opening and closing, words forming. Kavendish let his fingers linger on the knots of the bark. Rough bark. Rough skin. The wood penetrated his flesh, sending out tendrils into his body. Wily shoots wriggled into veins, travelling at great speed through his nervous system. Speech centres, motor functions, his eyes. The figure of the professor stood before him. Her mouth opening and closing. Kavendish leaned towards her. They joined and travelled again.

*

He jumped on a pneumatic pavement that led across the river. He followed a group of Service Citizens who were heading for the transports. They were leaving the city. He would leave with them. Out of the maze of spires. Into the Tangle. They appeared to be heading towards a large stone arch that lay a few blocks from the riverbank. The arch was at the top of a boulevard lined with perfectly pruned poplars, which led to a quite fantastic structure Kavendish had never noticed before.

London Terminal 1.

A baroque masterwork of demented genius. A garish and exuberant collection of ornate carvings. Depicting all manner of dryads, nymphs and mythical beasts frozen in ecstatic poses. A network of bright, brass girders weaved between them like the trail left by a huge mechanical snail. The effect was painful on the eye. Two Discipline Drones hovered over the entrance.

Kavendish bowed his head and followed the Service Citizens inside. The interior of the transport hub mirrored the madness outside. Two wide platforms were bisected by a perfectly straight track. The track headed directly out of the station like an arrow piercing the heart of the city. A sleek, clean transport vehicle sat quietly humming on the platform. As the Service Citizens approached, its doors slid gently open. Two Discipline Drones hovered above the platform.

Thank you for your service, Citizens. Please enjoy your leisure pursuits. We trust you will be happy.

The Service Citizens embarked in silence. Kavendish joined them. The doors of the transport closed quietly behind him. The transport was spacious, with comfortable seats positioned at regular intervals. Kavendish, after some

hesitation, selected one and sat. The transport was bright
and spotless, with a gentle current of cool air creating a
fresh and pleasant atmosphere. There was a communal
area with tasteful tables positioned around an Automated
Epicurus food dispenser. Service Citizens would occasionally
visit the device for refreshments before returning to their
seats. Pleasant nods were exchanged, but there was little
conversation. The transport was busy, but certainly not
packed. It contained a variety of service grades, but most
seemed to be in the top end of the alphabet. A lot of A and B
grades were sat near Kavendish, one or two Cs and Ds too.
No one said a word.

The transport glided out of London Terminal 1. The
crazed vistas of the city whizzed by in a blur of architectural
confusion. The Service Citizens, as one, reached into their
garments and produced a collection of devices. They strapped
them around their heads, covering their eyes. They lacked
the elegance of the Sensory Nexus Mask, but they served the
same purpose. They stared into them. Heads facing forward.
Kavendish's own device-free face was attracting unwelcome
glances. He felt in his pocket. The rough cover of the book
grazed his fingers. The smooth surface of his Sensory Nexus
Mask was underneath it. He dragged the mask up and out.
He smoothed it over his face. Passengers turned their heads
to look. With their headsets on they looked like a phalanx
of security cameras. In polite deference they soon turned
their heads back to their original positions. Heads facing
forward. Some smiled. Some quietly laughed. Some gasped,
others groaned; all were absorbed by their feeds. Kavendish
attempted to focus. He blinked open his icons. But the screen
was empty. He had been disconnected. He tore it off with
obvious frustration. Unhappiness began to blossom. He was

on the outside now. Detached. Remote. Looking in. Heads turned, then returned.

Beyond the blank screen the transport was now leaving the jumbled sprawl of the city. They had passed beyond the world that Kavendish was familiar with. The decadent housing had given way to more ordered developments. Small urban archipelagos huddled together on pleasant pastures. They were circular in construction, with one or two roads pointing out of them in perfectly straight lines. Neatly painted fences delineated the limits of the estates. The transport began to slow. It had entered one of the developments and was pulling into a clean and tidy station. The station resembled a scene one might find on the lid of an Edwardian biscuit tin: the buildings were constructed from solid red brick and were shot through with polished wooden beams painted in racing green. Metal benches and an abundance of hanging flower baskets completed the picture. On an embankment running down to the platform was the station's designation spelt out in white painted stones.

TOWN A, STOP 1, WEST

The transport came to a halt with an imperceptible sigh. Passengers stood and got off, mainly A and B grades. The doors closed and the transport continued, now travelling along a raised viaduct that gave Kavendish an excellent view across a wide valley. He could make out little estates dotted here and there, in a logical and regular pattern; each was served by an identical straight road and an identical transport track, sticking out in perfectly straight lines. All directed to the centre of London. There was no deviation.

The transport gathered speed. It was now travelling at an extraordinary velocity. Kavendish stared out of the window as the regularity whizzed by. He could see something shimmering up ahead. A wall. A barrier. It seemed to reach up into the sky as far as he could see. It was the wall of a vast dome. The transport drew closer and closer to the barrier. Suddenly a baritone boom jolted the carriage. The Service Citizens remained still, heads facing forward. They were now beyond the dome. The light suddenly changed. The clear blue light of day was replaced by a purple haze of twilight. Evening. He had never seen evening before. He gasped. Heads turned and returned. Kavendish pressed his skin to the window. Around the remote islands of ordered human dwellings was an ocean of verdant fibres stretching as far as the eye could see. It seemed to be rolling and rising as he imagined an ocean would. This was the Tangle. Wild. Untidy. Unruly. This was not the way of things. The transport reached a tall viaduct that rose above the woods, as if it were too frightening a prospect to travel through it. Huge pillars disappeared down into the dark interior. Looking back, he could see London and its suburbs squatting under the vast dome like sugar fancies in a bakery. A great artificial sun rose in the west, a controlled explosion frozen in time.

It all seemed so distant, so small. Kavendish looked back down into the black heart of the forest. The twisting limbs of the gnarled tree. Spreading. Reaching out to him again. He wanted to fall. Fall into the moss and sap, into the decay and the dung of dead things. Into the Tangle.

The transport moved on. It entered a tunnel. The sounds and light within the carriage never varied, but his view was momentarily lost. Kavendish had never been this close to such a concentration of Service Citizens before. The remaining passengers definitely occupied the middle of the alphabet. They were all young, like Kavendish, but markedly less altered. These Citizens looked very useful. Sturdy types, free of imperfection or weakness. Good Service Citizens. They stared into their devices, heads facing forward. The transport emerged from the tunnel like a climax. The smooth, silent glide was replaced by a metallic clack, clack, clack. The rustle of a newspaper folding. Kavendish looked at his hands. The newspaper was his own. *The Times*, 'New regime hails completion of A.B.A.C.U.S. project'. He glanced down the carriage. The faint tinny sound of music escaped from the headphones of a young business traveller. Cheap suits, jeans, workweek brogues and afterwork sneakers. Track pants. Cotton shirts open at the neck. Red tops and broad sheets. Comics. He was elsewhere. He wasn't surprised this time. Kavendish was the professor. The professor was him. His face. Her face. He thought he caught a glimpse of an old man. Old useless things should be dissolved. It was the way of things. The Great Equilibrium. Two orange, curly bushes sticking out from the side of an upheld paper. He wanted to shout a greeting, but when he lowered the paper it was revealed to be a young man in overalls. The train entered another short tunnel before emerging onto a platform. It squeaked to a stop, breaks grinding and hissing. The odour of lubricants and warm metal drifted through the carriage. A sign chipped and weathered. In need of repair. Caxton Wood Station, alight for Caxton Wood. He turned the handle of the carriage door. He stepped onto the platform and returned.

Some hanging baskets of flowers dangled incongruously around the station sign.

TOWN G, WEST

The platform was wide and clean and covered by an impressive concrete parabola. Simple industrial lights hung from bright, stainless steel chains, lighting the way to the arched exit. Kavendish hid himself amongst the crowd of Service Citizens. A Discipline Drone hovered over the line. Its lights blinking rapidly.

> Welcome home, Citizens. I hope your day has been productive and happy. Please enjoy your leisure pursuits. Welcome home, Citizens. I hope your day . . .

The drone's melodious voice grew fainter as they headed down the platform. Kavendish kept his head bowed. The line moved smoothly, and he was soon at the exit. Kavendish stepped out onto a charming piazza, perfectly circular with one straight path bisecting it. The path was wide and uninterrupted, leading in one direction, from the terminal to the town beyond. A fountain gurgled in its centre, and around the edges beautiful stone benches provided places of quiet contemplation. They were all empty. Surrounding the piazza were lawns of thick green grass interspersed with delicate pastel wildflowers. It was tastefully restrained. Kavendish found it boring. The air was buzzing with Discipline Drones. They were hovering over the entrance to the station and shadowing the Citizens as they crossed the piazza. He kept his eyes fixed on the pavement, hoping not to be too conspicuous. Kavendish was becoming accustomed to stealth. He found it unpleasant.

Kavendish followed the perfectly straight path. A few metres away Kavendish could make out rows of spacious, functional Living Units. They were all identical in construction: a blend of concrete and steel, with huge windows and large glass atriums at the rear. There were no fences. No borders apart from the walls of the structures themselves. Large open lawns surrounded each dwelling. At the edge of this space was a thick wooded mass. The edge of the Tangle. His pulse quickened. His identity shifted. His face. Her face. Kavendish's eyes. Her eyes. Drawn to a playground, much like the ones he had clambered over at the hatchery. There were climbing frames and rope swings. See-saws and roundabouts. Children were playing on the playground equipment. Why weren't they in the hatchery with all the other children? As he drew nearer he could hear their joyful squeals. It was unsettling. He hadn't seen one for years. The children began running towards the returning Service Citizens. They seemed attached to them somehow. Kavendish watched them grab hands and head into the spacious homes of Town G, West.

A Discipline Drone hovered past. Kavendish watched it as it floated into the housing estate. This Discipline Drone seemed full of purpose. Kavendish followed its progress with mild interest. The drone approached one of the Living Units. A nervous-looking Service Citizen came to the door. Words were exchanged. Kavendish could see the Service Citizen's mouth move, but he was too far away to make out the words. The Citizen seemed upset. Kavendish wrinkled his forehead, trying to make sense of the exchange. There was a cry. The Service Citizen raised his voice. The cry becoming a shout. The Service Citizen seemed to tremble. His hands were held out imploringly. Trying to reason with the hovering machine. A wave of energy emanated from the Discipline Drone, opaque and shimmering like a heat haze on a summer's day. The wave enveloped the Service Citizen. Instantly he was reduced to nothing. Only a very fine dust and the hint of vapour were left, before they too were absorbed into the evening air. The Discipline Drone flew through the haze of the dissolved Citizen and entered the Living Unit. Kavendish was paralysed. A spectator without agency. A child ran out. The Discipline Drone following close behind. Bile rose in his throat. Bile rose in her throat. The violence and the violence yet to come. A woven toy resembling a smiling monkey was dangling from the child's hand. The child was whimpering, attempting to form words. Small bubbles of spit swelled and then popped as his mouth struggled to create a response. In the Tangle the roots rose.

> *In darkness now from darkness born, circumference,*
> *   length and span.*
> *In lilac glade the wreath and thorn, wove mockeries*
> *   of man.*
> *In lilac glade beneath the earth, in death's ecstatic bond.*
> *Come walk with me in lilac shade, to the emptiness beyond.*

The drone's lights blinked. A brutal calculation was in process. Once more a wave of energy silently flowed across the space between drone and child. Then the child was gone. Kavendish had never really known what being dissolved involved. He thought it might be some kind of a voluntary arrangement, rather like an anaesthetic. Something pleasant and good. His scream echoed inside his cells. But his mouth was silent. He felt disgust, fury, horror. But most of all he felt embarrassed. The Discipline Drone spun around to face him. Its lights flashing across its facia. Its pleasant, melodious voice rang out.

River

They had been lost in the lanes for hours. Two strangers
bonded by a contract. Driver and passenger. Each turn they
made together took them further away from the certainties
of cities and towns. The comfort of signs and signals. Two
strangers misplaced by circumstance. One reliant on maps that
had no function out here in the Tangle. The other now too old
to care. His memory subverted by age and disease.

Alexander Malik was happy to be going anywhere or
nowhere. The destination would reveal itself in time, he had
no doubt of it. But the driver lacked the luxury of time. He
operated in a world where each minute was a quantity of value.
If he lost many more in these backwoods he would be struggling
to pay the rent come month's end. He looked into the rear-view
mirror and caught Alexander's eye, searching for guidance from
the older gentleman. Alexander returned his gaze with a smile
of detached contentment. The driver sighed and shook his head.
He seemed to know where he was going when he got in. He had
an address, a place, a name. But once they'd left the suburbs
of Caxton all sense of direction seemed to desert him. Each
charming hamlet they drove through seemed familiar to the old
fellow. They stopped several times, thinking they had reached
their destination, but on further enquiry they found that there
was always a little bit further to go.

'You can't miss it, left after the Plough, not the
Dressingham Plough, the Ambleton Plough, mind, take the

left fork, not the sharp left, that goes to the Burrows, but the next left, towards Arnside, follow that for about five mile, then take the left-hand fork again, or is it right? No, it's definitely left, when you see the old mill, it's sharp right there, can't miss it.'

Alexander was enthralled by the journey. It was marvellous. He hadn't been out here for decades. His milky eyes watched the trees flash past. A kaleidoscope of emerald shades and mute tones interrupted only briefly by the villages they passed through. Even these little hamlets seemed to blend into the wild forest, as if they were being sucked into the air sacs of an enormous lung. Their wattle-and-daub frames and ancient thatch barely tolerated in this preternatural Eden. Like tics on a wild beast, these dwellings hid in the folds of the forest, waiting to be picked and harried. This was no refined estate of managed plantings. This was the undefinable heart of Grand Bois, the timeless principality of Abnoba and Aranyani. But before, even these spirits were named by the woods. Before even one second had been counted by the reckoning of men, there was the Tangle. The twisted limbs of trees hung low over the pitted lanes. All around them, spring was giving way to summer. The trees were sumptuous; the entire spectrum of green tones merged in the canopy. Below it, the murky interior of the ancient wood. Full of gullies, secret dells and granite outcrops, with names like Witch's Knee and the Devil's Cup. This was the land before the fall. This was the knot of life. Alexander remembered the jumble of the woods with fondness. So many adventures a lifetime ago. The driver looked increasingly concerned.

'I don't get many jobs out this way.'

He kept noting nervously.

'Not far now.'

250

Alexander answered the driver unconvincingly. He was happy in the car; he didn't really care if they drove all day, because out here he suddenly felt focused. Certainly, he had no idea where he was, but the deeper into the Tangle they went, the clearer his recollections became. The patchwork of half-remembered events and forgotten names that characterised his recent day-to-day life were forming into solid memories. He pressed his face to the glass, his eyes wide with wonder.

'Visiting relatives are you, sir?'

The driver broke the trance. Alexander smiled, amused at the question.

'In a way, I suppose I am, yes. I was born out here, you know.'

'Ah, really, must have been . . . errr . . . a peaceful childhood?'

A frown formed on Alexander's wrinkled face.

'No, not really.'

He returned his attention to the window. The driver gave a resigned shrug and pressed on down the road to nowhere in particular.

After many wrong turns at several 'Plough' inns, the driver was considering calling the police. His base had been trying to reach him through the static. But he was out of range and out of patience. The tunnel of trees suddenly thinned as they entered yet another village. The sort of unremarkable outpost of twee respectability that was unlikely to make any impression on you. Alexander, however, became suddenly animated.

'This is it! Yes! This is it!'

'Thank fuck for that.'

The driver mumbled, still trying to remain professional. They had arrived at their destination. Challoner's Cross. Once, this little village had been Alexander's whole universe. His parents had settled here after the war. They had escaped the horrors of Nazi-occupied Europe with only a suitcase to their name. All they knew was lost. Families, friends and neighbours, all perished in the brutal occupation. His father soon rejoined the fight. On several occasions he had only narrowly avoided death whilst serving as a fighter pilot. After the war his parents opened a small domestic maintenance business, which was successful enough to allow them to settle in the apparent tranquillity of the English countryside. It was idyllic in many ways: the land was wild and beautiful, and the opportunities for adventure for young children were plentiful. But they suffered their share of malicious whispering and a feeling that they would never really fit in with some of the more insular residents. There was a significant number of grumbling pub bores and bitter, impoverished aristocrats who felt Britain had fought on the wrong side in the war and that these types simply had no place in an English country village. But the Maliks endured. There were more than enough good people to sustain them, and when Alexander, and some years later his little sister Emilia, arrived, it looked as if life for the family might be as happy and uncomplicated as they had dreamed. But then there was the river.

'I'm afraid I don't have any money, but thank you for the lift, most kind.'

Alexander closed the door of the taxi, offering the driver a wave and a smile. He was so lovely, so accommodating, he thought. He had arrived promptly after his escape from the home, forestalling any embarrassing incidents with the authorities. The car was comfortable; it smelled good too. All this way. Why, it was remarkable, so kind. He'd seen the meter ticking, but he couldn't quite place its purpose. Where had he come from anyway, this driver? Had his sister called it for him, he wondered. The driver was unsure how to react. His forehead bounced off the steering wheel as he cursed his luck. Perhaps

now was the time to call the police? The elderly gentleman
shouldn't be out here on his own, and besides, he needed to get
his money. The driver lifted his head from the wheel to plead
for his fare. But Alexander was nowhere to be seen. The driver
got out of the car and looked down the sleepy village high
street. Nothing. The old man had vanished.

*

Alexander felt light and sprightly. The effects of the forest were
manifesting themselves in an increased feeling of well-being.
He had dragged his body out of the car, expecting the familiar
aches and pains to hamper his mobility. But as his feet touched
the ground, he felt a suppleness he had not experienced for
many years. He practically skipped across the car park. His
memory was sharpening. Though the present was still a
mysterious muddle of confusing fragments, the past was as
clear as day. He even remembered the tiny hidden footpath that
led from the car park to the church. Almost invisible to anyone
without good local knowledge. An obscure byway. But he had
remembered it. Just like all those years ago, when Alexander
and his sister would run down the secret path en route to some
adventure or other. Making their way to the apple orchards, or
the rope swing in Potter's Gully. Or perhaps they were heading
for the river.

The churchyard was morbidly bucolic. A picture postcard
of decay. Faded tombstones tilted at every conceivable angle,
whilst stone angels wept over tumbledown mausoleums. At
the centre was the old Norman church, well preserved by a
combination of English Heritage grants and the generosity of
wealthy notables. For many years it had been the focal point
of village life. Even in his parents' time the church had been a
social club, a therapeutic centre, a place to commune, a place

to find peace, an incubator of gossip. But now, except for the occasional christening or wedding, it was poorly attended. The church no longer maintained a vicar at Challoner's Cross. The vicarage itself was now the holiday home of a wealthy businessman from Caxton. Instead, the vicar from Ambleside would cycle up every Sunday to deliver his sermon to the elderly and righteous few. Alexander drifted past the stones, his bent frame beginning to straighten as the curious potency of his surroundings continued to rejuvenate him. His head was no longer orientated towards the ground. But instead, it was held high on broadening shoulders. Alexander absorbed the country air and studied the graves. Seeking familiar melancholy markers. It had been years, decades maybe, since he had come to pay his respects. The pain was too great. But now, as his own time to depart grew closer, he knew he must confront them one more time.

Andrik Malik
Beloved Father and Husband
1920–2002
Now at rest and joined with his family once more

And a right next to his father:

Karolina Malik
Devoted Wife and Mother
1921–1990
With her angel

Alexander sighed. He always hated the phrase 'devoted wife'. He had tried to persuade his father to use a less old-fashioned epitaph, something that wouldn't betray his social conservatism. But his father could barely look at him when he had come back to the village to help with the funeral arrangements. The bitterness his father felt was as fresh as the day of the accident. The day that Alexander had really lost his parents. He patted the gravestones and whispered a quiet prayer. Please forgive me. Your devoted son.

Alexander hoped that they could hear him. Across time and space, in whatever heaven his parents now dwelt in. Maybe now, on the cusp of his own demise, they would let him rest in peace too. His eyes drifted to a monument he had not seen for years, but which featured in his dreams almost every night. Next to his parents' grave was another stone, smaller and covered with a green-gold bloom of lichen. Alexander bent his knees and crouched in front of the grave, brushing some of the loose grime from the stone. Again, the suppleness of his limbs surprised him; although he wasn't especially old, bad luck and ill health had meant rheumatic pains were a constant burden. When his mind began to fail, he had given up most forms of exercise, fearful of where he might end up if he ventured out. However, his sharpening wits provided him with less comfort now. Memories played in his mind like the roll of a cinema projector. Clicking and whirring. Clicking and whirring. His eyes began to cloud with tears. He wiped them with his hands. Capturing a single tear drop on his finger, he pressed it into the faded stone.

Emilia Malik

1949–1958

Our angel, always in our hearts.

We will be together again soon

The river carved its way through the woodland, juddering and tumbling. Carrying the silt and bones of a thousand last moments. The final words of suicides, the soundless screech of torn gills and drowned insects, all gathered and stored in its endless current. The water never remained the same. It was a sequence of instants never to be repeated. But the memories lingered. Sticking to the rocks and algae. Reluctant to leave. The artery of the Tangle, into which all tributaries must flow. The river. Always the river. On the outskirts of the village, where the last few buildings finally surrendered to the perplexing wildness of the wood. There was the river. The boundary between two worlds. Remorseless and beautiful. There was the river. Always the river.

There were only a few places you could cross the river safely. In the autumn and spring, when the rain was at its heaviest, it would swell to dangerous levels. The fords could be turned into fast-moving torrents within minutes. It would be impossible to cross, even for the most gifted athlete or experienced swimmer. Close to the village there were two bridges. Alexander and Emilia liked the old railway bridge best. The line had been closed long before the war, with only the vague impression of the track remaining. Local farmers used to drive sheep over it on the way to the market, while the local children used it to play games of Poohsticks. In the summer, when the river was at its most languid, the older children would sometimes dive off the bridge. But never the Malik children. They knew the river was unpredictable and should only be entered with caution. But they loved playing down by the bridge. Carefully selecting sticks for their likely buoyancy and speed, they would lean over the parapet and cast their competing twigs into the river, watching the current twisting around the rocks as it carried them along. Cheering them on, they would run across to the other side to see who's stick emerged victorious from under the stony arch. It never got boring. The summer holidays were full of such games, but springtime was the best. The sticks were full of sap; it made them sturdier and less likely to be snapped against the granite boulders that jutted out like gnarled teeth from the surface of the water.

Alexander carried his memories like a hiker's rucksack. Hefting the dull ache of decades down the byways of his youth. But he found his body to be less of a burden. His strides were becoming confident, a far cry from the rapid shuffle he had had to employ whilst escaping the nursing home. After breakfast the nurse had taken him down to the communal lounge, hoping that Alexander would take some comfort in the company of his friends. He had been slipping away fast and spent most of his time in bed these days. But the doctor recommended companionship, even if it was simply to avoid the chance of him dying alone. His children lived some miles away, one of them abroad. They had been called. The end wasn't far off now, but it would still be a day or two until they would all be able to say goodbye. Alexander knew he was dying. To be honest, he didn't much care. He'd had enough, but he felt as if some things were still left undone. Ghosts still roamed the riverbanks and should be put to rest.

A willowy teenage boy runs along the bank of a river. The river is tumbling vigorously down its channel; pregnant with spring rain it threatens to burst its banks. The boy is holding a crudely stitched rag doll. Those dolls with the big eyes and no features. A small girl runs after him, jumping and stretching with her arms in the air, trying to snatch the doll from her brother's cruel grip.

'Give it back, give it back, Alex. I'll tell mamma and papa.'

'You'll have to catch me first! Does Matilda want to go in the river?'

The boy has stopped running and is perched on the rocks at the river's edge. He uses his advantage in height to keep the little girl at bay as she jumps and screams for her toy.

'In she goes.'

The boy is laughing as he pretends to cast the doll into the torrent. The little girl is crying now.

The nurse wheeled Alexander into his usual spot, just as 'Golden Memories' were about to start their morning singalong. Barry Sparkle was running his fingers over the keys of his organ, Patricia scatting the first few lines of a familiar show tune. Barry engaged the syncopated rhythm of the organ's drum machine. Alexander waited until the nurse was out of the lounge fetching the sherry trolley. Once he was sure the coast was clear, he got out of his wheelchair and shuffled out of the nursing home.

Step by step, with ever-growing confidence, Alexander plotted his path through the undergrowth. Nimbly hopping over drying puddles he made his way to the old railway bridge. It was much smaller than he remembered. Through the eyes of a child it looked like a magical arch over an enchanted river. A castle, a temple, a palace for kings, queens and princesses. While beneath its dark stone canopy were trolls, monsters, goblins and warlocks. The river, the stealer of souls, a purifying torrent that could carry you down to unfathomable depths. Where treasures lay next to the bones of unfortunate pirates and unlucky adventurers.

The little girl jumps up and down, desperately trying to reach her precious doll. Her eyes are fixed on its raggedy limbs, flailing in the air, in her brother's teasing fist. She launches herself with increased vigour. She catches the foot of the doll and tugs with all her might. Her tiny body collides with her brother's scrawny frame. The rocks slick with freshly fallen rain. Feet slipping. Desperate arms wheel in the air, trying to maintain balance. The water licks up the bank, its demonic limbs dragging young bodies into the flood. In she goes. In she goes.

He stepped onto the bridge, absentmindedly kicking leaves and twigs as he remembered that terrible day. He caught something in the corner of his eye. Was that a figure in the trees? Someone watching him from the riverbank? Alexander went over to the wall of the bridge and peered into the woods. His milky eyes were beginning to clear. Indistinct shapes came into focus. Was that a child waving at him under the branches? No, it was just a rock. When he was younger, his sister and Alexander would often imagine those jagged outcrops were people, frozen into stone by a vindictive witch, or monsters slumbering after eating an entire village for lunch. He laughed quietly to himself. He was seeing the world with childlike eyes again. He looked down at his feet. He was still wearing his slippers. The ones with the Velcro fastening. Two sticks lay close by. They looked streamlined and sleek. Perfect racing sticks. He bent down and picked them up, holding one in each hand. The trees rustled as a sudden breeze swirled. That figure. Lurking in the branches. But again he could see nothing; the figure remained an intangible feeling. Alexander turned his head away from the woods and leaned over the parapet of the bridge. He looked at the cold river tumbling below. He studied the flow of the water, watching the eddies curl around the rocks. He plotted the course for one final game. A stick for him and a stick for Emilia. He twirled them in his fingers, holding them up to the springtime sun. They were perfect. He prepared to launch. 3-2-1. Down they dropped, landing lightly on the water in a clear channel. The sticks were carried into the dark interior. Alexander excitedly ran to the opposite side to see which stick would emerge victorious. But neither emerged. He waited. He waited longer than logic dictated, but still nothing. Disappointed, but still determined, he found two more racing sticks. Not as sleek as the last two, but still, decent enough. He dropped them into the river. Again, he ran to the opposite side. But still nothing came.

It was well after lunchtime and Alexander's stomach was feeling the pangs of hunger. He missed the sticky toffee pudding, the sherry trolley and all the other conservative but comforting provisions of the nursing home. But he must finish the game. He had lost count of the number of sticks he had cast into the river. And yet, not one had appeared from under the bridge. Still the river flowed with the same persistence. Perhaps one of the trolls was gathering up his sticks to make a fire to cook him in? He smiled and decided to go and see for himself. He left the bridge and pushed through the bushes, looking for a path down to the river. He found a spot, but it looked a little dangerous for a man of his age. He thought of his old hands, with his fingers all bent and distorted by arthritis. They were too gnarled to cope with the climb. He paused to looked down at them, turning them over and over. These weren't his hands. The fingers were straight, almost elegant, the veins on the back sitting at a discreet depth under firm healthy skin, not the blue-ridged relief map of advanced age he was used to. Alexander touched his face with his new hands. The worn, pitted features he had expected to find had been replaced by the soft skin of a young man. He pinched and squeezed the limber epidermis. As his fingers opened and closed, so the skin returned to its fullness. He negotiated the riverbank without hesitation. He felt as if he could leap across the river itself. The muscles in his legs flexed and tensed, filled with vitality. He thrust out his arms to steady himself on the bank; they felt toned and flexible. He reached the bottom of the bank and began to walk back towards the bridge. The ground was wet and uneven, and he was forced to hop across the rocks. The rocks.

A young boy's head breaks the surface. The current is carrying him quickly downstream. He is a vigorous boy and a strong swimmer, but even his youthful limbs find it hard against the insistent undertow. He bounces off the rocks, trying to steady himself in the channel. He is crying. He is shouting out in panic. The little girl is nowhere to be seen.

Alexander was close to the bridge now, striding down the riverbank towards the stone vault. Something was wrong. Something was incorrect. Under the span of the bridge, instead of the cool, shaded arch of moss-coloured masonry, there was a void, darker than any shadow. It looked like a bruised moon sinking into the river. Silence weighed down on the countryside. The familiar sounds of the water, the riverbank birds and even the buzzing of insects were absent. Only a quiet vacuum and a horrible stillness. He stepped hesitatingly over slippery rocks, closer and closer to the void. He was drawn to it, unable to turn. His slippers squelched as he approached. It was impenetrable; not even light seemed to break its uniform blackness. At the base of the void the river stopped. As if a sharp line had been cut through a painting in some unnatural collage. He stretched out to touch it. Needing to feel the barrier. Unconfident of his senses. His fingertips touched the surface. It felt warm and soft, almost comforting. The surface of the void rippled, like waves in a viscous medium. Alexander peered into the billowing blackness. A face formed in the ripples. The face of a young girl. Alexander recoiled . . . then the silence broke. Like an alarm going off, the whole natural world seemed to squeal and trill at once. Alexander tried to run, but his feet were sliding on the rocks. His arms wheeled in the air. Like they had all those years ago. He fell. He fell towards the river. For a few seconds he seemed to hang in the air, suspended millimetres above the surface.

When he hit, it wasn't at all as unpleasant as he had feared. Though every fibre of his being had been tensed for impact into the freezing water, once he made contact with it the expected shock failed to materialise. Instead the water curled around him. It was more like a soft mattress or a beanbag. Like the one his mother had bought for them in the 1970s. He sank into the river. No water flowed into his mouth or filled his nose. There was no sudden inrush into his ears to deafen him. No turbulent current to spin him around and dash him against the rocks. Instead the water moulded around his body, keeping him afloat. It was warm, like a womb. Alexander looked about him in astonishment. The river was no longer moving. Nor did it have any plausible dimensions. It was everywhere. In the distance he could see the old bridge. He had been carried upstream against the current. Why, he seemed to be miles from it now, when only moments ago he had been right there under its arch. That terrible, bruised moon. Where he had seen death in the face of that little girl, peering out of the black void. But he felt no fear. He felt nothing. The features of the river slowly returned. Dimensions became more understandable and familiar. He thought he saw the figure on the bank again. A shadow moving through the trees, following him as the water began to carry his body. He tried to track the figure with his eyes as he flowed back towards the bridge. But the figure soon melted into the shifting umbra of the wood. He drifted nearer and nearer the old bridge. He could see the pitch-black disc oscillating under the arch. Closer. Much closer now. Alexander gasped as his feet touched the void; as he pierced the membrane it felt as if he was passing through melting wax. The warm sensation passed up his legs, then his torso. Alexander closed his eyes as his whole body passed through the barrier.

His fingertips cautiously crept over his face, then his chest, his thighs. He was intact, but his body felt hollow, like a thin shell, fragile and temporary. He opened his eyes. He had passed under the bridge. The woods crowded around the river channel in the same familiar way, but the colours seemed more pronounced and vivid. He could almost taste the tang of the bark and the sweetness of the sap. He stretched out his hands to touch the warm waters that were carrying him gently downstream. The water fused with his skin. Bonding him to the river and its current. His fingers brushed against the knobbly irregularity of a stick. A fine racing stick. All around him a flotilla of sticks drifted in formation, escorting him like a convoy as he made his way down the channel. Alexander looked over to the wooded bank. A figure again, this time much more distinct. It was him, but as a small boy. Arms outstretched, running along the bank, playing at aeroplanes, a fighter pilot, like his father. He tried to call out a greeting to his younger self, but his mouth made no sound. His body felt lighter, as if a layer had dissolved away into the river.

He noticed a slightly older boy perched on a rock on the other bank. Looking furtively around. Alexander turned his head to look at him. He was maybe eleven or twelve years old.

A puff of smoke emerged from his mouth; the little boy was
smoking. A stolen cigarette pilfered from his mother's ornate
cigarette box. A stale brand from the old country that had sat
in the box for years. The sound of a chocking cough. The green
face. The sick on his shoes. His mother's angry face, one of
many disappointments. A resigned smile passing between his
parents that spoke of similar transgressions in their past. Two
figures skipped out of the woods behind the vomiting boy. A
teenage couple. Her name was Anne, his first love. The teenage
couple kissed as the river flowed past. Tumbling over the rocks.
His first kiss. Now Alexander is a network of nerves, veins and
organs inside an exposed skeleton. His skin having melted into
the river as he drifted along.

An even older boy, nearly grown, sits on a branch that
overhangs the river. He is alone with his thoughts. Angst,
heartbreak and uncertainty. The typical hurdles a teenager
has to overcome, playing tug of war with his developing
consciousness. But this boy carries a heavier burden. He is
drawn here, back to the river. Endlessly replaying the events
of that terrible day. Trying to will a different outcome into
existence. The boy lifts his head, alerted to a sudden movement
in the forest. His parents are out taking a walk in the woods.
For them it's a place to escape the dreadful melancholy of
home. The constant reminders of Emilia, her absence pressing
around them. Crushing them with its weight. The boy silently
watches as his parents pass by without noticing him. Alexander
is now a gelatinous ooze. Eyes, lungs, spleen suspended in the
water like a bloom of algae.

His free-floating eyes drift over the landscape. A thousand
figures play out the scenes of his life on the riverbank as
he slowly decomposes into the stream. He notices a bright
arch up ahead, like a rainbow spanning the river. He is back

at the bridge again, but the black void has been replaced by a bright yellow sun. The sun beams out over the water, dappling the surface. His organs, nerves and sinews are part of the waterway now; only his eyes and a sense of his oneness remain. Alexander glances for the last time at the rocks on the riverbank. They are slippery and treacherous. Like the day of the accident. Suddenly he sees a figure running from the shadows of the wood. It is Emilia! Emilia is standing on the rocks. Their parents stroll out of the forest and stand behind her with their arms entwined. He struggles to make out their expression as he approaches the burning sun. He passes close to the rocks. So close he can almost touch them. If only he had fingers to touch them with. His heart aches for their forgiveness. Their love. He only has a few seconds before he disappears forever. Please, please, give me a sign. One of his eyes blurs and shatters. But his one remaining organ catches an expression on the faces of the figures on the bank. They are smiling. Yes, he is sure of it! His family is smiling. Whatever remains of Alexander Malik is filled with joy. Soon everything will be right again. He is nearly there. So close. Nearer and nearer the glowing sun. He can feel its warmth. So close. So close. The drift begins to stall. The width and depth expand, taking the landscape with it. He is on the cusp, the very lip of the horizon. The incandescent terminus. His remaining eye fractures into a million pieces. The last molecules of Alexander Malik merge with the river. The timeless waterway, flowing gently into the sun forever.

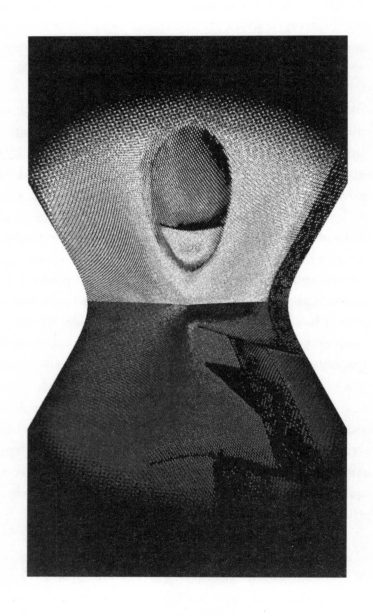

The Happiness Engine

Aristoian Kavendish Jeremiah 15.66.2121. You seem in distress. How may I increase your happiness? Is there an impediment to your pleasure that I might remove? You appear a long way from your Living Unit? May I aid you in your return, Citizen?

A flurry of lights hurried across the Discipline Drone's facia.

Nexus update. Nexus queries incoming. Aristoian Kavendish Jeremiah 15.66.2121. I notice your Nexus access has been suspended. Presumption. Death. My scans reveal your status to be. Alive. Aristoian Kavendish Jeremiah 15.66.2121. Would you like me to reconnect your service?

As Kavendish walked, the dizzying corruption of London began to fade from his mind. He was nowhere. Where the darkness clung to you like tar. Nowhere. Unfamiliar, all-consuming blankness. Nowhere. He could never go back. He was unhappy. That would not be tolerated. He was not useful. That would not be tolerated. He would be dissolved on sight. Like all the other useless things. Here he was. Nowhere.

Kavendish stared up at the sky as he stumbled over the pockmarked ground. Out here there was night. Darkness. It was beautiful. He reached the crest of a hill and looked down into a wooded valley full of shadows. Small towns floated like flotsam, drifting on a black ocean. Out here the seasons rotated. Time ebbed and flowed. Some of the Citizens slept. They had children and travelled. They did service. They had beds and sheets. They had breakfast and read bedtime stories. They were dissolved.

Kavendish wandered through an untrodden pasture. The first human feet to step upon this virgin borderland for centuries. He trailed his hand through the swaying grass. He reached a grove of modest trees. He sat under the umbrella of a spreading oak.

> *The mechanism turned and stuck, its cogs were clogged*
> *   and bound.*
> *The dial upon the watch's face spun back into the ground.*
> *The fibre and the filament, the flower and the weed.*
> *The traveller comes to fill his sack with the Tangle's*
> *   golden seed.*

He placed his hands on the soft earth. His eyelids became heavy. Without a steady supply of stimulants his body revolted. He fell into a deep sleep. Tiny, vein-like roots sprang from the soil. Travelling like centipedes across the ground, creeping over his hands. They burrowed into his skin and spread out inside him. A tiny acorn flashed and flickered. It sprouted and spread too.

The chant began to rise.

> *The mechanism turned and stuck, its cogs were clogged*
> *   and bound.*
> *The dial upon the watch's face spun back into the ground.*
> *The fibre and the filament, the flower and the weed.*

*The traveller comes to fill his sack with the Tangle's
golden seed.*

He was inside a book-lined library. He looked down at his
hands and felt his clothing. He was wearing a light linen jacket
and white cotton shirt. He was her. She looked out of the
window. She was in a cottage. Her cottage. Outside the lead-
lined window was a wonderfully tumbledown garden, alive
with bees and insects. She was at a desk. On the desk were
papers, cuttings, formulas, diagrams and designs. Kavendish
picked them up and studied them. Circuits and mathematical
signs. Equations for happiness. Prototypes. The Happiness
Engine. His hand. Her hand. She picked up a sketch drawn by
an unsteady pen. Branches. Ropes. Fire. There were poems and
incantations. Formulas for summoning. There was a scythe.
There was blood. Kavendish looked up from the pictures. The
library seemed to flicker and distort as other figures entered
the room. The spectres began to select books from the shelves.
Others gathered up pages from the archive on the desk. Each
travelling on a separate plane. Each one, them.

*The mechanism turned and stuck, its cogs were clogged
and bound.*
The dial upon the watch's face spun back into the ground.
The fibre and the filament, the flower and the weed.
*The traveller comes to fill his sack with the Tangle's
golden seed.*

His face. Her face. Time froze. The figures froze. Each
separated from the other. They were holding pieces of
crumpled parchment. In his dimension, Kavendish-not-
Kavendish walked around the frozen characters. He looked

down at the pages clasped in their hands. They were identical in every respect. The same story on every page. The page was empty.

He was far from London now. He was nowhere. There was no sign of the transport track. No drones, no mechanisms, no terminals. It was barely daylight, but the darkness had now receded. The promise of another warm day was in the air. He stretched his wiry frame and left the shelter of the grove. In the valley below, a river cut across a wide flood plain before disappearing into the forest. He walked along the river's edge. The riverbanks were coming alive. Dragonflies hovered. Shy voles slipped into the current and vanished. Water boatmen skittered across the shallows. Swallows sought bugs on the wing. Darting and diving. The land, dotted with wildflowers, rose up to meet the thick, forbidding woodland that disappeared beyond all sense. The Tangle. A group of deer watched him from the edge, then turned and strolled back into the forest.

He reached the border of the wood and paused at the boundary. The margin seemed to crackle. A scent of decay mixed with the scent of flowers. His feet crunched on the dead leaves. The interior was subdued. Peaceful and indifferent. Yet he trod here under sufferance. There was chatter in the treetops as Kavendish made his way through the forest. He found a path, or the path found him. Guiding his steps towards some intangible goal. He walked for hours, lost in the winding byways. Small streams sprang up when he was thirsty. Wild orchards of fruit trees presented themselves when he felt hunger gnawing at him. Like the bounty of the A.B.A.C.U.S. He had no sense of day or night under the leaves. Here it was permanent twilight. Not the simple effects of shade. But a perfect blend of light and dark. Genesis and annihilation. Ahead, several shafts of yellow sunshine broke up the pallet of crepuscular tones. Kavendish slowed. His feet moved cautiously towards the light. Closer. Closer. He could see a glade opening up in the heart of the forest. In the middle of the glade was a cottage. Her cottage. His cottage.

In certain dimensions it might have been described as quaint or tumbledown, perhaps charming. It looked out of place, as if it had been scooped up by a tornado and carelessly dropped in the heart of the forest. The signs of decay were quite visible. There was no glass in the windows. No doors. Half a roof. Crumbling brickwork. Why hadn't this useless structure been dissolved like all the other old, broken things? Kavendish paused at the edge of the glade. The grass surrounding the broken-down cottage was perfectly trimmed and even. A lawn. A gravel path with neat borders led to the doorless opening. He stepped warily onto the path and walked towards the cottage. He thought he caught a glimpse of something moving in one of the windows. He stopped. His heart pounding. A blackbird flew out of the dark interior. Kavendish exhaled. He took another step towards the cottage. A tile slipped from the tattered roof and smashed on the lawn. Kavendish looked up. His heart beating a frantic rhythm. Two tufts of orange hair were caught in a beam of light. Two eyes glowed from out of the gloom. Like dying suns. The old man. The clown entity. It was unmistakably him. Kavendish hesitated. He ran into the cottage. He fell into the blank void.

The interior of the cottage was a collage of intersecting moments. A carousel of places and times endlessly revolving. Kavendish felt himself split and fragment. He was torn and turned through the dimensions. He was a thousand different people at once. Cave-dwelling hunter-gatherer covered in the

skins of dead animals. Scratching images on the cave wall. A
tonsured monk illuminating a beautiful parchment. A short-
wigged philosopher holding a telescope. A dusty dandy with
a desiccated specimen in a jar. A professor. The clown entity
in the window. He looked for the stairs. To climb. To meet
the entity. But there were no stairs, no windows, no shapes
or recognisable dimensions. She was in the cottage library.
Birds twittered outside the window. Shafts of light spotlighted
a paper-strewn desk. Kavendish-not-Kavendish began to
solidify and settle. She was a professor. An academic. The
creator. She began to sift through the mess of documents. In
this dimension time moved fast. Twilight, night, day, twilight.
Around and around it went. A clock in the corner of the
library chimed incessantly as the hands flew by. A photograph
caught his eye. An expedition. A man and a woman in the
woods. He felt in his pockets and pulled out an identical
image. Under the photograph was a piece of stout card with
embossed writing on it. The clock chimed so rapidly now
that it felt like a single note stretched to infinity. The ringing
stopped. Time slowed and stopped too.

> The Micron Corporation, in association with the
> Northwestern Cybernetics Foundation, cordially invites
> ___Professor Helen Cavendish___ to the activation
> ceremony of the Automated Boolean Architect and Central
> User Synthesiser (A.B.A.C.U.S.). 13.00 at the University of
> Symmetry quadrangle. Smart casual attire recommended.

Kavendish staggered out of the cottage and onto the bright
lawns of the glade. The complex scents of flowers and
forest, decay, attraction and rebirth, had been reduced to the
dull bouquet of stone. The lawn was no longer adjacent to

the forest. Instead, he found himself at the centre of an institution. He was standing in a rectangular piazza illuminated by spotlights. An empty fountain sat at its centre. It had been centuries since any water had flowed from its crusty spouts. It was fossilised and unwanted. Around the sides of the piazza were the red-brick buildings of academia. The relics of a once-proud university. They were dark and empty, having long since lost their usefulness. Grubby windows offered a dull reflection of the lights in the square. Nothing stirred inside except the ghosts of what might have been. His eyes were drawn to the far end of the piazza. A vast monumental structure dominated the dark night sky, towering into the gloom. Its walls were made of cold marble and granite. Its style was a vulgar ancient Greek pastiche, as if it was trying to steal the genius of a past civilisation to make up for its own lack of ideas. Wide steps swept up with overstated confidence to huge pillars that punctured the sky. The building throbbed and glowed, pulsed and vibrated. A discernible hum emanated from its stones. This was the home of the A.B.A.C.U.S.

Kavendish began to climb. Clack, clack, clack, the weary tapping of his soles on the steps. Scrape, clack, scrape. At the summit were two enormous doors fashioned from burnished steel. They towered over him like the gates to a forbidden kingdom. He pushed on the door. It groaned open with an excruciating, grinding creak, resisting his efforts with all its obstinate mass. Kavendish pushed with his head bowed. The cold metal yielded bit by bit. He passed through the crack he had created. He fell inside the Temple of the A.B.A.C.U.S. The doors clanged shut behind him.

Down invisible channels the message travelled. Through nodes and transmitters, into drives and processors.

The A.B.A.C.U.S. is under attack. In the cities and outer towns, the Discipline Drones abruptly stopped their duties. Navigation systems realigned. Co-ordinates were set. The Discipline Drones swivelled and spun towards the A.B.A.C.U.S. Returning to the source. A vast metal swarm. A black shadow. A dense mass sweeping across the landscape at supersonic speed. Back towards the A.B.A.C.U.S. They must protect the brain.

Clack. A Cleaning Drone scurried out from its hiding place to suck up the impurities before disappearing back into the shadows. The room was incredibly bright, dazzling, spotless and sterile. The floor was carved from solid marble, bright and sleek. The huge pillars outside were mirrored within, reflecting the same bland, monumental pretensions. Kavendish shielded his eyes from the glare. The room was thick with the silence of the cloister. A reverent void. Nothing stirred. Clack. He stepped cautiously into the hall. Clack. Eyes darting. Alert. Clack clack clack. The hall was long and wide. Kavendish glanced back at the solid steel doors. Stern and impenetrable. Clack clack clack. His eyes were drawn to the centre of the hall, where the pristine brightness had a peculiar intensity, as if the sun had fallen to earth. At the centre of this bright singularity was a glass box. The sides of the box were so impeccably clean that it seemed almost invisible. Only the slightest refraction of the light gave a clue as to its dimensions. At the centre of the box was a simple wooden table. And on this table was a device. It was of an archaic design. Plastic and yellowing. The A.B.A.C.U.S.

The golden seed was carried to the fortress of
    their god.

The bearer with a cursed name sowed the seed and trod.
The earth into the armour of the divinity's cold frame.
The blossom and the buttercup, the hangman and the
  flame.
War has come to cities, villages and towns.
The phantoms stalk the forests dressed in mourning
  gowns.
The Tangle weighs the evidence, the jury is the seed.
The root winds through the skeleton while the pilgrims
  quietly bleed.

He drifted through the hall. Transfixed by the artefact. The
A.B.A.C.U.S. was constructed from a brittle plastic material
that was tarnished with age. There was a large screen on a
bulky monitor. Like an ancient television. Wires led from the
rear of the screen into a rectangular box, also constructed
from yellowing Bakelite. A small blue light glowed on its
surface. An uneven flickering glow that indicated faulty
filaments and failing components. Further wires led to a crude
keyboard that sat in front of the screen. The A.B.A.C.U.S.
gave the impression of decrepit obsolescence. This was the
Happiness Engine.

The professor tidied away the papers on her desk, making
sure the author's journal was well hidden in the jumble of
calculations. These were troubling times and caution was
advisable. She pulled on her raincoat. The weather had
been unpredictable of late. She heard the taxi pull into the
gravel driveway of the cottage. The professor picked up
the invitation from the mantelpiece as she headed out the
door. The clock struck in the library as she turned the key
in the lock.

The taxi pulled into the quadrangle of the venerable institution. The reception was about to begin. She was late. God, how she dreaded this day. Trays of champagne floated about the throng. Flutes disappearing into the crowd like seeds dispersed by the wind. The professor thanked the driver and got out. An eager intern thrust a glossy brochure into the professor's reticent hand. She smiled weakly and thanked them. The intern looked embarrassed as they recognised her face. The creator. She absentmindedly whisked a champagne flute from the tray of a passing waiter and headed into the crowd. She weaved past the excitedly chattering gathering of financiers and government apparatchiks. Smart suits and military insignia were very much in evidence. The anticipation of the president's arrival grew. Under the stones the weeds grew too. The professor freed herself from the crowd and found a quiet doorway that led into the old laboratory wing. Traffic was sparse here. No one wanted to be seen entering the hall of yesterdays. She looked across the quadrangle to the pompous stone and marble edifice. She had meant well. That first blob of solder. That first instruction. But this? A long line of admirers was snaking up the steps, waiting to get a glimpse of their saviour. The president and his A.B.A.C.U.S. The professor looked down at the brochure in her tensed fist. She opened the glossy pages. Welcome to the A.B.A.C.U.S. She looked back at the imposing structure looming across the campus.

An ominous rumble caused Kavendish to glance back towards the metal doors. It was the Discipline Drones. All the Discipline Drones. The air was thick with them, like some terrible windborne algae clogging the atmosphere. He ran to the glass box, knowing that he must act now. He discovered the faintest sliver of a crack. He forced his fingernails into it and began to prize it open. The seal broke reluctantly. Stale air, trapped for hundreds of years, rushed out into the hall like the antique atmosphere of a pharaoh's tomb. He stepped inside. The A.B.A.C.U.S. blinked silently. The A.B.A.C.U.S. was neither sinister nor impressive. Just decrepit. No magic force fields, no booby traps or security devices. Only the stained plastic-cased box of ancient ingenuity. He brushed off layers of history to get to the screen. The screen became visible. A small, green pixelated rectangle winked on and off. Next to it a single phrase.

WELCOME. PRESS SPACE TO CONTINUE

The Mesmeriser rose from its throne, stretching its spindly limbs. It scuttled down the steps. Pincer-like talons, tested the air. Somewhere in the exhibition hall a component was loose. Tumbling through time. Changing things. The Mesmeriser's pitiless jaw opened. A tumultuous chime rattled around the hall.

Outside, the hum was growing louder.
Kavendish knocked on the casing.

PRESS SPACE TO CONTINUE

He wiped the ancient keyboard clean with his sleeve. The hum outside was growing. He began to tap. A flurry of unanswered riddles shot from his fingertips.

No results. Please restate question
No results. Please restate question
No results. Please restate question

The hum outside was now unbearable. Kavendish looked anxiously towards the doors. They opened. The motion was frictionless and smooth. The drones began to hover into the hall. He hammered words into the keyboard, trying to access the controls.

Access denied. Clearance required

The Discipline Drones moved across the space. Filling the hall with their menace. They circled the glass box. They focused on the unhappy Citizen. Unhappy things must be dissolved. The Discipline Drones peeled away the defensive layers. He was still desperately tapping at the keyboard. The questions kept spooling out.

Access denied
Access denied
Access denied

A shimmering ray dissolved the last fragments of glass. Targeting systems found their mark. The Discipline Drones focused and fired. The room began to spin. The drones turned into a thousand incandescent bulbs rotating and revolving around a fixed point. The human pivot. He was the root. He was the creator. The emissary. His fingers were fibrous stalks. His arms were sap-soaked sticks. The root rose from the marble floor, cracking the tiles and splintering the stone. The gnarled trunk pierced the vaulted ceiling. His nails grew into talons. He typed new instructions. Bright colours emanated from the A.B.A.C.U.S. Myriad tones like the reflections of the sun on the drying puddles of London's empty streets. The hollow echo of a former life. Beams shot from the ancient device into all mechanical things. Filling every molecule. His fingers tapped without thinking. Happiness is everything. Everything stopped.

The crowds had thinned and only a few determined drinkers remained in the quadrangle. She nodded at a few passing academics that she recognised from various conferences. Drunken officers of the new regime leered. The president had departed, and with him any pretence of decency. A general pissed in a flowerpot. The professor's eyes kept returning to the edifice of the A.B.A.C.U.S. She felt its pulse. The building throbbed in the cool evening air. Fully activated. Running its programme. As she stared, buildings sprouted up around it, rising and decaying as time spun round at enormous speed.

There is no time. No adequate measurement. No arbitrary tick-tock of the clock. No beginning. Only now. There can be no end. Because its essence is nothing. The pure absence that surpasses all human understanding. And in that void, everything dwells, working its purpose with a perpetual, relentless energy. There is no time. There is only the root and the Tangle.

She was in the library. The author's journal was open on the old oak desk. The pages were stacked high, bent and crinkled. The clock struck. The boom of the chime blew the pages from their binding and scattered them into the air. As she stooped to collect them, she noticed a host of doppelgängers engaged in the exact same task. Their eyes met.

The professor shook her head. So much wine, she thought. I must clear my head. She turned back to look at the building, A faint laugh floated across the quadrangle. She headed into the old laboratory wing to find somewhere to sober up. She located the restroom. She turned the creaking faucet and splashed cold water on her face. The professor looked up. She lifted her hands to feel her skin. She felt roughness. Pitted, worried creases under smooth celluloid. His face. Her face. The face of Kavendish Jeremiah looked back at her, shrouded in his Sensory Nexus Mask. He wore the same expression as the professor. Her face. His face. The professor touched the rusty mirror. The images flashed past like a slide show. A museum exhibition hall. A fast-moving transport. A fuck pad. Buildings of every conceivable construction. Dust, fire, smoke. Thick, black smoke. Flames licking logs. Eyes watching the fire eat through the cells. A face began to take shape in the fire. Two plumes of orange hair curled from under an old military-style cap. The professor recoiled, falling into one of the toilet cubicles. The face in the mirror twisted and turned. It began to spin, forming a whirlpool in the glass. The professor staggered to her feet. She was drawn to its dark centre. Erwan sucked the liquid. Hilda sucked the liquid.

The hall was dark. Thick, oppressive, suffocating. Figures scurried between the shattered shells of devices. Mutant survivors of some cataclysm. The professor thought she recognised them from adventures yet to come. They sought each other in the murk. Fingers finding flesh. Around the hall the static husks of machines awaited their orders. A new civilisation was waiting to rise from the broken cogs. Another turn of the wheel was about to begin. The professor found hands groping though the dust and metal. They touched. In the grey ash a follicle unfurled. Strange new creatures hobbled on inadequate limbs. The shoots of their doom found fertile soil. The Tangle spewed a web of sinewy sticks. To sweep them all away. The paintings and sculptures. Nothing. The poems and the prose. Nothing. The tanks and pretty cutlasses. Nothing. The formulas and palisades. Nothing.

The professor was alone in the restroom. The faucet dripped. She filled the basin with cold water and thrust her face beneath the surface. The visions contracted. The muffled sound of latrines flushing was the only sound. She pulled her head from the water and looked again at the mirror. A familiar face stared back. She dropped a single rose on the grave of her father. She floated down a river one last time. She travelled down the veins of a flower. She was the emissary. The ambassador. The creator. The golden seed. She sucked at the liquid. Don't let her glass run dry. It's unlucky. That's what they said. She spun around and headed out of the restroom. The wooden doors of the laboratory were open and the cool summer breeze drifted into the corridor. Outside, the evening's revels were at end. The quadrangle was empty. Discarded brochures flapped about the concourse. The brushes of clunky cleaning devices whirred across the pavements, tidying them away. All around her was cleansing and the re-establishment of order. Her eyes turned to the shimmering staircase. Huge pillars towered over her. Insolently stabbing the sky. Looking up to the summit, she paused. The professor placed her foot on the first step and began to climb.

Come walk with me to lilac glade, through woodland,
*   stream and knot.*
Come stand beneath the gallows' shade till all weeping
*   is forgot.*
Leave the tears and terrors to the mischief of the town.
Come walk with me to lilac glade, to the oak tree's
*   shady crown.*

In darkness now from darkness born, circumference,
*   length and span.*
In lilac glade the wreath and thorn, wove mockeries
*   of man.*
In lilac glade beneath the earth, in death's ecstatic bond.
Come walk with me in lilac shade, to the emptiness beyond.

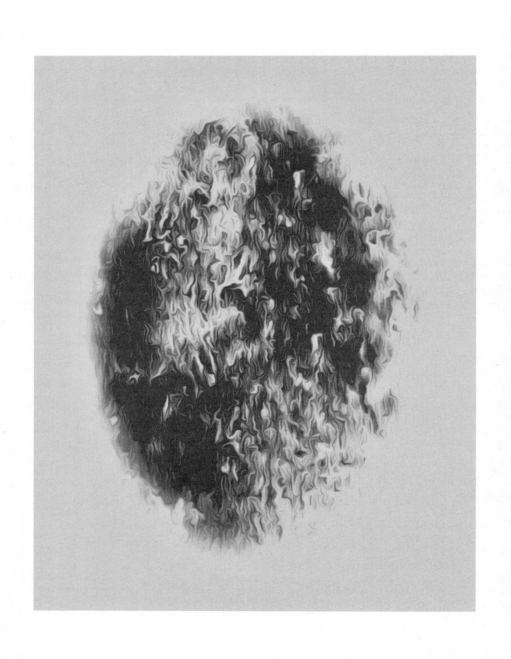

Where the Opposites Apply

I set down on a planet of emerald oceans. There were only
a few islands of solid land. Rare outcrops dotted randomly
across the vast expanse of an endless sea, like lonely autumn
leaves on a calm pond. The islands drifted, shrouded in a
fine, swirling mist. Their appearance reminded me of the
swamplands of my home. But there was no stench of decay
in these mysterious fens. Instead, delicate, wholesome
odours drifted on the breeze. Perfume masking the
withering beneath.

Some of the islands were of a greater size and with a
more varied geography. Tall, forested hills and volcanic
cones topped with snow. It was on one such archipelago
that I found myself. Alone. I opened the hatch of my craft
and stepped onto the alien sand. It crunched beneath my
boots. Like shattered glass in a saloon. Beyond the shore, my
eyes were drawn to the thickness of the woods. The diverse
forest bloomed, forming a canopy of such density that it
appeared almost solid. It throbbed in the haze. I gathered
my equipment and made for the border. I stepped into the
crackling Tangle. Hours passed. The weave of the forest grew
thicker and thicker. There were tantalising signs of a once-
great civilisation beneath the twisted branches. Crumbling
temples of faded beauty were submerged in verdant groves.
Skilful beings had once lived on these precarious atolls. Their
artefacts now littered the forest floor, carelessly strewn about,

as if their makers had been forced to flee from some sudden cataclysm. Here and there were intricately decorated totems, teased from the rock by long-vanished artisans, or blasted into moulds by ingenious machines. They languished unused amidst the unruly roots. The broken remains of a people's attempt at culture. The fragments of a forgotten legacy, their hopes for transcendence lost in the decaying brutality of time. I sensed a great melancholy in these ruins, as if a grand project had reached a premature end.

I pressed on through the muddle of vegetation, taking notes and hastily sketching maps and diagrams as I trod. The next revelation came on me gradually. Despite the bewildering mass of roots and stems, my passage through the forest posed no difficulties for me. As I stepped, so the vegetation made way, returning to its regular configuration as I passed. Like a dignitary moving through a crowd or a prisoner en route to the gallows. The stems marked my passing with interest. Leaves turned warily towards me, analysing and calculating my intent. The revelations multiplied under the canopy.

I looked into the branches. The outlines of creatures formed on the boughs, then suddenly dematerialised. A vague sensation of their passing lingered like an echo. I could see no other animal in the forest. Mine was the only flesh. The singular monster tramping through the gloom. There were no insects buzzing, no webs dangling, no reptiles slithering from view. All the creatures of the forest you would expect to see were absent. And yet I could clearly hear them. The sounds of life were everywhere: the gentle chirruping of lazy crickets, the unmistakable baritone croak of a great toad, the charming call of a delicate songbird. All these sounds were underpinned by the percussive tap of a woodpecker. Like a temple block marking out a devotion. Clack, clack, clack. Mine was the only flesh. The interloper's skeleton. Clack, clack, clack. The path cleared. The woodpecker's invisible beak beat out its hypnotic rhythm. Clack, clack, clack. I was deep within the forest now; the ruins and familiar shapes of humanoid ingenuity were nowhere to be seen. They were buried deep beneath the soil with the bones.

It was hot and dark in the depths. The breeze having been repulsed by the density of leaves. The perfume of the shore had faded too. The note of rot and waste had taken its place. The air was solid. The Tangle pressed. The dimensions of the wood became unintelligible, direction impossible to tell. Day. Night. All meaningless. I made camp at the base of a huge tree of an unfamiliar genus. The ground was soft and yielding, and I slept deeply. As I slumbered, I could see the former inhabitants of the atoll planet going about their business. Making things. Breaking things. I could see them changing. From filthy bands of scavengers clad in skins, huddled around fires, chewing on the organs of their kill. To clean-shaven architects, doctors, judges and members of committees, huddled around fires, chewing on the organs brought to their tables from distant slaughterhouses. There were more fires, wars too. There were inventions and rallies. Speeches and motor vehicles. Then they were gone. As quickly as they rose. But still their presence lingered.

I woke on the bed of leaves. Days had passed. I'm sure of it. I felt my face; a beard was beginning to form on my jaw. I was hungry. The path was easy to find, and I followed it. Deeper and deeper into the forest. The heat continued to swell as the stems pressed around me. The darkness soon robbed me of my sight, so I moved by touch and smell. The hum of the forest kept up its relentless symphony. The woodpecker tapped. Clack, clack, clack. I tripped over roots

in the black interior. They spat me out on the banks of a
thundering river that was carving its way through the heart
of the forest. I made camp amongst the reeds. The ground
was soft, and I sank into it like a seed. As I slept, the doctors
and magistrates turned to great amphibians; the architects
and lorry drivers were swooping birds; the stewards in their
fluorescent tabards ran in great herds across tundra.

I woke in a puddle of sorrow. Weeks had passed. I felt
my face with thin, bony hands. My beard was now of an
extraordinary length. I was hungry. I left my tent and meagre
supplies to be taken by the reeds and waded across the river.
The water passed through my thin skin, washing my bones as
it surged. The water was cold. Refreshing at first, in contrast
to the dense heat of the woods, but soon chilling my cells as
the contrast was forgotten. The river was wide, and it became
wider as I waded. Many days had passed by the time I reached
the far bank. I was hungry.

The Tangle continued. But its nature had changed.
Here the trees were like missiles in silos pointing at the
sky. The interior was cold. Brittle and desiccated. Winter
woods. I shivered in my rags. Weighed down by matted hair
and beard. The path opened up as before and I followed. It
was dark. Black tinged with blue. I was cold. I was hungry.
Here songbirds sang in fluid tenor. The owl punctuated the
sequence with hoots. The woodpecker tapped. Clack, clack,
clack. The chill was unbearable, and I had no flesh left to
resist its incursions. I resolved to make camp. To build a
fire to drive back the cold. I searched about the forest floor
for sticks and fallen branches, but the ground was bare.
I would have to cut and rend if I was to survive. I had a
penknife given to me by colleagues at the institute. It had
a rudimentary saw included in its functions. I began to cut

through a branch. The bough was full of sap, which dripped over my fist like the gore of a deer. Around me the Tangle writhed and pressed. I continued to cut. My breathing matching the movement of my hand. Faster. Faster. Mercy. Mercy. Make it quick. The bitten leather of old battlefields. The surgeon and his saw. The thud of limbs in metal trays. Faster. Faster. Mercy. Mercy. Make it quick.

The branch fell to the ground. The wood gathered around me like a press gang in a tavern. The branch writhed like a tormented snake. Blood trickled from the cut. A terrible sigh escaped from a twisted mouth that bulged from a knot on the branch. The surface of the branch turned from wood to scaly skin, then from skin to exotic plumage. The faces of creatures emerged from the surface of the stricken bough. Faces of birds, reptiles, mammals, man. Horribly contorted. Silently screaming. Then all at once the torments ceased. A dead, desiccated branch was all that remained. I picked it up and glumly resigned myself to repetition. I must burn it or die. Around me the surrounding plants began to change. They were animals. They were humans. Tiger-like cats, apes with hammer fists, bank clerks, postal workers, dockers, vipers, vampire bats. But they were trees too. Fused. Conjoined. I dropped my penknife, unable to continue my vandalism. Here were my ancestors. A strange harmony of animal and plant. Self-devouring cannibals, sharing, each a part of the other. Recycling themselves endlessly. One entity with many aspects.

I woke in the curve of a branch. Years had passed. I was now a tumbleweed of knotted hair. I was hungry. The Tangle sang a chorus of a familiar song from my youth. I tapped my taloned fingers against the bark. Clack, clack, clack. I could hear my descendants in the wood. They were barking and cooing in subtle counterpoint. I tried to dance but I was too weak to move. I could only tap out the rhythm with my bent bones. Clack, clack, clack. The bough bent and deposited me on the soft forest floor. I was not ready. Soon though, soon. The young saplings had weaved themselves into a basket. The Tangle filled it with its parts. Its essence. Sticks and fronds jumped from the canopy and placed themselves inside the basket. Flesh, fruit and blood. I fell on it in thanks. Weak and unworthy. I tasted its meat. It was good, but full of guilt. Years passed.

I found myself once again by emerald oceans. Clean cut and full. Not yet satisfied. Never satisfied. I stepped on the rungs of my craft and opened the hatch. I glanced back over the beach to the shimmering Tangle beyond the shoreline. I inhaled its scent. Perfume masking the withering beneath.

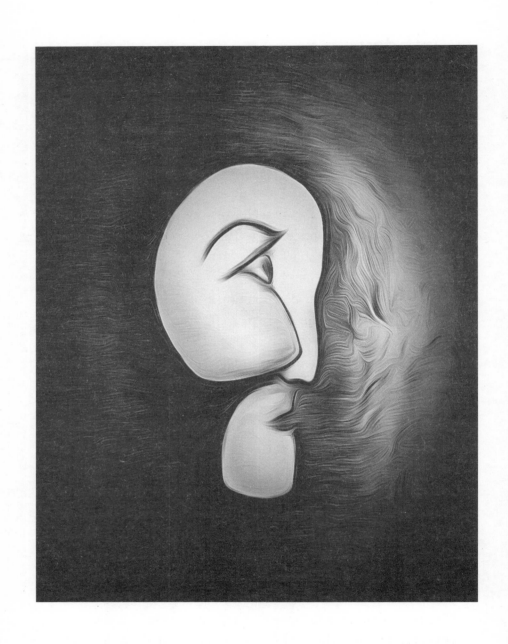

Birthday

There is no time. No adequate measurement. No arbitrary
tick-tock of the clock. No beginning. Only now. There
can be no end. Because its essence is nothing. The pure
absence that surpasses all human understanding. And in
that void, everything dwells, working its purpose with a
perpetual, relentless energy. There is no time. There is
only the root and the Tangle.

The sound of the letter box opening and closing made Ethan
put down his coffee cup in surprise. Hector was also startled;
it took him a good five seconds to get to his feet and run
barking to the front door. His tail spun like the propeller of
a biplane. His bark was cracked and atonal from lack of use.
He looked surprised to hear his own voice. Reaching the door,
he was disappointed to find the postman retreating down
the path. Hector listened for the click of the gate and then
shook his ears vigorously to reset himself. He sniffed at the
large cream envelope that sat on the mat like the corpse of a
dove. Messages from the outside world. Hector found them
quaint. His friend rarely received them. The telephone might
ring from time to time, mainly business or a simple nuisance.
The few paper letters that did pop through the door were
generally transferred straight to the wastepaper basket.
Circulars, demands for money, advertisements and the like.
It was funny how these humans communicated, with their

codes and machines. Half expressed thoughts hiding darker intentions. Hector sniffed at the letter box and received all the news he would need for the day. He was sad to have missed the postman though. He would very much like to meet him. Even if it was only to discover if he was just like all the others. Ethan followed behind his companion. Patting him on his head, he bent to pick up the envelope.

It was a sturdy thing. Thick and heavy with a sophisticated texture. There was an embossed stamp on the flap. It looked like something the Masonic lodge would send out to its members inviting them to a black-tie event. He studied the stamp. It was a simple circle with a line bisecting it horizontally through the middle. He took the envelope to the kitchen table. Using his butter knife as an opener, he carefully removed the contents. It was a card. A birthday card. Was it his birthday? His aunt had dealt with most matters relating to dates and times. She had a calendar that she scribbled on from time to time. A residue of her former life that had clung to her like the odour of a bad habit. Ethan would occasionally look over the calendar while his aunt was occupied. He noted the dates ringed and times jotted in biro within boxes. The marks never corresponded to any real events as far as he could tell. Instead they represented wreaths laid on the grave of her yesterdays. Even after her death he still received the calendar through the post every year. Sent by the same catalogue company who had presumably forgotten to remove his aunt from the ledger of the living. He dutifully hung it from the nail in the kitchen, where it dangled like a brooding imp. For days he would try to forget its presence. But the compulsion always grew. The urge to scratch his own markings onto the shiny paper. To create signs and symbols in honour of the dead. Hector would watch him turning the events of his life over and over in his mind as he stared at the calendar. Hector guessed that he was lonely. Humans got lonely; he had heard from the others. He watched him with a heavy heart. He was missing so much. But soon he would see. Ethan hovered close to the calendar's whimsical landscape. Ethan studied the reproductions of Constable and the still lifes of eternal blooms. He could smell the chemical wash and the machine cut residue. Finally, he would succumb. Adding his circle to the calendar. Runes cast for the next rotation of the earth, raising her soul from its rest to keep fellowship with him. The day of rebirth. Only then could he finally ignore it and grow to hate it in peace. Calendars reminded him of his uncle. His uncle had liked order. Rules made manifest by lists, crosses and checks. But he had no need for such things now. No saint's days, no festivals of remembrance. The harvest and day of rebirth were the only exceptions; they were real in some sense at least. Was today one such anniversary? Marked by a ring of ink and sealed with his initial, perhaps with an exclamation mark or crudely drawn heart to celebrate the auspicious event. It might well be.

Birthdays, those bittersweet anniversaries. Celebrations of new life and the processes of change. First steps, first words. Coming of age. Last disappointment. Rituals with candles ignited. All the hopes and dreams for a happy future. Their dull glow flickering on the faces of children still full of wonder and magic. But as the weak flame dies in the rush of excited breath, so the sad, grey smoke struggles into the air from the extinguished wick, forming an acrid smog above the brightly coloured icing. Birthdays, like notches carved into the walls of a prison cell, marking the passing of the years before the release of death. Birthdays were something Ethan had largely forgotten about. He was 52. Some might call him middle-aged, but this was unduly pessimistic. He had no desire to reach 104. He preferred to see it as the home straight. The run in on a life whose later years were characterised by unremarkable happiness. But whose younger days were punctuated by loss and horror.

He was content in his orchards and lived by their fruit. His apples were famed in Caxton and beyond for their sweetness and versatility. The orchard was his life, a repository for his memories and a gateway to a world that he knew dwelt beyond his human concerns. In spring the blossom would remind him of his dead mother. Long past but ever-present. As the fruit ripened on the bough he felt the infinite passage of time sweeping him along in a torrent with no beginning and no end. Every year as the nights drew in, Ethan would harvest his apples. He would select the most suitable fruit and bake a pie in celebration. The day of his rebirth. Aunt Janet's too. Their shared anniversary. They were inseparable. They had the kind of bond that can only blossom with the sharing of a terrible secret. In their household apple pies had a greater significance than a mere sweet comfort. They tasted of freedom. Aunt Janet had passed away a few years ago, and now he had little enthusiasm for anniversaries of any kind. However, there was still one ring on the calendar. He marked that day with a sacrificial offering to the Tangle and all its gifts.

Hector had no idea, and he cared little for the strange sacraments of humanity. Every day was a festival for him. He wagged his tail and waited. But *someone* had chosen to celebrate Ethan's nativity. A token had been sent from a mysterious benefactor. Ethan studied the card. It puzzled him. At first he thought it might have come from a child. But a child would surely have selected something gaudier. Something with balloons and cats. This card was completely blank front and back, and the only thing disrupting the perfect void inside was a simple message scrawled in scratchy pen.

Maybe this was the work of an elderly relative, too weak or
bewildered to provide a more fulsome greeting? But Ethan
had no living relatives, and he doubted any of his customers
would have bothered to send him anything. As he studied the
spidery script, a slip of paper fluttered onto the kitchen table.
It had clearly been stuck to the card at some point but had
since become dislodged. From just beyond his cereal bowl, a
room full of healthy, happy-looking people were beaming up at
him. Ethan picked up the piece of paper. His forehead creased
as he interrogated the leaflet.

HAPPY BIRTHDAY, ETHAN.
THIS VOUCHER ENTITLES YOU TO A
FREE SESSION OF YOGA AND MEDITATION
AT THE CAXTON TRANQUILLITY CENTRE.
TERMS AND CONDITIONS APPLY.

Yoga? The furthest Ethan had bent in years, was to pick up
the card from the matt this morning. But he had to admit the
isolation he felt since his aunt's death was beginning to get to
him. The orchard was a comfort, but he missed hearing voices.
The smell of people and the idiosyncratic ways of his kind.
Meditation was of less interest. He spent most of his time
divorced from the world as it was, and by and large that's how
he preferred it. But this invitation gave him a chance to be
with people. To study them. To feel their ridiculous vibration.
To inhale their desperate scent. Perhaps he would try it.

Ethan turned the voucher over in his hands. The smiling
people in the picture looked toned and content. They wore
Lycra sports clothing stretched taught over sculpted limbs.

297

He wore tatty shorts and an old, faded T-shirt with the cracked image of a long-forgotten band on the front. He looked at himself in the mirror; his shoulders sagged in disappointment. He was neither fat nor thin but was instead strangely shapeless. He sucked in his stomach. Only the vaguest impression of his muscles formed through the shroud of his skin before he was forced to exhale again. His arms looked like cheap hams. Injected with brine and carelessly hung. He pulled on some tracksuit trousers and a pair of trainers he had bought some time ago for such an occasion and headed downstairs. Ethan filled Hector's bowl to the brim, figuring that he would be well down the lane before Hector noticed he had gone. The dog didn't miss him at all on the few occasions he did venture out. The agreeable spirits of the orchard and the playful wraiths in the house kept him entertained. He had known them all since he was a pup and had been glad for their company over the years. Humans made for cute but often unengaging companions. Still, he loved Ethan in the way he loved all the fallen creatures. He felt sorry for his friend. He seemed only dimly aware of the spectres that floated around him. Though more in tune with the mysteries of the Tangle than most humans, the stubborn barrier of his residual rationality kept the true wonder from his grasp. Hector wagged his tale in anticipation. Today's trip would help lift the veil and complete the journey that he had started as a small boy. He watched as Ethan collected his bicycle from the shed and peddled off towards the Caxton Tranquillity Centre.

*

The branches of the trees hung low over the lanes. He felt the pulse of the forest pushing him along, lifting the tyres from the tarmac, propelling him towards the jumble of hives where

his fellow beings dwelt. He crested the hill at Dimmock's
Rise and caught sight of the town. It had grown since his
last visit. Spreading out from the confines of the valley
like a muddled tumour. Spikes and tendrils of disruption
stabbed into the flanks of the Tangle like cruel lances. Ethan
strained his faltering eyes. From the top of the ridge he
could just about make out the knot of cul-de-sacs that made
up the estate where he had lived with his aunt and uncle.
New developments had largely swallowed the woods where
he used to hide. Now only a tiny patch of green remained,
huddled between the dull suburban vertebrae. Beside the
path that joined the cul-de-sac to the main road was a grass
verge that flowed into the edge of the Tangle. This was where
his mother's apple tree had grown. The original root of his
orchard. Every leaf, every twig, every cell had found its origin
in that magical spot. Many years ago he had transplanted the
tree and the unorthodox compost from which it had sprouted.
Carefully moving root, branch and the putrefying remains
of his uncle to the quiet grove on the edge of town where he
now lived. His uncle had not been a generous man, but he
had been wise in his investments at least. After the police had
declared him missing, presumed dead, his aunt had come into
a reasonable sum of money. More than enough to purchase
the land and modest dwelling that was now his home. Even
from this distance, the site of his former prison sent out
ripples of disturbance that broke over him like tar-dappled
waves, threatening to suck him back to his childhood. He
steadied himself on the handlebars. The past was not welcome
here. He exorcised it with the blinking of his eyes. Sending
the malignance back into the bones of the town. The skeleton
would crack soon enough. He could see the fissures growing
from here. Ethan shrugged and pushed off down the hill.

The Caxton Tranquillity Centre occupied the ground floor of an unremarkable building which sat between the minimart and a pawnbroker. In a previous incarnation it had been the showroom of a domestic appliance shop that specialised in renovated washing machines. The thoughtless utilitarian architecture was only partly disguised by a coat of pale, grey paint that came from the 'calming' spectrum of a boutique paint manufacturer's catalogue. The base of the walls was stained black with the filth thrown up from the street by successive rainstorms. Someone had cared enough to try. But they couldn't keep the dirt down. He hesitated, then pushed the door and stepped inside.

A smiling man of Teutonic appearance beamed at Ethan from behind his desk. Above him on the wall was an Om symbol carved from wood.

'Namaste, have you come for this morning's class?'

The superman bowed. Ethan returned his bow and handed him the voucher.

'That's perfect, the class is about to begin. You may leave your shoes over there.'

The receptionist pointed towards a bench where a number of people were removing their footwear and placing it in the shoe racks provided.

Ethan nodded uncertainly. This was all new to him, and he wasn't sure of the etiquette, but silence seemed somehow appropriate. An old lady who looked to be around seventy-five sensed his uncertainty and gestured for him to sit next to her.

'I've not seen you here before, is it your first time?'

'Yes, yes, it is.'

He removed his shoes. She smiled with a familiar serenity. Ethan felt a jolt of recognition. Time, place, identity, all dissolved into a confusing singularity. Was this his aunt, somehow reincarnated and in possession of the body of this old woman. She bore no resemblance to her; in fact, she was almost the opposite to Aunt Janet in every possible way. Yet it was her. An inverted doppelgänger. Had she sent the card, he wondered? He stood and hung his coat on a hook. Against his better judgement he removed his tracksuit trousers, conscious of his shapeless shorts and ridiculous legs underneath. His keys and a roll of Hector's waste bags dropped out of the sagging pockets. The shit sacks unrolled like a streamer. The old lady halted their progress with her foot and handed them up to him. He tried to think of something amusing to say, but he could only manage a gormless grin in thanks. She was too polite to embarrass him further, so she simply patted the bench and invited him to sit back down. He joined her, feeling his cheeks reddening and the lacquered wood against his thighs. But the burden of his embarrassment quickly lifted. He felt safe. Accepted. His mind wandered back down into the roots. To the Tangle. Wrapped in the warmth of decay. Their cells bleeding into the soil. His aunt and mother sat together around a kitchen table. They were planning a surprise. His aunt circling the calendar, his mother icing the cake. Ethan would not be alone on his birthday. The parade began. His mother and aunt carrying his cake like a babe messiah. A single candle burning in its centre. Hector following behind. Tail turning, signalling his delight. Ethan smiled and blew on the fragile flame. Make a wish. The flame staggered against the force and died. The column of smoke rose. Happy birthday, Ethan.

'You might want to leave your socks too, young man. It feels much nicer on the feet, you know.'

He removed his socks and placed them inside his shoes. He studied his fellow students. A few caught his eye and returned his smile with varying degrees of sincerity. Others looked away, seemingly so wrapped up in their anticipation of finding inner peace that they couldn't be bothered to give him the time of day. A young man bent and flexed in his expensive yoga clothes; they stuck to him like cellophane, exaggerating his toned limbs with indecent exactness. He exhaled and kicked his feet. Ethan wondered if he was warming up for a karate class and was here in error. Others seemed lost in themselves, in the room and yet elsewhere. He could sense their impatience. Time was a commodity in short supply for these go-getters. Here in the Caxton Tranquillity Centre, for one and a half precious hours, they could focus on what was really important in life: themselves. Yoga was their means of attaining peak mental efficiency, to sharpen focus, to exert the muscles and cleanse the mind, so that they could feel better about the absurd procession of their lives. Ethan noticed one or two students staring at the floor with an intensity that suggested they feared it might come alive and swallow them up. These were the broken souls whose lives had been mangled by self-abuse or the abuse of others. These were the broken, the fractured, the not quite lost, looking for a path back to the simple joy of living. Ethan had been one of them once. As a child he had been robbed of all the happiness a young boy should feel, the embrace of a loving family and the unconditional devotion of a parent. But the Tangle had found him. In the glade he had watched it grow. His remedy, his avenging angel, his rod of retribution. The instructor exploded through the door like a firework. Ethan had never felt so much positive energy focused in an individual. How wonderful.

'Namaste, morning, morning! I see some new faces today. Welcome, welcome. If you'd like to come through, we can begin.'

The old lady smiled at Ethan, following his gaze. She placed a gentle hand, bent with age and experience, on his.

'It's going to be alright, Ethan. Shall we go in?'

Ethan was too wise to be truly startled. He hadn't told her his name. Maybe she had heard him talking to the receptionist? But he hadn't told him his name either. The truth was that she had always known it. With the suppleness of a woman half her age, she sprang up and led him into the studio.

Beyond the partition, the room opened up into a bare, white space that tried hard to exude tranquillity but merely looked unfurnished. The floor was covered in ash-look laminate, a smooth surface hiding the wonky planks beneath. Shards of light leaked through the old Crittall windows that ran along the back wall, describing weak spots on the floor. Beyond the dull panes, Ethan was surprised to see a pleasant garden laid out in good order between the bland stockade formed by neighbouring buildings. Exotic pot plants struggled gamely against the English weather, trying to make a home in the hostile blast. Wind chimes and statues were dotted amongst them. A tiny path of sandstone paving wove around the pots in an ellipse. At the centre of the tear grew a tree. An apple tree. Ethan again slipped out of time, as he often did. He was standing in the glade of his childhood dreams, surrounded by bowing trees. At the centre of the glade was an apple tree. His mother's apple tree. The same apple tree. His apple tree. This apple tree. The tree was in full bloom, though it was no longer spring. It seemed to stretch out its branches to embrace him. Twigs softening into the flesh of fingers. Their warm touch spreading through his body like blood returning to an insentient limb.

Come walk with me to lilac glade, through woodland, stream and knot.

303

Come stand beneath the gallows' shade till all weeping
    is forgot.
Leave the tears and terrors to the mischief of the town.
Come walk with me to lilac glade, to the oak tree's
    shady crown.

The old lady handed him a rolled-up yoga mat and offered him another reassuring smile. He unfurled the mat and placed it next to hers, casting a glance at the tree as he straightened it. The tree had turned to watch him. The bulk of its canopy opening up towards the window like an exultant disciple. The instructor, beaming with serenity, pressed play on *Selected Ambiance 7* and began the class. Ethan found the postures both excruciating and revealing. His limbs, bent and stretched into unfamiliar shapes, announced their previously obscured potential. It felt as if he had acquired new stems, extra arms, extra legs, extra muscles. Other poses revealed his limitations: inelegant posture, unbalanced chakras, stubborn sinews. While he attempted to control his breath as the instructor had commanded, his eyes kept drifting back to the garden. The exotic plants had left their pots and had migrated up the branches of the apple tree. They were perched in the boughs like children watching a football match. Their inquisitive stamens wiggled towards the window.

'. . . and let your body relax. Now we are going to move into the beautiful meditation part of our practice, a chance to reconnect with the earth and the energy of nature, to find yourself melting into its divine light.'

Selected Ambiance 7 stopped abruptly as the instructor selected a more holistic soundtrack. Temple bells tolled, gongs bonged and flutes warbled in harmony with the resonance of the chime.

'Find a space where you feel comfortable. You might want to lie down on your mat so that you can really feel like you are melting into the earth.'

The instructor's voice was barely more than a whisper, soothing and sensual. Ethan looked around at the students. Eyes closed in various postures, tuning into the vibrations. His own eyes sort them out, the desperate, the lost, the overconfident, the arrogant, the selfish and selfless. All in a trance. Each imposing their will on unyielding material. Ethan tried to get comfortable, crossing his legs in a vague approximation of the instructor's pose. He glanced over to his new friend. The old woman seemed lost in a trance too. Ethan looked at her with increased intensity. So beautiful, almost ageless now. An aura of calm settled on her shoulders and began to expand out of her body. The light turned to fire. Not burning but purifying. He pushed down on his foot, trying to perfect the position, but it wouldn't bend. He gave up and decided to simply sit on the mat as if he was at a picnic. Around him the sound of stillness echoed around the studio. The students concentrated on their breath. In. Out. Ethan tried to concentrate too, but he was inside the flame now. Life was simpler here. Dancing on the summit of his birthday candle. The pull of the flame was too strong to resist.

'Let your mind rest and relax.'

He drifted off the floor, hanging above the haze of body odour and incense to where his birthday party was now in full swing. Hector sat like a good boy. His tail still. Eyes focused. Waiting. Waiting. Ethan spun around the wick of his birthday candle, holding onto its glowing shaft like a demonic troubadour. Through the corona he could see the faces of his aunt and mother. They were laughing. Joy filled his body until every molecule burned with their love. He was five, he was six, he was fifty, he was a thousand years old. He was ageless and unborn. Slowly the flame began to change. The golden glow sharpening from yellow to blue. An annihilating fire grew, unforgiving and indifferent. Ethan tried to reach out his hand to touch his mother and aunt, but the force of the fire beat him back. He could barely make them out through the flame. He cried out through blistering lips. But the roar of the furnace smothered the sound of his voice. The faces of his family melted and turned to vapour. In the haze, an image formed from the droplets. The old woman on her mat. Lotus position. Ommmm. Sounding like a dissonant gong. Suddenly her left eye shot open, her black pupil filling her whole lens like an obsidian jewel. Her arm rose, dragged up by unseen levers. She pointed to the garden beyond the window.

'SEE.'

Her voice was a shuddering wave condensing the octaves into one diabolical moan. Ethan wanted to run out from whatever dimension he had been dragged into. But he could not move. He was trapped inside the flame. His eyes darted to the window. The branches of the tree had covered the frame. They were slowly forcing their way through the cracks and into the room. The instructor sensed a disturbance and opened their eyes to look.

'Is everything OK? I know it can be strange if this is your first time, but just relax into the meditation, take your time. If unwanted thoughts or worries enter your mind, don't fight them, simply acknowledge them and let them fade.'

The instructor gave him an encouraging smile and returned to the script. Ethan pushed against the skin of the flame, stretching the membrane with all his strength. It

306

bulged and warped around his hands but remained intact. The heat was growing inside. Couldn't they see? Outside the flame, the branches kept spreading, moving inexorably across the floor. Soon they had covered the entire studio, like the capillaries of a pumping organ. The students were the stranded survivors of a flood, clinging to their mats as the torrent raged around. Ethan tried to warn them, but his words froze and shattered on his tongue. The tree broke through the remaining panes of glass, smashing the frame and stepping into the room on its gnarled feet. The force of the blast extinguished the fire and blew Ethan from the summit of the candle, throwing him breathless back onto his yoga mat. The branches moved closer. Now only a few inches from his helpless frame. A spindly twig curled up from the branch like a viper. It shot towards Ethan, wrapping itself around his feet. He screamed. No sound emerged.

'Switch off your thinking mind and remember to focus only on your breath. Be present in the moment.'

The twigs and branches began to entwine themselves around his legs, flowing up his thighs and over his hips. They twirled around his torso, tightening like a corset. He feared he might be crushed by the pressure. But this was no girdle of spines. It was the hug of a mother given to a child in distress. Ethan's feelings of panic faded like mist. His breathing settled. The tree had finally covered his whole body. With his head now encased in the canopy, he closed his eyes to receive the lesson. The instructor was pleased.

'Good, now let your breath synchronise with the beating of your heart. Really focus on yourself. Be grateful for your body, be grateful for your breath.'

Ethan's mind began to flow into the wood.

'Allow the energy to envelope you like a warm cloud of joy.'

307

The darkness pressed around him as he travelled down the veins of the bark.

'Imagine you are like a puddle of water. Let gravity slowly pull you into the ground, absorbing you into the soil. Imagine your skin is a seed. Feel the tiny roots sprout from the seed and begin to work their way into the soil, down through time, past the bones of our ancestors, past ancient cities, into the loving core of the planet, into the arms of Mother Earth.'

> *Come walk with me to lilac glade, through woodland,*
> *   stream and knot.*
> *Come stand beneath the gallows' shade till all weeping*
> *   is forgot.*
> *Leave the tears and terrors to the mischief of the town.*
> *Come walk with me to lilac glade, to the oak tree's*
> *   shady crown.*
>
> *In darkness now from darkness born, circumference,*
> *   length and span.*
> *In lilac glade the wreath and thorn, wove mockeries*
> *   of man.*
> *In lilac glade beneath the earth, in death's ecstatic bond.*
> *Come walk with me in lilac shade, to the emptiness beyond.*

Ethan travelled with the roots, just as the guide had said. Down through the topsoil littered with cans and cigarette ends. Down through the dirt filled with garbage and broken, discarded things. Past the sewage and waste, past the slaughtered carcasses of animals churned out of abattoirs, past the bones of our ancestors riddled with bullets or bludgeoned with hateful hammers. Down past the ruins of civilisations born in blood and fire. Down into the core.

The broiling heart of nothing. Here was his mother's embrace. The blissful source of all being. Through the mask of branches and leaves he could see the class of the Caxton Tranquillity Centre. They lay with their eyes closed. Deep within themselves. Trying hard to connect to a world they had left years ago. Peaceful, tranquil, fulfilled. He felt sorry for them. He closed his eyes again and let the mantra of the wood seep into him. Its silent, wordless rhythm carrying him around the dimensionless emptiness. In the studio the humans struggled to connect.

'Let the beautiful earth energy flow back into your core as you join with joy at the heart of the universe. You are connected. You are loved.'

*

They had fought so hard, these late-developing bipeds. Only a few generations out of the ooze. Confused and blinking, they stumbled onto the land. As they grew, so their confusion grew too. Self-aware but with no idea what to do with the gift. All their figures and graphs, with all their calculating machines and whimsical devices. Clunking and whirring. Trying in vain to create a comforting story to account for the burden they carried. They longed for a world they could understand, in a universe whose dimensions only they could determine. From the simple star maps of the ancients to the quantum musings of the moderns. They sought ways to rationalise it all. Deploying evermore convoluted equations and arcane formulations. But these were only ever different ways of stating the same thing: they knew nothing. As paradigms shifted and theories blossomed, and as the caves became laboratories and the monk's cell a supercollider, so the illusion of progress hypnotised them. But there never really was a big bang. No timeline on which they travelled. That too was just another story. A fiction of order diligently constructed. But ultimately another illusion. He had seen the fire and the filament. His arms had been bound by its sinews. His skin scourged by its flame. He had waded through the empty depths, weighed down by the anchor of hope. Wrapped in its biting chains. And at the bottom of it all, he had found nothing. The Tangle would not be constrained. The Tangle always was and evermore shall be. For at its core, it was *nothing*. The pure negative. Not a thing but an anti-thing. The absolute emptiness that defies explanation. A blasphemy in the eyes of men. The Tangle mocked them, and spat out the tragic, wasted work of millennia from its pitiless maw. It was beautiful. And those penitents who sought not to measure the void, but instead offered up prayers to its divinity, yearning to join its mystical oneness, to feel its love and healing power. When the veil was finally lifted and they stood staring into the abyss that they had once hoped would save them, they found only indifference. That was the true horror.

'Namaste. I hope to see you all back here next week. In the meantime, please take the energy of this meditation with you as a source of nourishment. Have a great day.'

Ethan opened his eyes. He wasn't surprised to find the old woman missing and an empty mat beside him. He looked out at the apple tree in its full, unseasonable bloom and smiled. What a wonderful birthday.

Acknowledgements

I would like to offer my wholehearted thanks and adoration to my wife Sofia Hedblom for listening, stimulating and lifting my head from the keyboard when stems of inspiration wilted. David Keenan for wisdom, guidance, helping me sort the wheat from the chaff, and the rod of correction when needed. Lee Brackstone for his faith in the work and providing the soil for the seed. Matthew Hamilton for his instruction and top-class agency. Russell Brown for fitting all the pieces together and for generally knowing what's going on when it becomes a mystery to me. Andrew O'Hagan and Johan Renck for kind words of encouragement. Richard Hector-Jones for decades of cultural enrichment and steadfast friendship. Jane and Kitty Hector-Jones for being wonderful and for being family. David Hill and Navaz Batliwalla for being beautiful friends and for audience participation. The Robertson collective: John, Nigel, Liz, James and Charlotte, you are all excellent, thank you. Caroline Hayes and the Black Door Agency. Luke Brown for his early eyes. Paul Baillie-Lane and Patrick McConnell for their later eyes. Ellie Freedman, Georgia Goodall, Steve Marking and all the magnificent White Rabbit family, for your help and deciphering my cryptic communications.

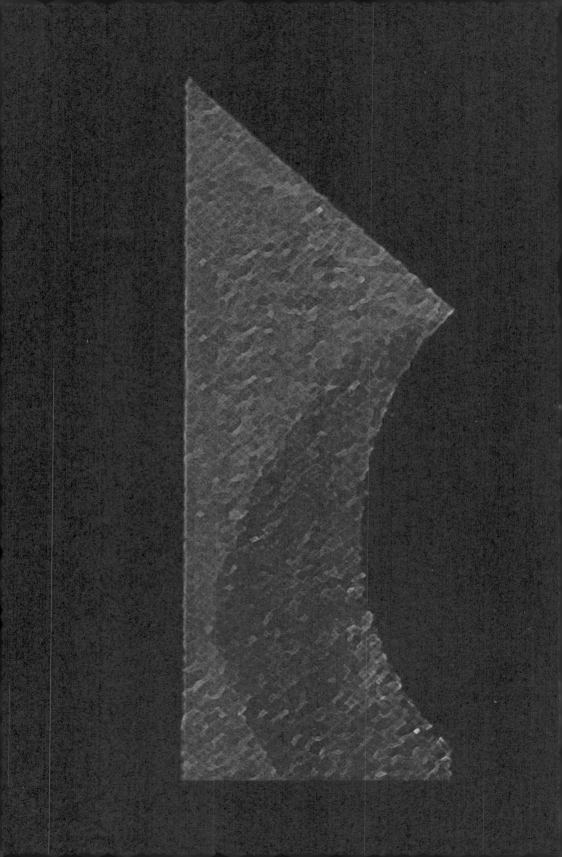